BENJAMIN SILLIMAN

Pathfinder in American Science

Books in
THE LIFE OF SCIENCE LIBRARY

VICTORY OVER PAIN
A History of Anesthesia
BY VICTOR ROBINSON

SUN, STAND THOU STILL
*The Life and Work of
Copernicus the Astronomer*
BY ANGUS ARMITAGE

BENJAMIN SILLIMAN
Pathfinder in American Science
BY JOHN F. FULTON
AND
ELIZABETH H. THOMSON

*Publication No. 16
Historical Library
Yale University School of Medicine*

BENJAMIN SILLIMAN

From the miniature painted on ivory by Nathaniel Rogers in 1818

BENJAMIN SILLIMAN

1779—1864

PATHFINDER IN AMERICAN SCIENCE

BY

JOHN F. FULTON

AND

ELIZABETH H. THOMSON

HENRY SCHUMAN · NEW YORK

Manufactured in the U.S.A. by H. Wolff, New York

To
MARIA TRUMBULL DANA
Granddaughter of Benjamin Silliman

"Lord Macaulay, in his famous paragraphs on the Puritans, expresses the theory that their narrowness and bigotry are to be attributed to a religious fervor that absorbed all emotions and left room for no other enthusiasms. However that may be, versatility was not often a quality of the Puritan character. All ages and almost all countries have their fashions in thought, and the 'time spirit' of Puritan New England was not favorable to a cultivation of the grand manner, the sophistication, the ability to handle many affairs without effort, that constituted the ideal of the polished gentleman on the other side of the sea at about this time. So it is that when one encounters a New Englander of this general period who seems to have had an adaptability and a ready liking for many things, one's interest is inevitably and agreeably arrested."

(Francis Parsons, *Six Men of Yale*, 1939)

Preface

BENJAMIN SILLIMAN played two prominent rôles in the development of this country. In the nineteenth century—at a critical period in our history—he fostered the sciences more persistently and effectively than any other figure, particularly in relation to their applications to industry and to the uncovering of the vast natural resources of the North American continent. Still more important was Silliman's rôle as an educator, for through his efforts in teaching the sciences at Yale he laid the foundations of graduate education in the United States.

On the occasion of its centenary, the Sheffield Scientific School, which owed its beginnings so largely to Silliman, takes pride in hailing its founder not only for inaugurating the first department of graduate study in the sciences, but for the part he also played in advancing higher learning in the humanities —to Silliman there was no basic conflict between these two branches of intellectual endeavor. Although Silliman's original contributions as a laboratory investigator were not of the first rank, his influence on science education was tremendous, and we offer this biography as a timely reminder of the man who provided the initial impetus which has been in such large measure responsible for our present international prestige in science.

The Silliman source materials are voluminous and our primary problem in preparing a biography for the general reader has been one of selection. In the official "life" published a year after Silliman's death, the late George Parks Fisher, Professor of Ecclesiastical History at Yale, included a large assemblage of material essentially without critical evaluation. This two-volume biography, although admirable in many regards, lacks perspective, for in 1865 it was not possible to foresee the extent to which the innovations introduced by

Silliman were to influence American academic and scientific life.

Silliman left an unpublished, nine-volume autobiography entitled *Origin and Progress in Chemistry, Mineralogy, and Geology in Yale College and in Other Places, with Personal Reminiscences* (written between 1857 and 1862); he also left the manuscript volumes of his travel diaries, his account books for his first trip abroad and the early years of his professorship, a volume on the foundation of the Trumbull Art Gallery, as well as a seventeen-volume daybook (1840-1864). In addition to these original materials, now chiefly in the Yale University Library, there are innumerable letters—in the Library, in the possession of his heirs, and in various other college libraries and historical institutions about the country, the Historical Society of Pennsylvania alone having eight hundred items.

In preparing this record we have been aided by the active cooperation of the staff of the University Library, particularly Mr. James T. Babb, the Librarian, Miss Marjorie G. Wynne of the Rare Book Room, Miss Anne S. Pratt, Reference Librarian, and Mr. Alexander O. Vietor, Curator of Maps; and of Mr. Theodore Sizer and Miss Josephine Setze of the Yale University Art Gallery (formerly the Trumbull Gallery). Of the many readers who have enriched the text, we must particularly mention Miss Maria Trumbull Dana, youngest daughter of James Dwight Dana, who has read the entire manuscript and given us access to family papers not otherwise available. We are similarly indebted to Dr. Charles H. Warren, formerly Dean of the Sheffield Scientific School, Mr. George L. Hendrickson, Lampson Professor Emeritus of Latin and Greek Literature at Yale, Mr. J. Dwight Dana of New Haven, great grandson of B. Silliman, Sr., Mr. Carl A. Lohmann, Secretary of the University, Miss Lottie G. Bishop, Executive Secretary of the School of Medicine, Professor Donald H. Barron of the Department of Physiology and Mrs. Barron, Miss Madeline E. Stanton of the Historical Library, Mr. E. DeGolyer of Dallas, Texas, and Mr. Henry Schuman, the publisher, for their constructive scrutiny of the manuscript and their many valuable suggestions. Mrs. Henrietta T. Perkins of the Historical Library and Miss Stanton have given us assistance with the index. There are also others who by reading individual chapters or by offering helpful comment have contributed to this record of a great educator and pathfinder in American science.

J.F.F.
E.H.T.

Historical Library, Yale University,
June 1947.

Contents

List of Illustrations

BENJAMIN SILLIMAN

Pathfinder in American Science

CHAPTER I

Connecticut Boyhood
1779-1801

EARLY in the morning of March 19, 1889, a life-sized bronze statue was overturned in front of Farnam Hall at Yale College in New Haven, Connecticut. It was the work of mischievous students on their way home from a local tavern, but the prank called forth no mirth from any quarter. Instead, the student body and the faculty were righteously indignant. The conniving night watchman was dismissed, the faculty began a diligent search for the culprits, and the students circulated a petition of protest. For the statue which the unknown pranksters had toppled was that of Benjamin Silliman, beloved professor of chemistry and geology, who was said to have done more for Yale than anyone in the history of the College. Although he had been dead for twenty-five years, the indignation of students and faculty alike gave clear indication of the affectionate regard in which he was still held.

EARLY YEARS

"Sober Ben," as he was called when he entered Yale College in 1792 at the age of thirteen, was born in the midst of the American Revolution. His father, Gold Selleck Silliman, lawyer and well-to-do landowner of Fairfield, Connecticut, served as a Brigadier General in the Revolutionary Army and was charged with the defence of the southwestern frontier of Connecticut. Since the British had long occupied Westchester, New York, and Long Island, this was a particularly responsible assignment requiring diligence, ingenuity, and considerable strategy. So thoroughly did General Silliman discharge his duties that the British were eager to capture him; accordingly they sent an armed party by night, surprising him as he lay asleep in his house overlooking Long Island Sound and taking him and his son William prisoner.

Mrs. Silliman, although seriously frightened by the sight of the armed men and by the thought of what might happen to her husband in their hands, courageously gathered together her infant son—named Gold Selleck after his father—and the rest of her family and servants and proceeded inland to a less dangerous area. She found haven in the town of North Stratford (now Trumbull), Connecticut, and there three months later (on August 8, 1779), while her husband was still in the hands of the British, she gave birth to a son who was christened Benjamin. Not long after this she was able to return to their farm on Holland Hill.

The house in which Benjamin grew up was a large, hospitable mansion where both friend and stranger were given a warm welcome. He recalled that many interesting people sought the good company and enlightened atmosphere of his father's household. "In my early days," he wrote many years later in his Reminiscences, "much company resorted to Holland Hill—not a few lodging guests; and it was a favorite excursion from Fairfield, especially with young people of both sexes—and in Mr. Eliot's family there were sensible and agreeable daughters [the Reverend Andrew Eliot had settled near the Sillimans when he was driven out of Boston by the British occupation]. The reverend gentleman was not forgotten by his Boston friends, even the great. I remember on one occasion the celebrated Governor Hancock, President of Congress, drove up to Mr. Eliot's in his coach and four, and while he made his call, the coachman drove farther up the road to find a place wide enough to turn the horses and carriage."

From the description Benjamin left of his father there emerges a vivid picture of the "gentleman of the old school" whose charming manners, affable company, and gracious hospitality made him a most genial host. As Prosecuting Attorney for the County he enjoyed a considerable prestige, as had his father, Ebenezer Silliman, before him, also a lawyer. Both had been graduated from Yale College and as educated men, wise and just in their administration of the law, and deeply reverent but not severe in their religious practices, they had been acknowledged leaders in the community.

Benjamin's mother, Mary Silliman, was the eldest daughter of the Reverend Joseph Fish, a graduate of Harvard College, and her mother, Rebecca Peabody, was a great granddaughter of John and Priscilla Alden. She, too, had had the advantage of being brought up in an enlightened household and was given the best education available to the girls of her day. Since the colleges of that time were designed primarily for the preparation of ministers, the minister was often the most highly educated man in each community and was, therefore, not only a spiritual leader but a cultural influence as well; and her father was such a man.

Mary Silliman taught her boys to read and gave them thorough religious training. While she combed their hair and helped them dress she heard them recite prayers and hymns and guided their progress in reading the Bible and religious books. Warm-hearted and generous, she was held in affectionate regard by her sons—an affection clearly discernible even in the formal language characteristic of the period in which Benjamin wrote of her many years later:

. . . As to my mother, in the course of long experience I do not remember to have seen a finer example of dignity and self-respect, combining a kind and winning manner and a graceful courtesy with the charms of a cheerful temper and a cultivated mind, which made her society acceptable in the most refined and polished circles. Her delightful piety, adding the charm of sincerity and benevolence both to her action and conversation, attracted the wise and the good, and won the thoughtless to consideration. It is a great blessing to have had such a mother. I loved and honored her in life, and her memory is precious.

From the hill on which they lived the youngest Silliman
liked to look out over Long Island Sound and to watch the
white canvas of the sailing vessels and the ever-changing face
of the sea—the deep blue of calm days and the snowy crests of
the waves whipped up by storm winds. When he was still quite
young he was sent to a small school about a quarter of a mile
from their house on the Fairfield road. The boys loved to fish
and these good times were so engraved on his memory that
he could clearly recall them in his maturity:

There was a fine fishing-ground at some distance from the shore, and
the long clams standing erect in the sand afforded the requisite bait.
Fishes also for the seine flowed with the refluent waves into the narrow
inlets in great numbers, especially at the head of Black Rock Harbor,
among which the striped bass were the most esteemed; and seafowl
flitted across the spit or bar which ran out almost a mile from Fairfield
Beach, and at low water appeared a naked rocky reef, resembling an
artificial breakwater. We boys loved to wander, when the tide was out,
on the hard flats, which were so firm that the human foot made hardly
any impression, and they were hardly marked by the iron shoes of a
horse. . . .

When Benjamin was but eleven years old and Selleck
thirteen, their carefree days were abruptly terminated by the
death of General Silliman. The day after he died the grieving
widow took her sons to the room where the body lay and together they read psalms and prayed for guidance. It is small
wonder that Benjamin developed a seriousness of mien which
earned him the nickname of "Sober Ben."

Mary Silliman was now left with a large estate to administer
and two boys to educate. Before she could be sure there would
be funds to finance their education, she resolutely went ahead
with the plans she and her husband had made for them. High
schools being unknown in that day, their neighbor, the Reverend Andrew Eliot, was asked to prepare them for entrance
to Yale College. "Mr. Eliot was a thorough scholar," Silliman
wrote, "and was so fully imbued with classical zeal that he was

not always patient of our slow progress. He, however, devoted himself with zeal and fidelity to our instruction in all good learning that was adapted to our age and destination, and carried us safely through. . . . Mr. Eliot took great delight in reading aloud to us from the *Aeneid*. Being excited and animated both by the poetry and the story, he evidently enjoyed the subject, and would fain have imparted to us a portion of his own enthusiasm."

On Sundays the two Silliman boys continued to attend public worship and their mother assumed their father's place in directing family prayers. Selleck and Ben sometimes had each to take one of Mr. Eliot's daughters with them on their horses to the Sunday services because there were not enough horses and carriages on Holland Hill to carry them all to town. They were at an age when the jeers of their school-fellows made this a rather embarrassing duty.

YALE COLLEGE

In this wise they came to the end of their preliminary training and in September 1792 the brothers entered Yale College, Benjamin being thirteen and the youngest but one in his class. Yale was then under the liberal leadership of Dr. Ezra Stiles, a man of independent mind and unusual intellectual attainments. A Congregational minister whose flock had been dispersed by the war, Dr. Stiles had been reluctant to assume the presidency for he doubted his fitness. "An hundred and fifty or 180 Young Gentlemen Students," he confided in his diary, "is a bundle of Wild Fire not easily controlled and governed—and at best the Diadem of a President is a Crown of Thorns." But having accepted the responsibility, he set out to discharge it with vigor. He had a great zest for life and much natural curiosity, and to his inquisitive and adventurous spirit is largely due the beginnings of an interest in science at a college where the emphasis had been up to this point almost entirely on classical and religious training. Prior to his marriage Stiles wrote his fiancée a long discourse on eclipses and on the moon's influence upon the tides, illustrated by carefully drawn diagrams. The letter, which contained nothing in addition that might have been of interest to a young girl in love, was signed "I am, my dear, Your Affectionate Philosopher, Ezra Stiles." Astronomy fascinated him, no language was too difficult for him to learn, and he was so much interested in chemistry as to have "incurred the suspicion—peculiarly menacing, of course, to the repute of a minister of the gospel—of flirting with alchemy."

President Stiles' insatiable curiosity gave fresh impetus to life at Yale; but fearful lest he not rise to the dignity of his office, he stringently invoked the rigid rules of conduct that had been set down for students many years before—outmoded rules that did little to enhance his popularity. He enforced, for example, the rule that: "The Freshmen, as well as other undergraduates, are to be uncovered, and are forbidden to wear their hats (unless in stormy weather) in the front door-yard of the President's or Professor's house [there was only one professor—Josiah Meigs—besides the President], or within ten rods of the person of the President, eight rods of the Professor, and five rods of a tutor." It is said that the students were ever zealous in showing their proportionate respect. Early in his career Benjamin incurred presidential displeasure by kicking a football in the college yard, and his friends at home were highly amused to hear that "Sober Ben" of all people had run afoul of college rules.

A former historian of Yale has left a description of its rural surroundings in the early days: "It is not extravagant praise to say that New Haven, enclosed by an amphitheatre of precipitate and lofty mountains, at the head of a beautiful bay, spread out amidst gardens and shady walks, in simplicity, perfect neatness, and unostentatious elegance, presents one of the most attractive places for literary pursuits that the country affords. It realizes to the student all the quiet beauties and charming retirement which the school of Plato enjoyed: 'In sacred Academus' shady walks.''

The entrance requirements might also have been appropriate for a "school of Plato." "Candidates for admission to the Freshman Class are examined in Cicero's Select Orations, Virgil, Sallust, the Greek Testament, Dalzel's Collectanea Græca Minora, Adam's Latin Grammar, Goodrich's Greek Grammar, Latin Prosody, Writing Latin, Barnard's or Adams' Arithmetic, Murray's English Grammar, and Morse's, Worcester's, or Woodbridge's Geography. Jacob's Greek Reader and the four Gospels are admitted as a substitute for Græca Minora, and the Greek Testament." The Silliman boys had assimilated enough of the Reverend Dr. Eliot's teaching to pass these formidable examinations without difficulty and they now continued their study of the classics in the vigorous intellectual atmosphere created by Ezra Stiles.

Although these were rough days when, despite the strict rules, students were wont to express their displeasure with their tutors by stoning their windows or attacking them with clubs if they chanced out after dark, Benjamin, after his first exuberance expressed with the football, seems to have been among the orderly. He studied, but by no means all the time. He made a conscientious effort to be regular in his attendance at chapel night and morning and at the daily sermon, not solely because it was required, but because he had no wish to depart from the religious practices he had followed all his life. However, if he had been up very late the night before, he was not above sleeping through morning prayers. The diary that he began during his third year in college, although a naïve, boyish document, preserves for us an excellent picture of college life in his time and also a glimpse of Ben himself,

happily not always as sober as his nickname would suggest.
On the cover of Book I he wrote:

JOURNAL OF A VOYAGE ON BOARD THE SHIP ASSIDUITY
TO THE HARBOUR OF SCIENCE, THROUGH THE OCEAN OF
LABOUR, KEPT BY BENJAMIN SILLIMAN, COMMANDER
BEGUN JULY 27, 1795 AND OF MY COLLEGE LIFE THE 3D
(AETATIS 16 YEARS AND 4 MOS)

On July 28th cloudy weather in the morning did not keep
him from dancing in the afternoon. Numerous references to
dancing would seem to indicate that while not a legitimate college activity, it doubtless kept the young men from less appropriate forms of amusement. On this day Mr. Meigs took
charge of the Class of '96. And also, alas, a member of the
moral society was detected using profane language!

On July 30th he studied in the forenoon as usual. At four
o'clock "notwithstanding the rain some patriotick sons of
Yale were determined to have dancing at all events, and for
that purpose hired a hack in which they gallanted the ladies
through mud and water to the dancing room. Notwithstanding
the bad weather we had a very pleasant afternoon."

The 5th of August was full of boredom. "Nothing worthy
of record has turned up. College life is a continual round of the
same transactions. I hope if I live to get into active life, at least
to have a little more variety." August 11th was another cloudy
day and very hot. He writes: "I studied in the forenoon, but
felt rather dull as I had not sufficient sleep the night preceding.
I studied in the afternoon until half past 3, then went out with
a number of my class to make experiments with the electrical
kites which I mentioned yesterday, but as there was not wind
enough we met with no success. I can study very little in the
evenings, as the candle hurts my eyes."

On August 13th, after a rainy, cloudy day, he attended in
the evening a meeting of the Brothers in Unity Society

(formed in 1768 and with Linonia the earliest society at Yale).*
By August 15th the weather had improved and on that day he
records:

> Fine, clear, wholesome air—very cool. I studied in the forenoon, and
> came home in the afternoon determined to write, but as I felt in a
> poor mood for study, I went and danced in the hall; however, I might
> as well have kept to my books. I have been this evening at Bishop's room,
> when the conversation turned upon swearing, and a profane person
> who was present said that he was determined to break himself of swear-
> ing; but I fear that his promises are more easily made than kept. I have
> just now come to a resolution to write down every material error of my
> life in this journal, that by a retrospective view I may keep myself free
> from error. I hope I shall be enabled to do myself justice and not to be
> partial. . . . I think of no material error of which I have this day been
> guilty, but in general I would observe that I am in some degree addicted
> to detraction, but I hope I shall be able to cure myself.

On August 19th he spent the day writing a paper for the day
following. He found it hard to concentrate in the evening,
however, for Selleck and Bassett, a classmate, were in his room
talking "upon this, that, and the other pretty thing," and
Selleck was advising him not to fall in love again "etc., etc.,
etc."! In the same paragraph with Selleck's admonitions about
love, Benjamin reported that dysentery and yellow fever prevailed in the town.

Two days later (August 21st) he wrote: "I have spent the
greater part of the afternoon of this day in making a writing
book. Page has been here this evening, and we have had some
agreeable conversation, sung a song or two, etc., etc. I have
just now finished my recitation. I am very well, thank heaven,
while many are sickening and dying." The next two days were
full of trial for him:

* In December of the preceding year (1795) he had read a twenty-page "Discourse upon Natural History" to the Brothers, which he concluded thus: "I
have been obliged contrary to my inclination to omit many things in the latter
part of this piece which I hope my audience will excuse, especially considering
that it is already swelled to an immoderate length."

August 22. . . . I went to prayer meeting in the evening where the sweetness of Robbin's elocution lulled me to sleep and I did not wake until the assembly were going out, nor then for I was awakened by Atwater. I started up in a maze, hardly knowing where I was, and it was some time before I discovered that it was simply B. Silliman in college hall. I then got my hat and made the best of my way home where I might sleep securely without fear of disturbance.

August 23. Cloudy and cool. I attended meeting all day as usual, but felt very drowsy in the afternoon and fell asleep in the course of the sermon, and slept so sound that I did not wake until the assembly rose to pray, and then I was moved by Fairbanks. I jumped up very suddenly, dropt my handkerchief into the alley, and if I may judge from countenances, I made a pretty droll appearance. This is the second time I have been caught so, and I must take care for the future. . . . I have been this evening to Col. Snoyt where we played cards all the evening and flattery was dealt out by the whole sale. I heard of an observation made concerning me which I ascribe to Miss . . . viz., that when I was in the burying yard at a funeral this afternoon, I could have been seen even if I had not stood upon a high stone. It touched my Dutch blood and I feel a little miffed, but perhaps I am mistaken as to the person. . . . The girls I find have tongues and happy he who escapes the lash. But since I feel my bile a little disturbed, I will upon my pillow seek the repose which I cannot find in the circles of the gay. I detest flattery. I should detest anyone who makes use of it were I convinced that he or she had any design. But perhaps I have been too hasty in my decisions.

In May of 1795 the College had been saddened by the death of President Stiles after a brief illness. On the 8th of September at Commencement Dr. Timothy Dwight became his successor. The induction ceremony was to have taken place at ten o'clock, but some misfortune prevented, so Benjamin copied tunes and "fluted" during the morning. At six p.m. he attended the inauguration of the President in the chapel "which was filled with clergymen, students, &c. The ceremony was begun by an anthem; then a Latin oration and address to the President-elect, by Mr. Williams. The President then made a Latin oration and addresses to the corporation, and the whole was concluded by an anthem called 'The Heavenly Vision.'"

After supper there was an "illumination" and fireworks. Ben reported that the illumination was partial, as well as the fireworks, but the music was very good.

Directly after this the brothers left on vacation (seven weeks) and Benjamin did not resume his diary until October 29th. He apparently passed the time pleasantly and, according to his lights, not unprofitably:

. . . I think that upon the whole I have never spent a vacation more agreeably than the last. I have been blessed with good health and good spirits, and an inconsiderable portion of my time was spent in the company of the ladies, which I think not an unprofitable employment—which is a very happy circumstance, seeing it is so agreeable. I have attended four balls, or, more properly, one ball and three dances. I stayed for more than two weeks at Mr. Eliot's, while my mother was gone on a journey with my brother Selleck, and this I reckon among the most pleasant parts of the vacation, as he has two very sprightly, agreeable daughters. I have done nothing of any consequence this day, as I have been in town only two days, and am hardly settled in my studies. I board at present at Mrs. Hill's but expect soon to live in Commons. I have been this evening to the meeting of the Brothers' Society, where I read a composition and returned, and am now sitting in my great chair, but hope soon to be in bed,—so goodnight to you all. . . .

By October 31st he was already full of admiration for their new President—not only were their recitations made more interesting by the useful and entertaining instruction of Dr. Dwight, but his sermons were excellent. "He is truly a great man, and it is very rare that so many excellent natural and acquired endowments are to be found in one person. When I hear him speak, it makes me feel like a very insignificant being, and almost prompts me to despair; but I am reëncouraged when I reflect that he was once as ignorant as myself, and that learning is only to be acquired by long and assiduous application."

On the 4th of November he went with a member of his class in the early evening to look at the planet Jupiter (through the large telescope from the Museum), which with its four

moons they easily discovered. Upon his return he had a call
to go into Bacon's room and help despatch some wine—
"which I very readily obeyed," he wrote, "and I presume acted
my part faithfully. . . ."

On November 9th he spent the afternoon reading and writing on the perplexing question as to "Whether the mental
abilities of the females are equal to those of the males," he
being a strenuous advocate of the affirmative. He believed, he
said, "that the difference in the appearance of the sexes (as
to their minds) is owing entirely to neglect of the education
of females, which is a shame to man, and ought to be reme-
died." After attending a meeting of ΦBK in the evening he
continued writing on the above question until half past ten.
The next morning he marshalled more arguments until it was
time for the eleven o'clock recitation to begin. His efforts were
rewarded, for after a hot debate of more than two hours, the
contest was decided in the affirmative. In the afternoon he
rested on his laurels, studying being impossible in any case because the boys who were bringing up wood (each room had an
open hearth) were making such a din.

November 11th found him writing poetry in the morning,
afternoon, and also in early evening "with tolerable success." He made no explanation as to whether it was a required
assignment or prompted by one of the sex whose cause he
had championed so vigorously the day before. But the Muse
was banished when Marsh, a graduate, came in with several of
his classmates. They drank a few glasses of wine and then
"the conversation ran upon politics in general," he recorded,
"and particularly upon the corruption of some of our great
men, the state of France, of England, &c. Matters ran pretty
high, as is generally the case in politics. Many men who in
private life are of the most amiable and gentle dispositions,
when they come to converse upon politics are ravenous wolves.
The company did not break up until past ten. . . ."

November 17th found him in a reflective mood:

I sat down to study in the evening but not feeling very well disposed for study & feeling the want to exercise I went to walk with Prince. We perambulated the principal streets in town as far as the wharf and kept up a spirited conversation. I find that Prince possesses a warm imagination and a good heart very susceptible to friendship. We returned to my room and there I found Sherman. Soon after Belden came in and King. We drank metheglin [a beverage, formerly Welsh in origin, made of fermented honey and water], ate apples, conversed, &c., &c. As my college life begins to draw towards a close I begin to be more sensible of the happiness which I enjoy. I find great pleasure in pursuing my studies but still greater in the company of my classmates and other college friends and particularly with those to whom I dare unbosom myself without reserve, which number is however very small. Cicero's maxim ought to be adopted with regard to the greater part of our college friends, *viz.*, "So to live with your friend that if he should become your enemy he can do you no injury."

On November 23d the Senior Class found it necessary to send a petition to the steward concerning their food. The Commons, where as many of the students as could be accommodated were required to eat, was ever a source of contention. The fare was plain, with as much variety as the surrounding region afforded, and reasonably ample. Beer was no longer supplied at table, but in general the food was probably equivalent to what the majority of the students were accustomed. However, there were frequent protests, such as this by the Senior Class, which sometimes reached alarming proportions. For instance, the Bread and Butter Rebellion some years later was staged by the entire College, and a large part of the students went home after they had knelt in a great circle on the grass and sung a parting ode written especially for the occasion to the tune of *Auld Lang Syne*. (After an interview with their parents, most of them promptly came back.)

In addition to the food supplied at meals, the Latin Laws of 1748 authorized a "concession" in the lower front corner of South Middle College called the Buttery where the Butler (always a graduate of excellent character and good standing) could sell cider, metheglin, ale, porter, strong beer to the amount of not more than twelve barrels annually (this was increased to twenty as the College grew), together with loaf sugar, raisins, almonds and native nuts, lemons, ginger, honey, eggs, biscuits, cakes, pies, candles, pipes, tobacco, and "such other necessities of the scholars as were not furnished in the Commons." Books, stationery, and fresh fruit were among these latter. Also available were pitchers, bowls, mugs, decanters, glasses, and corkscrews. Students were not allowed to buy beer elsewhere.

The Freshmen Rules made it incumbent on a Freshman to run any errand demanded of him by an upper classman and trips to the Buttery were frequently required. Although he was not permitted any back talk, an enterprising Freshman might express himself while sticking to the letter of the law as did one, sent with a dollar for "some pipes and tobacco," who brought back ninety-nine pipes and one cent's worth of tobacco! Benjamin recorded in his diary that he was called upon to settle a dispute between a Junior and a Freshman, but in this instance the Freshman doubtless did not tarry long enough for a dispute.

Silliman himself did not take advantage of the privileges of the upper classmen, for even at this age his innate kindliness was apparent. He constantly endeavored to keep himself from "material error." On November 23d, the same day the Senior Class found it necessary to complain to the steward, he discovered several shortcomings on which to reprimand himself. "I find that I am very apt to be guilty of scandal," he wrote, "although I acquit myself of doing it through any malicious design. I desire to make it a rule from this time never to say anything concerning any person (if I cannot speak in his favor), unless it is absolutely necessary. . . . I ought likewise to be more careful of speaking concerning myself.

No person ought to speak of himself unless when it is absolutely necessary, and even then with the utmost modesty. For if you speak well of yourself, it argues vanity; if ill, you will be called a hypocrite. I hope I shall observe these particulars, and any others which may tend to make one a Christian scholar and gentleman."

Four days later he returned to this theme:

November 27. . . . I am every day more and more convinced of the importance of modesty in a young person; it is his letter of recommendation. A bold and loquacious air may dazzle the thoughtless and ignorant, but modesty alone will procure the good-will of persons of real worth. If you wish to be noticed, say but very little of yourself, and that with the utmost modesty. Speak well of others; make them pleased with themselves; and there is no danger of their being displeased with you. Never strive to hurt the feelings of any person. Do not affect to despise others. Finally, put on modesty, and it will procure you a reception in all good company. . . .

Following this entry, which is the last in Book I of the diary, Silliman wrote the year before he died: "Good observations on the last page. I perused this juvenile journal again May 28, 1863—it was written almost 68 years ago."

Late in the autumn, when he was at home for a week-end, Benjamin cut the instep of his left foot while chopping some firewood, and although the cut was not serious, it became infected and was the cause of considerable pain and discomfort and a prolonged interruption of his college activities during the early weeks of 1796. He recorded in his diary that he feared lockjaw, but from his description of the illness, which he set down in minute detail, it is probable that he had developed a generalized bloodstream infection, not tetanus.

In September, 1796, Benjamin was graduated from Yale College. Timothy Dwight, whom he so intensely admired and respected, had the vision to see in the boy a man who could do much for Yale, for he stood out among his classmates. He was tall and handsome, with dark eyes and dark hair; his manners, on which both his father and his mother had laid much stress, were gracious beyond his seventeen years. Although appearing to be a man of the world, he strongly disapproved of some of the escapades of his classmates. But while he was somewhat self-righteous in his reactions to sin and seduction, he had an engaging sense of humor and a healthy curiosity about life, all of which lightened the heritage of Puritanism and made him a person to whom we react warmly today.

FARMER, PEDAGOGUE, LAWYER

Since the infection in his foot had affected his general health, it was decided that Benjamin should remain at home for a year and endeavor to help his mother straighten out their affairs. His father's law practice had been seriously interrupted by the war and his property had deteriorated, and not having been on the payroll of the Continental Army when the war ended (being in the hands of the British), he received no reimbursement for his considerable personal expense. He died before he had been able to put his affairs in order so that Mrs. Silliman, who had managed as best she could while the boys were in college, was now in real need of assistance.

On May 9, 1797 Ben wrote to Selleck, who was teaching in a private family in South Carolina, that he was doing all he could "to lighten the cares and to cheer the spirits of that mother to whose anxious care and unwearied exertions we owe those superior advantages which it has been our lot to enjoy." He had taken over the entire care of the farm, had been supervising the repair of fences, reseeding of the land, cleaning up of the orchard, and in general restoring the estate to its former prosperity and usefulness. "We calculate," he wrote, "that the productions of the farm will, this year at least, support the family, which you know was far from being the case last year. My present employment is far from being one to which, at the

January. 1796

Cloudy, not very cold. & a light snow has fell
this day. Altho I have ~~not~~ been out of doors only once in a whole week, yet I took cold yesterday
& felt quite unwell this ~~for~~ morning. My foot
altho it does not occasion much acute pain, does
not seem to be getting well very fast. Confinement
for so long a time, & the tediousness of sitting almost constantly still, are more irksome, than
the pain occasioned by the wound itself. The
forepart of this day I employed in fluting, reading
&c, & the afternoon in reading letters, written by
my hond father while he was a prisoner of war
among the British, upon Long Island, very interesting & entertaining to me. In the beginning of the
evening, the two Misses Eliots, came to our house, & we
spent our time very agreeably in _____ Well! Shall
I begin (as usual) to scold, & fret, because the females
do not talk more sensibly: or shall I, since I can
not remove the cause, patiently bear the effects? Pru-
dence says the latter. But these two ladies, are in
some measure, honorable exceptions, to the general
observation. I sat up untill about 11 P.M. &
feeling very sleepy went to bed.

SILLIMAN'S STUDENT DIARY

A page kept during his senior year at Yale when seventeen years of
age (Jan. 1796)

BROTHERS IN UNITY

A page from the minute book of the student society for December 3, 1795 showing that Silliman had been elected Vice-President. In September 1795 he had been elected to the student post of "Professor of Rhetoric" present period of my life, I should wish to give my time. But I have found by experience that it conduces to my health and to my interest, and therefore I think it is clearly my duty to pursue it until a return of health shall enable me to prosecute that employment to which I have been educated, and which is my delight. Think not, my brother, that I pay no attention to books. As often as leisure and health permit, I improve the opportunity in reading or writing, and not infrequently in wooing the Muses. . . ."

During the following year, when his health and the family fortunes were improved, Silliman accepted the opportunity of taking charge of a select private school in Wethersfield where some of his pupils turned out to be almost as old as he. One of them, John Marsh, who later became an eminent lawyer, wrote that "during his residence and instructions at Wethersfield, Mr. Silliman was as marked for the elegance and courteousness of his manners and his efficiency in all the business that was committed to his trust, as at any period of his life."

After a year at Wethersfield, he returned to New Haven in October 1798 and with his brother entered the office of the Honorable Simeon Baldwin to begin the study of law—the profession to which he felt most drawn, probably because his father and his grandfather had followed it. He commenced his studies with enthusiasm, glad to be once more in New Haven. The following year, in 1799, he accepted the tutorship which Dr. Dwight offered him at Yale because, as he confided to his brother, "my principal pecuniary weakness has been a *taste f*or elegance, which in circumstances more eligible would have been perfectly proper, but in mine was certainly reprehensible."

During this period of his apprenticeship in the law he thought very seriously about the future and in a letter to his mother he set down with engaging frankness and naïveté a youthful *confessio fidei:*

New Haven, December 15, 1798.

. . . I find no propensity in my system stronger than a wish to be highly *respectable* and *respected* in society. I must act in a particular sphere, and that sphere which is assigned me is the *Law*. This affords a boundless field for the display of every great and good quality. In a country like ours this profession is a staircase by which talents and industry will conduct their possessor to the *very* pinnacle of usefulness and fame. This pinnacle is constantly in my eye. I am not content (as I once thought it best) to walk obscurely along through some *sequestered vale* of life. . . . No. I must embark on the great business of life; and that reputation and usefulness may attend me, my *present* time must be devoted to laborious study. A lawyer ought to be an *able counsellor* and an eloquent man. *Intense study* is the only means by which he can attain the first character; and practice, with unremitting attention to the great models before his eyes, and a constant habit of elegance and accuracy of language, are the principal means for attaining the second. This same thirst for respectability influences likewise all my conduct. I wish to make myself the easy, agreeable, and endearing man in society. With the grave, I wish to be sententious; with the girls, easy, affable, and polite, nay, sometimes moderately trifling; but with the *friends* of my *heart,* open and sincere. In short, I wish to make myself "all things to all men," as far as decency, morality, and religion will suffer me to go. Another strong propensity is that which impels me to associate with females of equal age and respectability, and from them to cull out some guardian angel, some tutelary diety, who may be my protectress and the object of my care. . . . Should I meet a congenial soul I should be a *happy* man, but my ardor may drive me to an improper connection, and then I shall be truly miserable. These, my dear parent, I believe to be the great traits of my present character. I could enlarge upon them and trace them through all their various ramifications, but I should tire you with egotism. Now, my dear parent, is there anything in all this which is *unworthy?*

The matter of his religion also concerned him deeply, and although he was outwardly a devout Christian, one finds human doubts in his heart that he courageously and with candor admits to his mother:

New Haven, March 15, 1800.

My dear Parent,—This evening brings us repose from the fatigues of a four days' examination, and I sit down with satisfaction to converse a little while with my dear parent.

Your affectionate parental and instructive letter I have perused again and again. I wish, indeed, that I could give you an account of my religious concerns sufficiently pleasing to repay your exertions and to satisfy my own anxious feelings. I can say with truth that this great subject dwells in my mind when I am at liberty to think, "but shadows, clouds, and darkness rest upon it." Not that I doubt, but that I do not *feel*, although I readily assent to the proposition that these things are so. When I read that one of our frigates has fought a severe battle with a ship of superior force, I feel it at once. I trace every circumstance in my mind, and fancy that I hear the roaring cannon, the shouts of victory, and the groans of the dying. But—whether it is owing to some fatal cause, or merely to the triteness of the subject, I know not—when the awful truths of Christianity are announced from the desk, I do not always feel that interest which the subject ought to command. But I will reserve this subject until I see you. . . .

In 1802 there was a "Revival" at Yale College and Silliman was sufficiently touched both in heart and imagination publicly to profess his faith. In his senior year there had been a growing number of so-called "infidels" at Yale—students who denounced the religious tenets of their forefathers, possibly because of an overdose of piety or because they considered it more "enlightened" to find a new way to salvation. To Timothy Dwight, this attitude was a challenge he accepted fearlessly. In the autumn of 1796 only one Freshman and one Junior were "professing Christians," the Sophomore Class was unanimous in its godlessness, and the Senior Class could claim but eight or ten. By 1802, Dwight had brought the College back to Christianity, not by inciting mass hysteria, but by calm reasoning and persuasion. In the religious revival one third of the two hundred and thirty students became converted, and Benjamin, although he had never strayed far from the path, and then only in his mind, experienced a spiritual rebirth that sustained him as long as he lived. Throughout the rest of his life the depth and sincerity of his religious convictions influenced all that he undertook. Only in this way was he able to accomplish in that age the work which caused him to be described by another Yale President as "the father of American scientific education."

On the 19th and 20th of March 1802 Silliman successfully passed his law examinations, but he was destined not to practise law. Timothy Dwight had other plans for him—plans which opened up a new and exciting world to Benjamin Silliman and took him far from his appointed course.

CHAPTER II

The Young Professor of Chemistry
1802-1805

ONE VERY warm morning in July 1801, Silliman was cross-ing the college grounds when he met Dr. Dwight, who had now been President of Yale College for six years. He held President Dwight in highest esteem:—"a divine, a poet, a rhetorician, a scholar, and a high-bred gentleman, he, when physical science did not sway the universal mind as now, still saw with a telescopic view both its intrinsic importance and its practical relations to the wants of man and to the progress of human society." And Dwight in turn looked with a kindly eye on this handsome, earnest son of his former close friend, General Silli-man, so that when Ben asked his advice about accepting an appointment at a flourishing academy in Georgia, he thought the time had come to outline his plans for him at Yale.

In 1798 President Dwight, building on the interest in science created by Ezra Stiles, had recommended to the Yale Corpora-tion that a professorship in chemistry and natural history be established at Yale as soon as funds were available. This last condition was possibly included not alone because of the finan-cial condition of the college, but because the idea was a revolu-tionary one and required some consideration on the part of the theologians on the Corporation. Harvard, Pennsylvania, and the "College of New Jersey" (later Princeton) already had professorships of chemistry, and President Dwight did not want Yale to lag far behind its rival institutions.

So under the elms on this July morning he suggested to young Silliman, since three years had passed and since the funds were now forthcoming, that he present his name to the Corporation as the first Professor of Chemistry and Natural History. Silliman, who had his future planned, records that he was startled and almost oppressed by the proposal. But he went on to say that "the good President perceived both my surprise and my embarrassment, and with his usual kindness and resource proceeded to remark to this effect:—'I could not propose to you a course of life and of effort which would promise more usefulness or more reputation. The profession of law does not need you; it is already full and many eminent men adorn our courts of justice. . . . In the profession which I proffer to you there will be no rival here. The field will be all your own. The study will be full of interest and gratification, and the presentation which you will be able to make of it to the college classes and the public will afford much instruction and delight. Our country, as regards the physical sciences, is rich in unexplored treasures, and by aiding in their development you will perform an important public service, and connect your name with the rising reputation of our native land. Time will be allowed to make every necessary preparation; and when you enter upon your duties, you will speak to those to whom the subject will be new. You will advance in the knowledge of your profession more rapidly than your pupils can follow you, and will be always ahead of your audience.' "

These persuasive words were full of challenge to Silliman whose selection of the law had been largely because of family tradition and not because of any strong predilection for that profession. Dr. Dwight's placid acceptance of the fact that his candidate for the professorship knew little or no chemistry and that it would be necessary for him to go away to take a course of instruction before he could enter upon his duties seemed to remove this rather formidable obstacle. And, as he so realistically pointed out, the subject would be quite new to Ben's audience; this also was comforting. During the course of these arguments Silliman finally recovered himself, thanked the President appropriately for the honor and advantages so unexpectedly offered, and "we then emerged from under the shade of those noble elms, and I retired, thoughtful and pensive, to my chamber."

Unconsciously glad of a worthy excuse to turn aside from the law and not a little flattered at the confidence placed in him, a boy of but twenty-two, by this surprising offer from President Dwight, he accepted but not, however, without first seeking the advice of his mother. Until the matter could be brought before the Yale Corporation and until he could pass his legal examinations Silliman asked President Dwight to keep the whole affair secret. Meanwhile he obtained a few books on chemistry and hid them in his desk, occasionally reading them privately. He admitted quite frankly that the reading did not help him much, and that although he could understand some of the general principles he realized that he must see and perform experiments and become familiar with substances before he could make any progress in chemistry. The Corporation voted on September 7, 1802 to establish the Professorship of Chemistry and Natural History and to appoint Benjamin Silliman, now just twenty-three years old, to the chair. The new professor forthwith made plans to go to Philadelphia "which presented more advantages in science than any other place in our country" to learn something about the subject he had been appointed to teach.

PHILADELPHIA AND PRINCETON

He found life in a large city and his classes with some of the most eminent scientists and physicians of the time intensely interesting and stimulating. He attended lectures in anatomy and surgery, as well as in chemistry, for he seemed to feel that eventually there would be a medical school in New Haven. His enthusiasm for chemistry led him to engage in some original experiments in the cellar of his boarding house with one of his fellow boarders, Robert Hare, who, though a year younger than he, was already well versed in chemistry. Elihu and Charles Chauncey, two of his law school friends, had secured him his room at Mrs. Smith's lodging house, where he found that Hare and the Chaunceys were part of a group of eager young men of rather unusual character (many of whom attained eminence in later life).

Mrs. Smith set a generous, even luxurious table, and Silliman noted with some surprise that there was not a teetotaler among her boarders. "On the contrary," he wrote later in his Reminiscences, "agreeable to the custom which prevailed in the boarding-houses of our cities half a century ago, every gentleman furnished himself with a decanter of wine—usually a metallic or other label being attached to the neck, and bearing the name of the owner. Healths were drunk, especially if stranger guests were present, and a glass or two was not considered excessive,—sometimes two or three, according to circumstances. Porter or other strong beer was used at table as a beverage. As Robert Hare was a brewer of porter and was one of our number, his porter was in high request, and indeed it was of an excellent quality. I do not remember any water-drinker at our table or in the house, for total abstinence was not there thought of except, perhaps, by some wise and far-seeing Franklin." Having been accustomed to a simple diet without wine in New Haven, he reported that after his two seasons in Philadelphia he had made some progress towards incipient gout. However, vigorous exercise somewhat offset the luxurious living habits, and private prayers kept him from lapsing altogether into the worldly spirit of the Philadelphians.

Silliman was well aware, even at this early age, that of almost equal importance with his studies were the opportunities extended to him to meet informally the well-known figures in Philadelphia social and scientific circles, and he lost no opportunity to further his education in this way. Of all the men of science he met there, none impressed him more than Dr.

Joseph Priestley. It was natural that this eminent Unitarian divine should strike a responsive chord in the young chemistry professor-to-be, for Priestley in discovering oxygen, nitrous oxide, and four other gases, had successfully combined chemistry with his teaching and religion. And Dr. Priestley was a refugee from his own country—this made him the more fascinating and caused the details of their meetings to be so clearly impressed on Silliman that he was able to set them down at length many years later:

This celebrated gentleman was also a guest on one of these occasions, when I dined at Dr. Wistar's. As a very young man (of twenty-three or twenty-four years), I felt it an honor and advantage to be introduced to so celebrated an author and philosopher. He had become obnoxious in his native country on account of political and religious opinions, as he was a friend of civil liberty, and his religious creed was Arian, or Unitarian. At that time, during the early part of the French revolution, there was a strong excitement in England against revolutionary sentiments and movements. Dr. Priestley then resided at Birmingham, and during an anniversary commemoration of the destruction of the Bastile, although he was not then in the city, the mob proceeded to his house, which they burned, with his library, apparatus, and manuscripts. All were lost; and the outrage was said to have been countenanced by persons of consideration both lay and clerical. In 1794 he fled from persecution and took refuge with his family at Northumberland, Pennsylvania, on the Susquehanna River. Here he resumed his philosophical pursuits, and made occasional visits to Philadelphia. It was on one of these occasions that I was invited to meet him at Dr. Wistar's table, and the interview was to me very gratifying. In person he was small and slender, and in general outline of person not unlike the late President Stiles. His age was then about seventy [actually 69]. His dress was clerical and perfectly plain. His manners were mild, modest, and conciliatory, so that, although in controversy a sturdy combatant, he always won kind regard and favor in his personal intercourse. At the dinner, Dr. Priestley was, of course, the honored guest, and there was no other except one gentleman and myself.

Some of Dr. Priestley's remarks I remember. Speaking of his chemical discoveries, which were very numerous, he said: "When I had made a discovery, I did not wait to perfect it by a more elaborate research, but at once threw it out to the world, that I might establish my claim before

I was anticipated." He remarked upon those passages in the Epistle of John which relate to the Trinity, that they were modern interpolations, not being found in the most ancient manuscripts. He spoke much of Newton and his discoveries, and the beauty and simplicity of his character; and I think that he claimed him as thinking in religion as he himself did. He mentioned being present at a dinner in Paris given by the Count de Vergennes during the American Revolution, and the seat next to him was occupied by a French nobleman. At another part of the table were two gentlemen dressed in canonicals. When, said Dr. Priestley, I inquired of the nobleman the names of those two gentlemen, he replied: "One of them is Bishop So-and-so, and the other Bishop So-and-so; but they are very clever fellows; and, although they are bishops, they don't believe anything more of this mummery of Christianity than you or I do." "Speak for yourself, sir," I replied; "for, although I am accounted a heretic in England, I do believe what you call 'this mummery of Christianity.' " . . . Dr. Priestley died in his seventy-first year, at Northumberland, February 6th, 1804. After rejecting the doctrine of Phlogiston in early years, he resumed it at a later period of life; and it was reported at Philadelphia that he was occupied on his death-bed in correcting the proof of a new pamphlet on that subject. . . .

Silliman was principally engaged in attending the lectures on chemistry of Dr. James Woodhouse, which lectures "formed a part of the course of medical instruction in the Medical School of Philadelphia." He reported that the accommodations were not capacious enough for the 120 pupils and the apparatus was humble, "but it answered to exhibit some of the most important facts in the science." Benjamin also had the temerity to criticize the performance of the experiments, but he added that although imperfectly done they were still a treasure to him. He likewise comments on Dr. Woodhouse's personal characteristics: "Dr. Woodhouse was wanting in personal dignity, and was, out of lecture-hours, sometimes jocose with the students. He appeared, when lecturing, as if not quite at his ease, as if a little fearful that he was not highly appreciated,—as indeed he was not very highly. . . . In his person he was short, with a florid face. He was always dressed with care; generally he wore a blue broadcloth coat with metal buttons; his hair was powdered, and his appearance was gentlemanly. His lectures were quite free from any moral bearing, nor, as far as I remember, did he ever make use of any of the facts revealed by chemistry to illustrate the character of the Creator as seen in his works. At the commencement of the course he treated with levity and ridicule the idea that the visitations of the yellow fever might be visitations of God for the sins of the people. He imputed them to the material agencies and physical causes,—forgetting that physical causes may be the moral agents of the Almighty. His treatment of myself was courteous."

Silliman attended other lectures, many in the evening, including those of Dr. Benjamin Rush, Dr. Benjamin S. Barton, and Dr. Caspar Wistar, all men who enjoyed national prominence in medicine. The latter gave lectures on anatomy and surgery, and Silliman recorded: "I was not willing to resist the temptation to attend them, especially as I expected eventually to be connected with a medical school in New Haven; and chemistry, moreover, sustains important relations to anatomy." He was soon, however, forced to send the following note to Dr. Rush:

Monday, 4 P.M. [1802]

Sir—Finding it impossible, without preparatory reading, to do justice to *four* courses of lectures and at the same time make Chemistry a principal object, I have determined, tho very reluctantly, to relinquish *two* courses and confine myself to Anatomy, Chemistry & midwifery; hoping that I may next winter make up the deficiency. I therefore return my ticket and beg you to erase my name from your list.

I am, Sir, with very great respect y^r m^o obt, B. Silliman.

Thirty years later James Rush wrote a crisp annotation to this letter of his father's, indicating that there was one at least of Silliman's contemporaries in Philadelphia who was not impressed by the prestige he had by then acquired: "See here the Yankee. This Silliman by dint of conceit, impudence, and self puffing contrived to become a professor in Yale College—but there is as now, and the end of the man is no better than the beginning."

Silliman returned to New Haven in March of 1803 to resume teaching of his classes since he was not yet relieved of his duties as tutor. His experience in Philadelphia had broadened him in many directions, for his worldly contacts had thus far been limited and he was unaccustomed to the freedom of a metropolitan community that had largely thrown off the heavy hand of Puritan tradition. His enthusiasm for his life work had been greatly stimulated and he immediately began the construction of apparatus for his future classes. He also performed some experiments, but his time for these things was limited and most of what he could spare from his tutorial duties he devoted to reading and preparing for his second sojourn in Philadelphia.

This time on the way to his destination he stopped at Princeton because the College of New Jersey had secured for its first professor of chemistry (in 1795) the distinguished Scotsman, John Maclean, whom Silliman was eager to meet. Maclean came to Princeton from Paris where he had spent three years with Lavoisier, the great French chemist who, taking up Priestley's incomplete disclosures concerning oxygen, had established the elemental nature of the gas. Silliman gave Maclean the credit for solid guidance during this early phase of his career.

At this celebrated seat of learning [Princeton], an eminent gentleman, Dr. John Maclean, presided as the Professor of Chemistry, &c. I early attained an introduction to him by correspondence, and he favored me with a list of books for the promotion of my studies. Among these were Chaptal's, Lavoisier's, and de Fourcroy's Chemistry, Scheele's Essays, Bergman's Works, Kirwan's Mineralogy, &c. I also passed a few days with Dr. Maclean in my different transits to and from Philadelphia, and obtained from him a general insight into my future occupation; inspected his library and apparatus, and obtained his advice regarding

many things. Dr. Maclean was a man of brilliant mind, with all the acumen of his native Scotland; and a sprinkling of wit gave variety to his
conversation. I regard him as my earliest master of chemistry, and Princeton as my first starting-point in that pursuit; although I had not an
opportunity to attend any lectures there. Mrs. Maclean was a lovely
woman, and made my visits at the house very pleasant to me. She was a
sister of Commodore Bainbridge in Philadelphia at whose house I was
an occasional visitor. . . .

Silliman's second winter in Philadelphia extended from
November 5, 1803 to March 5, 1804, and since there was less
novelty in the experience, he recorded it in less detail. As during the previous winter he attended the courses in chemistry
and anatomy and resumed his experiments with Robert Hare.
"The familiarity," he says, "which I had acquired the preceding year with men and things enabled me to derive additional
advantage and made me feel more at home. My circle of acquaintance had been more extended, quite as much as was
consistent with my studies. I was admitted hospitably or so-
cially to some of the most estimable families—that of Judge
Wilson, son of him of the Revolution, the Bishop Whites, the
Dr. Strongs, Colonel Biddle, where there were beautiful daughters." He adds: "About this time I was elected a member of
the Philosophical Society founded by Franklin, and of course
had free access to its library."

From a letter of Moses Stuart, one of his fellow tutors at Yale,
it is evident that not all of Benjamin's social contacts in
Philadelphia were with men of science:

. . . We are all anticipating your return, and expect to be taught where
we may find, or rather how we may compose, the *"philosopher's stone."*
For my own part, I am so grossly ignorant respecting chemistry, that I
hardly know what it cannot effect. This business of *analyzing* sometimes
makes bad work. If you confine yourself to the laboratory of Woodhouse,
and do not happen to get analyzed in the laboratory of some Philadelphia
ladies, you will do well. But I fear the particles of which you are composed, and those of some fine ladies there, are sufficiently homogeneous
to possess in a great degree the attraction of affinity. If so, I am convinced

that on near approach they would cause such a fermentation as would produce a composition. . . . As to College affairs, they go on much in the old way. We had many convulsions last quarter, many furious "spasms of infuriated" Sophomores and Freshmen. Mr. Fowler's door almost split to pieces with stones; my windows broken; . . . nothing but wars and rumors of wars. This term there appears to be some disposition to enter into a treaty of peace; at least, a cessation of hostilities is agreed upon.

The time of your return is now so near that we begin to anticipate much pleasure from a relation of some of your chemical experiments. Wishing you a safe return, without leaving your heart in any *laboratory* in Philadelphia, I am, sir, Yours with esteem, Moses Stuart.

YALE'S FIRST SCIENCE LABORATORY

On returning to New Haven after his second year away Silliman entered immediately upon his duties as a professor of chemistry; and although his laboratory equipment was still meager and although he was yet without laboratory space, he gave his first formal lecture on April 4, 1804. His later account of it is modestly appreciative of his own efforts. "In a public room, hired for college purposes, in Mr. Tuttle's building on Chapel Street, nearly opposite to the South College, I met the Senior Class, and read to them an introductory lecture on the history and progress, nature and objects, of chemistry. I was then twenty-four years old. . . . My first efforts were received with favor, and the class which I then addressed contained men who were afterwards distinguished in life. . . ."

Suitable quarters for his lectures were imperatively needed and arrangements were shortly made to provide them. Silliman has left a diverting description of the obstacles which had to be surmounted before the laboratory was ready for use, the first of which was to convince the Corporation of the inappropriateness of the space offered him. Whether it was his sense of humor or the earnestness of a man with a mission that prompted him to suggest that the august Yale Corporation descend a ladder into the cellar, we shall never know.

In 1802 the Corporation of Yale College erected the building which has ever since been known as the Lyceum. Its position is between the old South Middle and the North Middle College. I understood that a deep excavation under the west end of the building was intended for a laboratory. This building was erected before my appointment, and soon after President Dwight had confidentially offered the Professorship of Chemistry to me. . . . After the prospect of my appointment had been opened to me by President Dwight, I cast anxious glances into that deep excavation, not exactly comprehending how it could be rendered available for the purposes of science; but my lips were as yet sealed in silence.

An English architect, Mr. Bonner, had established himself in New Haven, and had acquired a deserved reputation for knowledge, talent, and taste in his profession. He was charged with the erection of the Lyceum; but, having no particular knowledge of a laboratory, he placed it almost under ground. On my return from Philadelphia, in the spring of 1803, I found that a groined arch of boards had been constructed over the entire subterranean room. It rose from stone pillars of nearly half of the height of the room, erected in each of the four corners and on the middle of the opposite sides. The effect was, therefore, by the curves of the arches, to cut off the light, more or less, from all the windows,—one third, or half, and even two thirds in some of them. At once I saw that it would never answer, and I made my appeal to the Corporation at their next meeting. I invited them to visit the room, to which there was no practicable access except through a hole or scuttle in the roof of the arch. A ladder was therefore raised from below, or let down from above, and, Crusoe-like, the grave and reverend gentlemen of the Corporation descended, as Robinson did into his den, and arrived safely on the floor. President Dwight, Rev. Dr. Ely, Hon. James Hillhouse, and his venerable father, then fourscore or more, and others,—members of the College Senate,—found themselves in a gloomy cavern, fifteen or sixteen feet below the surface of the ground, into which, especially as there was as yet no trench excavated around the outside of the building, little more light glimmered than just enough to make the darkness visible.

To see was to be convinced. I had no difficulty in persuading the gentlemen that the model arch of boards must be entirely knocked away, the stone pillars removed, and the space opened freely to the roof of the room, which should be finished square up to the ceiling, like any other large room. It was indeed to be regretted that several hundred dollars had been worse than thrown away upon the preposterous arch. How did it happen? I suppose that Mr. Bonner, an able civil architect, as I have already said, had received only some vague impressions of chemistry,—perhaps a confused and terrific dream of alchemy, with its black arts, its explosions, and its weird-like mysteries. He appears, therefore, to have imagined, that the deeper down in mother earth the dangerous chemists could be buried, so much the better; and perhaps he thought that a strong arch would keep the detonations under.

Thus did shafts of humor lighten the sober traits of young Silliman's unfolding personality as he vigorously attacked the problem of establishing science at Yale. The Corporation, now conclusively convinced of the need for change, authorized the plans which Silliman presented—the model arch was knocked away, the stone pillars were moved, and the walls proceeded, without ornament or interruption, squarely to the ceiling. A wide areaway was also excavated around the outside so that "a cheerful light was thus reflected into a large and lofty room." But this did not remove the damp—"all articles of iron were rapidly rusting, and all preparations that attracted water became moist or even deliquesced." The only virtue of the underground chamber was that it tended to remain cool during the torrid heat of the average New Haven summer. In this room Silliman spent the best years of his life from the age of twenty-five to forty. And not only was it used as a chemical laboratory where experiments were demonstrated, but it was also a lecture room and his only research laboratory. He describes its scant furnishings:

. . . A gallery was erected on the side of the room opposite to the windows, access being made from the front of the tower or steeple through the intervening cellar, over a paved walk. Tables were established on the floor of the laboratory, in a line with a large hydro-pneumatic cistern or gas-tub, and a marble cistern for a mercurial bath. The small collection of apparatus which I had got together was duly arranged, and things began to look like work. Arrangements were made for furnaces, and for the introduction of water from a neighboring well. The tables were covered with green cloth; the stone floor was sprinkled with white beachsand; the walls and ceiling were whitewashed; the backs and writing-tables of the benches, and the front and end of the gallery, were painted of a light lead color; and the glass of the windows being washed clean, the laboratory now made a very decent and rather inviting appearance, like the offices, store-rooms, and kitchens that are seen almost underground in cities.

During the summer of 1804 he spent the greater part of his time watching building operations and getting his laboratory fitted out. In October he received his first class of seniors who were destined to graduate in September 1805, among them a number of men who later became prominent, including Dr. J. M. Scott McKnight. His chemical apparatus consisted of a few flasks which he had obtained in Philadelphia, some glass tubes, a Nooth's machine for impregnating water with carbonic acid gas (a device which he had found useful in Philadelphia), and a few glass bells which had once covered the philosophical apparatus. He remarked that since his audience were novices, probably the appearance of the apparatus was respectable. He also recalled that Dr. Priestley had told him that "with Florence flasks (cleaned by sand and ashes) and plenty of glass tubes, vials, bottles and corks, a tapering iron rod to be heated and used as a corkborer, and a few live coals with which to bend the tubes, a good variety of apparatus might be fitted up. Some gunbarrels also, he said, would be of much service; and I had brought from Philadelphia an old blacksmith's furnace, which served for the heating of the iron tubes. He said, moreover, that sand and bran (coarse Indian meal is better), with soap, would make the hands clean, and that there was no sin in dirt."

Since it was difficult to obtain glass chemical instruments, Silliman persuaded a glass manufacturer in East Hartford to make some for him. The state of general knowledge of science in those days is reflected in Silliman's account of this experience. He sent a model with side arm broken, but had included the broken piece so that the glass manufacturer could visualize what the finished retort should be. "In due time, however, my dozen of green glass retorts, of East Hartford manufacture, arrived, carefully boxed and all sound, except that they were all cracked off in the neck exactly where the pattern was fractured; and broken neck and ball lay in state like decapitated kings in their coffins. This more than Chinese imitation affords a curious illustration of the state of the manufacture of chemical glass at that time in this country, or rather in Connecticut; the same blunder would probably not have been made in Philadelphia or Boston."

The reaction of the students to the new course of study instituted at Yale College was very favorable. It was to be expected that Silliman would feel unsure at first in his lectures on a subject so recently learned—lectures given to students who were very little younger than he, but he soon gathered confidence and the interest of his audience grew in proportion. He reminisced in later years: "Even with my immature and limited acquirements I was encouraged to proceed by recollecting other remarks which I heard from Dr. Priestley. Being complimented upon his numerous discoveries, he replied to this effect:—'I subjected whatever came to hand to the action of fire or various chemical agents, and the result was often fortunate in presenting some new discovery. In teaching I have always found that the best way to learn is to teach, when you will be sure to study your subject well, and I could always keep ahead of my pupils. Thus while I was teacher, I was still more a learner.' "

PLANS FOR A TRIP TO EUROPE

In September, 1804, Silliman fell ill with dysentery and while confined to his bed he heard the astonishing news that at a meeting of the President and Fellows of Yale College nine thousand dollars had been voted for the purchase of books for

the library and for "philosophical and chemical apparatus."
This amount of money, to be viewed with respect at any time,
was extraordinary for those days, and in his excitement over
the news Silliman quickly conceived a bold plan. He forgot
his dysentery and hurried to call on President Dwight at his
house, finding him "at leisure in the front parlor, and in a
state of mind to receive my suggestions favorably." This was
well, for his proposal was that instead of Yale's purchasing
the books and apparatus through agents in London, he, Silliman, be sent to transact the business. If he were allowed the
agent's percentage and if his salary were paid, he believed it
would be sufficient to cover his expenses, and "I should in the
mean time have opportunity to improve in my profession." To
this proposal President Dwight reacted with his characteristic
decision and frankness. He then pointed out that the Corporation had adjourned, but that the members of the Prudential
Committee, which had authority to transact interim business,
were not far distant and Silliman could visit each one and obtain his vote. He immediately therefore drove to Repton (now
Huntington), fourteen miles away, to consult the Reverend
David Ely, and then turned his horse toward Farmington,
twenty-eight miles from New Haven, to lay the matter before
Governor Treadwell. Reverend James Dana of New Haven
was more readily approached. His enthusiasm caused the members of the Prudential Committee heartily to endorse President Dwight's proposal, and to Benjamin's infinite satisfaction it was settled that he should go to Europe. He entered
upon the duties of his course in chemistry with fresh stimulus,
and was cheered through the winter with the bright prospect of
what spring held for him.

Almost immediately he began to write to his connections in
Philadelphia and Princeton for letters of introduction to men
of science abroad and to anyone else who could help him attain
his ends during his six-month stay (later lengthened to a

year). He also began to make purchases for the trip—clothing and other necessities, including a pair of pocket pistols. These he carefully recorded in an expense book where he kept minute account of every cent he spent abroad. This was necessary not only because of his methodical nature, but because Yale was paying his expenses and he wanted to give an accurate account of his stewardship of the college funds. On the first page of his expense book, we find the following entries:

EXPENSES CONNECTED WITH MY VOYAGE TO EUROPE

1804			
Nov.	x	Tablet of memory	$1.25
	x	Picture of London	1.46
		Postage to and from Dr. Perkins	.20
	x	Scotch Pebble watch seal and cord	3.50
		Postage to Dr. Maclean	.12,5
		Postage to and from C. Chauncey	.34
Jan.		Do. to Dr. Dutton	.77
	x	Expenses during a tour to New York	18.56
	x	A pair of superfine breeches	8.00
	x	A pair of pocket pistols	10.00
	x	Cleaning do.	.50
		Postage from Hare	.34
	x	Four silk handkerchiefs	2.00
		Postage Dr. Maclean	.37,5
Feb.		Spencer	7.50
	x	Cassimer pantaloons	7.00
	x	Superfine cloth coat	17.50
			$78.82
		Postage (E. Dwight)	.20
	x	Gloves	1.08
	x	Penknife	.24
		Postage Mr. Gilpin	.66
			$81.00

The paper-covered account books are now browned with age but the forceful writing, still clear and legible, takes us back to that busy winter when between his classes and his other duties he was getting his umbrella mended for 37 cents, his portmanteau repaired for 8 cents, when he was buying flannel drawers ($1.43) as protection against the rigors of the North Atlantic, also cider, porter, and brandy ($14.92), as well as twelve bottles of sherry ($9), for the same purpose. There were entries for thread, buttons, soap, diary, and other necessities for the provident traveller. Finally, two days before he sailed there appears:

Passage money on board the Ontario	$163.34
Servants on board	1.00
Liquors	23.02
Prunes and raisins	3.00
	$191.26

He left a blank page here before he began to record his expenditures on the other side of the Atlantic, and at a later date he wrote:

London, Aug. 17, 1805. From the preceding pages I have it in contemplation to select all those charges which are marked with an x on the left side of the page and to subtract them from my expenses—they amount to the sum of $118.01 [these items were clothes and other personal expenditures]. Then the sum with which I shall charge the Corporation till my arrival in Liverpool May 3, 1805 will be $264.51,9.

He left New Haven on the 22d of March to allow him time to call for his letters of introduction in New York and Philadelphia. On that day he recorded: "Have closed my account in this town (New Haven) having paid every demand—being about to depart in the evening for Europe," and then he added: "If I had never returned, no one would have been a loser by me."

CHAPTER III

A Year Abroad

1805-1806

PROPELLED by a bold wind the sailing vessel *Ontario* moved out of New York harbor on the afternoon of April 6, 1805 with Benjamin Silliman aboard. He had said a solemn farewell to his mother and his brother and family because sailing the Atlantic in those days was a long and risky business from which many a traveller did not return. Indeed, next morning when he awoke to "tempestuous seas and angry skies," he deemed it "but an unpromising beginning." But bad weather was soon followed by fair sailing, and so it went until they ran into the "Islands of Ice" off the coast of Newfoundland. Although deeply awed and not unconscious of danger, young Silliman could not help being thrilled. "I felt a mixed emotion," he wrote his brother Selleck, "of pleasure and apprehension, from the expected contemplation of objects so splendid and magnificent, and still, so dangerous to our safety." He described them at some length:

They were all of a very pure and splendid white, with a peculiar brilliancy, arising from the situation of the sun, which was declining; while the Ice-islands constantly came into view from the east and north, and thus threw back a flood of light upon us, which rendered them more conspicuous as they came nearer, and afforded the pleasure of continued discovery. Few of them were larger than a house or a church, but there were two which might well be dignified with the name of floating mountains. They all rolled much with the waves, with a ponderous motion, that alternately immersed an additional portion of the mass, and then, by the returning movement, brought a great bulk into view, which had been invisible before; while streams of water, taken up by the inequalities of surface, ran down their sides. It is not easy to give a correct estimation of the magnitude of the largest islands. Their appearance was very magnificent. They covered many acres on the water, and towered above our top-gallant masts. So peculiar was their appearance, that it is not easy to compare them to anything but themselves; yet, they resembled most, some ancient venerable ruin, while the beauty and splendor of the materials made them look like a recent, highly polished work of art, which some convulsion had thrown into vast disorder.

At midnight he added: "Two men are stationed in the bow to look out for the ice; one mass has grazed our side, but without doing any harm, and as the moon has risen, and the weather continues fine, I shall retire to rest. I have not, however, forgotten the interesting history of the Lady Hobart British Packet, which perished last year in these seas, by the same accident to which we are now exposed."

He recalled an amusing bit the next day while he still watched the spectacle: "While contemplating these magnificent bodies, Dr. Darwin's whimsical project of employing the navies of Europe to navigate them to the tropical regions for the sake of cooling those climates, struck me with peculiar interest; what project or hypothesis has been too ridiculous to be proposed and defended by philosophy or to be embellished by poetry and fiction!"

After safely passing the icebergs they ran into a hard storm and heavy seas. Silliman made light of it in his humorous description of their difficulties:

We have been compelled to place our food on the floor, and to sit down around it, with all the simplicity, although not with the quiet and security, of pastoral life. You would have been much amused could you have witnessed our grotesque appearance; one might have been seen bracing a foot against a panel, and another against a trunk; a second and a third, not equally fortunate in their position, aided each other, by extending their limbs, and placing foot to foot, in opposite directions, while the walls of the cabin supported them behind. Thus situated, with our plates between our knees, we attempted the arduous business of dining. At every roll of the ship there was a kind of manual exercise to be performed. Besides his own plate, each one had to elevate some vessel to prevent its being overthrown; one held up a decanter of wine, another a gravy-dish, and a third the soup-bowl; and it was only in the critical moment between one roll and another, that the knife and fork could be used with safety. Notwithstanding our caution, it has happened more than once today, that a sudden and violent motion of the ship has thrown us all, with the loose furniture and table utensils, into a promiscuous heap, while more solicitude has been manifested for the preservation of the food than of our limbs. As no serious injury has been sustained, we have been very merry on the occasion, and have enjoyed our tumultuous repasts quite as well as on some occasions we should have relished a sumptuous entertainment.

But this was not the worst. "The storm increased in violence through the day," he wrote, "so that it far exceeded everything which I had hitherto seen. . . . Night, at length, set in, dark and dismal—the tempest raged with more violence than ever, and the fury of the sea was wonderful. To an old sailor it might doubtless have appeared no very uncommon thing; but to me, to whom these incidents were novel, the scene was awfully grand; and one who has never witnessed a tempest at sea, has not enjoyed one of the highest exhibitions of sublimity." The following night he recorded:

I spent an hour in the evening in viewing the phosphorescence of the waves. It was indeed a beautiful sight. The ocean was covered all over with luminous spots, occasioned by the foam of the waves, while around the ship, the water glowed and sparkled almost with the brilliancy of burning coals. When we shipped a sea the spray appeared like a shower of fire, falling among the shrouds, and the deck seemed to be covered with glowing embers. . . . The phenomenon, which is certainly beautiful in itself, is eminently so from its occurring, most remarkably, in tempest and darkness, when beauty is contrasted with grandeur.

It was the 27th of April before land was sighted and the next day before the green hills of Ireland became at all distinct. Another severe gale kept them off the coast for a day. "During the storm I took my station along with the master in the companion way. We split our fore-top-sail, and such was the fury of the winds and waves, that the captain was obliged to give his commands through the speaking trumpet, and his oaths, which were now more frequent and impious than usual, were thundered out from this brazen throat, with a voice that spoke 'louder than the tempest.'" After riding out another gale, they were able to proceed down the Irish channel and make their way slowly toward Liverpool. On the morning of May 3d, nearly a month after leaving New York, he writes: "We proceeded up the river Mersey, but the tide compelled us to drop our anchor three miles from the town, we went on shore in a boat, and, as we approached the town, the country around it presented a very pleasing view of green fields, windmills, villas, and other interesting objects; and the noise of commerce, 'thundering loud with her ten thousand wheels', indicated our approach to the busy haunts of men. A little before two o'clock we leaped ashore, and realized with no small emotion that we had arrived in England."

ENGLAND IN 1805

It was a restless and anxious England to which Silliman came early in the new century. The powerful forces which had brought about the French Revolution, though stifled for the moment by Napoleon, had done their part in stimulating the arts and the sciences, no less than political thought. Sympathy with the principles of freedom and equality which had caused the French people to overthrow their despotic rulers had inspired the magnificent Third Symphony of Beethoven, the *Lyrical Ballads* of Wordsworth and Coleridge which contained Coleridge's finest poem, "The Ancient Mariner" (1798). True, Beethoven had angrily torn the dedicatory page from his symphony when Napoleon had declared himself Emperor, and Wordsworth and Coleridge had retired with Southey to the Lake Country disillusioned, but the spirit of freedom was ascendent in all spheres of thought. Adam Smith's principles of free trade were being implemented; Thomas Malthus and Jeremy Bentham, in their different ways, were laying the foundations of modern liberal thought. In the arts the scene was dominated by the expatriate American, Benjamin West, who for nearly forty years had enjoyed royal favor. Another colorful autocrat, Sir Joseph Banks, was using his wide influence and vast wealth to further the cause of science by collecting a large scientific library and by sponsoring ventures such as the voyages of Captain Cook. Science had not yet begun to flourish in the universities, but Banks, during his forty-two years (1778-1820) as president of the Royal Society, had fostered its progress in non-academic institutions. The Royal Institution, founded by that versatile American, Count Rumford, was being directed by a precocious youth named Humphry Davy who, only one year senior to Silliman, had already gained international recognition through his studies on nitrous oxide (1800) and galvanic combinations (1801) i.e., the electric battery.

Into this vigorous atmosphere Silliman plunged with all the enthusiasm and receptivity of egocentric youth. He quickly became aware of the political situation which had developed into a real threat to England's very existence. On the French shore, Napoleon had massed a formidable army for an invasion of England, and throughout the summer of 1805, while Silliman was travelling and studying, he everywhere encountered evidence of anxious preparation for the dreaded signal. Meanwhile Pitt, England's great Prime Minister, who had been forced in and out of office three times in as many years, was feverishly working to persuade Russia and Austria to join with Britain in opposing Napoleon. As with everything that interested him, Silliman set down a full account of the tense political drama:

> The French emperor had prepared a vast flotilla at Boulogne, and other ports of France and Holland, contiguous to England. Armies which counted by hundreds of thousands, had, all summer, lined the French coast, and the array of war bristled and glittered from her maritime hills.
>
> The troops were the best in the world, fully provided with the means of annoyance, and marshalled by officers of the first talent and experience.

England, dimly visible from some points of the French coast, but intensely visible to the inflamed imagination of every soldier; hated with hereditary rancour, desired with immense cupidity; charged by France with a debt of blood, which for nearly a thousand years had scarcely ceased to flow; conquered once by a French invasion, and given in booty to the followers of the Norman;—England, contemplated with such feelings, was the prize held out by Napoleon to his armies, and from which they were separated only by a narrow sea.

It was true it was not England distracted by faction, and led by a va-cillating Harold; it was England, firm, loyal and powerful, that was to be assailed; but if the difficulties were immensely greater, so was the prize; another doomsday book was already in imagination prepared; and the palaces, villas, and manors of England, and above all, the unparalleled wealth of London, were, in anticipation, already divided among the fol-lowers of Napoleon. . . .

But although the situation was serious, it did not prevent Silliman from going ahead with his plans. He remained for a week in Liverpool, where he landed, exploring its museums, asylums, churches, literary institutions, the docks, a circus, and a quarry. He also visited a large Guinea slave ship and examined the inhuman cells in which slaves were confined. This called forth his righteous indignation: "My own country so nobly jealous of its own liberties stands disgraced in the eyes of mankind and condemned at the bar of Heaven for being at once active in carrying on this monstrous traffic, and prompt to receive every cargo of imported Africans. . . . Liverpool is *deep, very deep* in the guilt of the slave trade."

Many of young Silliman's reactions to the customs of the country are amusing and his journal entries could probably be found duplicated in the diaries and letters of almost any provincial young American who for the first time set foot on British soil. His observations and experiences were recorded in great detail and were later published, as he explains in the Preface to the printed journal: "At the request of the brother to whom the following pages are addressed, I commenced a journal, which was continued, from the first, without a single day's omission, till my return. . . . I wrote *at the time,* and *on the spot,* and was rarely a day behind my date; my information was derived almost wholly from personal observation and conversation. . . . Of course, I wrote with a degree of freedom which made it unpleasant to me to learn that it had been found impossible to confine the manuscripts within the limits prescribed, and when I returned, I was informed that they had been perused by many of my acquaintance, and their friends." Had he known that pressure would be brought upon him to publish these rather personal journal notes, he might not have been quite so ingenuous in his recordings.

The English servants caused him some concern for he found them "extremely assiduous and adroit and they ply the guest with such watchful attention that if for any reason he lays down his knife and fork, his plate is instantly caught away, and a clean one substituted." And not only did he lose his plate every time he became earnestly engaged in conversation, but he found that they had an oppressive way, especially in hotels, of arranging every detail of his personal life—at a considerable expense to himself. But he quickly learned about these things —learned too about local conventions which he zealously endeavored to observe, sometimes overzealously. After having dined at a Mr. Ewart's where every gentleman was in full dress with shoes and silk hose, he reached Mr. Roscoe's several nights later in a carriage in similar attire, only to find that the other guests turned up on horseback, their boots bespattered with mud.

His first social contacts were varied and he gives amusing examples of table conversation. On one occasion, after being profoundly bored with a prolonged discourse on politics and race horses, he was relieved to have the talk turn to vintage wines.

As to the ripening of wine, this is a subject of universal interest among convivial men, and forms a standing topic of discussion, on both sides of the Atlantic, in those circles where abundant drinking gives brilliancy to wit and ardor to patriotism; and while the faculties are thus sharpened, it is no doubt very natural to descant on the properties of this great cheerer of the heart of man. The bottle went round rapidly, and continued its circuit for several hours. Port, Claret, and Madeira were the wines; the two latter are very expensive in this country, and Port costs nearly as much in England as Madeira does with us.

From Liverpool he made a leisurely trip to Manchester where he visited Manchester College and was greatly impressed by its museums and its valuable library of 15,000 volumes. Much more important, however, was his meeting with John Dalton, the distinguished color-blind Quaker chemist who was then at the height of his activity. He attended one of Dalton's popular lectures at the Manchester Philosophical Society and was much surprised to find attractive young women in the audience, as well as a variety of laymen; in fact it seemed to be as well attended as the local theatre. "Mr. Dalton," he writes, "exhibited one experiment which I never saw so well performed before. A wire made several circuits around the room, being attached to the wall; its circuit was interrupted at small distances by the cutting of the wire; the room was darkened, and when a powerful electrical discharge was passed through the wire, it exhibited a brilliant corruscation at every interruption." Silliman was interested to note that the apparatus which Dalton had used to establish his great law concerning the equal expansion of gases at a given rise in temperature consisted of "little more than a collection of glass tubes, fitted up in a particular manner."

Another sight that stirred his interest was the recently completed Duke of Bridgewater's Canal, linking Liverpool with Manchester—a distance of 30 miles—over which coal was brought to Manchester. Robert Fulton, who had published his treatise on canal navigation in 1796, had helped his Grace to construct the canal; it became one of the most important additions to the system of canals which Fulton had envisaged, and no doubt was a factor in stimulating the construction of the Erie Canal in the United States several years later.

After leaving Manchester, Silliman spent three days in the "Peak" country of Derbyshire where he occupied himself with excursions into the Speedwell Mine and also the Owdin Mine, which had been started by the Romans or possibly earlier, where he "travelled half a mile into the bowels of a mountain." Since he had developed a lively interest in geology, the mines were of particular interest to him and he appended to his journal a special section entitled "Geological remarks on the Peak of Derbyshire." He examined the limestone deposits and the animal remains in some detail, and was able to reconcile his observations with biblical concepts. Thus he concluded:

> The submersion of the globe beneath an incumbent ocean is proved most abundantly by the records which it contains within itself. In sacred writ this submersion is distinctly stated to have occurred twice; first at the primeval period of chaos, when the earth was "without form and void, and darkness was upon the face of the deep," and secondly at the deluge of Noah. The structure of the earth is clearly reconcileable to these two great events, and were this the proper time and place, it could be satisfactorily evinced that the more geology is investigated, the more it confirms the truth of the Mosaic history.

From the Peak country Silliman continued his journey through Buxton and Leicester to Coventry where he witnessed a British election. It proved a startling experience. The whole town, according to his account, had gone 'hog-wild'; they were "all noisy and all drunk . . . even the softer sex seemed to be inspired with the madness of the occasion." At Birmingham he stopped only long enough to see the ruin of Joseph Priestley's house that had been destroyed by the mob in 1794; from there he proceeded to Woodstock and Oxford. At Oxford he met no one of eminence, for he anticipated a return visit (which, as it proved, never came about). Here there was no confused noise of commerce, only spacious, quiet streets and a great number of academic buildings rich with the historic associations of a university claiming Alfred the Great as its founder. "No place," he wrote, "ever impressed me with such feelings of admiration and awe and I presume it is without parallel in the world."

LONDON

On May 20th he reached London where he found lodgings at the Bell Savage, a century-old public house whose name, Addison had discovered, came from a romantic French story of a beautiful woman found in the wilderness—La Belle Sauvage. It was near St. Paul's which he called "a sublime building . . . and an exhibition of architectural grandeur which I had never witnessed before." To his brother he wrote: "I shall now cease for some months to be a traveller and shall become a settled resident of London." He found the Bell Savage too far away from the museums and libraries, so he later took lodgings near Cavendish Square in Westminster where he remained throughout the summer and until the middle of November, save for a brief trip to Holland in September.

At London Silliman was in his element. He first delivered his letters of introduction and then, while awaiting responses, he set about exploring the city. One of the first places he visited was the Tower of London where he was interested in the displays of ancient armor, the crown jewels, and particularly the lions, about which he had heard from childhood. In Westminster Abbey his attention was attracted to a monument in memory of Major André and he was gratified to see "that the inscription contained no reflection on General Washington." He was less pleased with the inscriptions on the monuments of Gay and Ben Jonson in the Poet's Corner: for on the latter he found "O rare Ben Jonson!" and on the former "Life is a joke, and all things show it; I thought so once, but now I know it." "Surely," Silliman expostulated, "a sepulchral monument is the last place on which a witticism ought to appear."

Following in his footsteps for the next weeks would have led one into places of strange contrast—from Pidcock's menagerie to dinner at Benjamin West's, from an exhibition of paintings at Somerset House to Drury Lane where he saw the King and Queen, the princesses, and all the royal entourage in its regal splendor. One would have been led into a London pastry shop to procure "sickly dainties which were, like flattery, delicious but unsubstantial," to the rag fair ('clothes, clothes, old clothes'), and back again to Westminster Abbey. "There is no object that I have seen in England," he told his brother, "of which I am so desirous to give you a correct impression as of Westminster Abbey, nor is there any task of the kind to which I find myself so inadequate. . . . Within its majestic walls history calls up, with powerful association, the actions of the illustrious dead. On one side, the monument of Newton fills you with impressions of the noble claims which science, intellect, and piety like his have on the admiration of posterity; while on the other, the tomb of Henry V recalls powerfully to one's recollection the conqueror of France. Over this tomb are suspended the shield which he bore, and the saddle which he rode, at the memorable battle of Agincourt."

From the sublime he turned to the slightly ridiculous, for in 1805 he was not yet air-minded (although balloon ascents had been made since 1784).

On my way home from Westminster Hall, I stopped at the Pantheon, to view a magnificent balloon which is now getting ready there. Lunardi, a well known aeronaut, is to ascend in it, with a party of a dozen ladies and gentlemen. They pay a high premium for the privilege of breathing among the clouds, and the chance of being killed philosophically. This balloon is ornamented, in a very expensive style, and will probably cost enough to buy the finest equipage in Europe; minds of a less ambitious cast would perhaps prefer the wheels and horses on the ground, to varnished silk and inflammable gas among the whirlwinds of heaven. . . .

YALE COLLEGE IN 1793

YALE COLLEGE IN 1796

YALE COLLEGE IN 1803

From the student notebook of Moses Bradford

THE LYCEUM

Silliman's first laboratory was located in the basement

Vauxhall Gardens—with its long tree-arched passages bright with "ten thousand lamps," with lighted paintings at the end of vistas and alcoves where a variety of refreshments was laid out, with music and elegant company and courtesans dancing —kept him up until dawn. "I went to bed with a violent headache, and completely disgusted with a place which, although superlatively elegant, is, I am convinced, a most successful school of corruption."

His interest in the political situation and in the men who were making England's history during this critical period led him to the House of Commons. "The room occupied by the House of Commons is merely neat; it has no appearance of splendor, and is really unequal to the dignity of this great nation." But William Pitt did not disappoint him.

Although Mr. Pitt remained silent with respect to the motion on the state of the army, I had the pleasure of hearing this great man speak a few minutes on a petition which he handed in. There was nothing in the subject which called for a display of eloquence; he made simply a statement of facts, but this served to identify his voice and manner. In his person he is tall and spare; he has small limbs, with large knees and feet; his features are sharp; his nose large, pointed, and turning up; his complexion sanguine; his voice deep-toned and commanding, yet sweet and perfectly well modulated, and his whole presence, notwithstanding the want of symmetry in his limbs, is, when he rises to speak, full of superiority and conscious dignity. I had a distinct view of him for six hours, during which time he sat directly before me. His dress was a blue coat with metallic buttons, a white vest, black satin breeches, and white silk stockings, with large buckles in his shoes. His hair was powdered. Notwithstanding the violence of the opposition, and their having been so long accustomed to his voice, when he rose, the House became so quiet that a whisper might have been heard from any part. He was very deliberate, so that not a word was lost; still energy was his most striking characteristic.

Silliman was also interested in Charles James Fox, Pitt's distinguished rival, then leader of His Majesty's loyal opposition.

His person is very lusty. His neck is short—his head large, round, and now quite grey—his chest is broad and prominent, and his body and limbs vast and corpulent, even for England. . . . His hair was not powdered; —he wore a blue coat, with buff cassimere under dress, and white silk stockings. I saw him in numerous situations, for he seemed very uneasy and changed his place many times: he walked about—went out and came in—went up gallery and down, and was almost constantly in motion. He spoke a few minutes on a petition from a person imprisoned in Ireland for treason. His remarks were very pertinent to the case; his manner flowing, easy, and natural, but without the dignity and impressiveness of Pitt.

He found that the general appearance of the House was very similar to that of the American legislative assemblies. "They have a custom of crying out hear! hear! when any thing is said to which they wish to call the attention of the House: sometimes this word is vociferated from so many at once as entirely to drown the orator's voice."

There were few men of prominence whom Silliman failed to see, either at a distance, as he saw Pitt and Fox, or to talk with at social gatherings, for although an unknown young American not yet "arrived," he managed through the warmth of his personality, grace of manner, and a little Yankee enterprise, to meet the foremost intellects living at that time in London. At Benjamin West's he had encountered his own countryman, the celebrated poet and liberal statesman, Joel Barlow, and through him, another fellow American. "This evening I went by invitation to take tea at his [Mr. Barlow's] apartments, where I met Mr. [Robert] Fulton, and Earl Stanhope: Mr. Fulton I had before seen at Mr. West's. This gentleman is at present the subject of considerable conversation in England, on account of his projects of sub-marine explosion, by which he hopes to put it in the power of all nations to defend themselves against naval attacks: since if a ship of war can be approached below water, and blown up without warning, it is obvious that the more ships of war a nation has, the worse she will be off. This project of Mr. Fulton's is at present the subject of some apprehension and a good deal of asperity and ridicule in England."

At the home of the Honorable Henry Thornton, M.P., to whom he had a letter of introduction, he met William Wilberforce, reformer, philanthropist, and foe of slavery, thus realizing one of his earliest youthful ambitions "to see this distinguished friend of mankind." He described him as "small and slender, and his countenance rather pale, but his eye is full of fire, and his voice uncommonly sweet; his manners are polished, and so conciliating, as to banish any unpleasant restraint in his society, and to place a stranger at ease." Mr. Wilberforce, during their several hours' conversation, asked him many questions about America—"particularly as to the state of literature, morals, and religion—the condition of the slaves, and the encouragement given to the slave trade; in all of which subjects, but especially in the three last, he manifested that strong interest which, from the tenor of his life and writings, and from the uniform character of his parliamentary exertions, you would naturally expect." Mr. Wilberforce was at that time pressing his bill in Parliament prohibiting the importation of Negroes into the British Colonies. Both Mr. Thornton and Mr. Wilberforce were interested in the course of studies, the discipline, the religious instruction, and the "ultimate honours and distinctions" in American schools and colleges, and Silliman was glad to enlighten them.

The eccentric Earl of Buchan, with whom he later had a lively and amusing encounter, also plied him with questions about America because he had been sympathetic with the Americans in their struggle for independence and was an ardent admirer of Washington. "On the present occasion," Silliman wrote,

he was full of Washington, condemning his own government not only in their treatment of the colonies, but for entering upon one unnecessary

war after another, thus involving the nation in debt and wasting human
life. Had things been ordered as his friend, Mr. Fox, and the party which
he led, himself included, had wished, all these evils would, he said, have
been avoided. As the Earl was short-sighted he came so near to me that
I was within the limit of his distinct vision, and when I retreated to gain
a little more offing, he followed me so perseveringly that I brought up
against the mantle and was rather inconveniently pressed between the
fire and his nobility. Without preface or apology he gave me the history
of his agricultural proceedings for the season, and especially in the culture
of the turnip; and he continued to pour forth an uninterrupted effusion
on agriculture, John Bull, Mr. Pitt, General Washington, and twenty
other topics, and I could find space only for an occasional interjection
of admiration or wonder. From the embarrassing effort to preserve the
gravity of my muscles, I was occasionally relieved by flashes of wit or
humor which now and then broke forth from the Earl, and the relief was
complete when a hearty laugh exploded between us.

On June 30th Silliman dined at six o'clock with Mr. Charles
Greville, brother of the Earl of Warwick—"the latest hour that
I have ever been invited to dine in England." Mr. Greville
was a member of the King's Privy Council and was well known
among scientists for his efforts in promoting the study of mineralogy, his own collection being probably the best private
collection in Europe at that time. At Mr. Greville's, Silliman,
with his usual good fortune in being in the right place at the
right time, met James Watt, the venerable "improver of the
steam engine," then nearing seventy. Mr. Watt, evidently
pleased to have so interested and receptive an audience, was
very expansive and talked at length of "mineralogy, chemistry, history, antiquities, or the fine arts." He also advised
Silliman about places of interest which he should visit, and
took Silliman to a *conversazione* at Sir Joseph Banks', Silliman
not having previously attended because Sir Joseph had failed
to call on him after he had left his card and letter of introduction immediately on his arrival in London. It was doubtless with a twinkle in his eye that Mr. Watt told him that Sir
Joseph "in consequence of the numerous demands on his time,

was, by the universal consent of society, excused from the common obligations of civility with respect to returning visits and sending invitations, and every stranger who had been introduced to him was expected to call again as a matter of course." Silliman reported that "my reception was such as to make me regret that my mistake had not been sooner corrected, and every embarrassment was removed by the courteous behaviour of this celebrated man."

Sir Joseph Banks is verging toward old age; he is now afflicted with the gout, and from this cause is so lame as to walk stooping, with the aid of a staff. His head is perfectly white, his person tall and large, and his whole appearance commanding though mild and conciliating. From his being President of the Royal Society, and from his having been long distinguished by active and zealous exertions to promote the cause of science, especially in the various departments of natural history, he has become, by common consent, a kind of monarch over these intellectual dominions. We found Sir Joseph in his library, surrounded by a crowd of the literati, politicians, and philosophers of London. These constitute his court, and they would not dishonour the King himself. Mr. Watt was so good as to make me easy in this assembly, by introducing me to such of the gentlemen present as I had a curiosity to converse with.

At this gathering Silliman met Major Rennel—"probably the first geographer living"; also other men of renown: "Dr. Wollaston, a chemical philosopher of eminence, and Secretary of the Royal Society; Dr. [Horne] Tooke, the historian of Catherine of Russia; Mr. Cavendish, who has done as much towards establishing the modern chemistry as any man living; Dalrymple, the marine geographer; Windham, the Parliamentary orator; and Lord Macartney, famous for his embassy to China." He continued: "In this assembly the most perfect ease of manners prevailed; there was no ceremony of any kind. They came and departed when they pleased, without disturbing anybody, and those present sat or stood, or walked or read, or conversed or remained silent, at pleasure. Eating and drinking formed no part of the entertainment, nor was any thing provided for this purpose."

Silliman was delighted with Sir Joseph's library which was "very extensive, for a private one, and is freely consulted by all persons who have been properly introduced. Sir Joseph lives in all the dignity of science; he has a librarian constantly attending in the library: he is a Swede [Solander] and himself a man of learning. There are also, I believe, two secretaries." He summed up his comments with these words: "On the whole, there is no man in England better entitled to lead in science, than this eminent veteran, and I imagine the august assembly at his levees, would give a stranger a more favourable idea of the intelligence and urbanity of the English than any other which he could frequent."

His next desire was to see the Royal Society in session and this he was able to do a few days later. Sir Joseph presided in a cocked hat with a star on his breast and Dr. Wollaston read a paper. "Although one may learn from their transactions every important and interesting fact which occurs in the Royal Society," Silliman wrote, "still it is a source of rational satisfaction to be present in one of the first scientific bodies in the world; a Society which has been honoured by the presidency of a Newton, and whose papers present a mass of science which has probably not been surpassed by the exertions of any body of learned men."

Although Silliman's journal represents an epitome of a liberal education, he was not spending all of his time investigating the wonders of London and talking with its prominent men. He had not forgotten that Yale College had sent him abroad for a specific purpose and he was as diligent in discharging his responsibility as he was in assimilating knowledge and culture. He had early made the acquaintance of a well-known practical chemist, Frederick Accum, who had been an assistant of Davy's at the Royal Institution and who was now greatly in demand for making chemical analyses and examinations. His knowledge of dealers and manufacturers of instruments was of inestimable assistance to Silliman, and Accum seems to have responded warmly to the young American and to have gone out of his way to help him. Silliman also worked with him on various experiments, and one day when he came to the laboratory he found Accum in high glee. Prime Minister Pitt had given him an order for chemical apparatus to be shipped to India and Mr. Accum was intending to clean out his laboratory and attic of all the old apparatus he could lay his hands on. Silliman assimilated this thoughtfully. "Well," he said to himself, "Mr. Pitt is not here to look after his apparatus and if he were present he would probably not be a very good judge; but I am here, and shall keep a sharp lookout for my own concerns."

He was learning, through contacts with men like Accum and through attendance at lectures such as Dalton's, the practical aspects of teaching science, how to make it attractive to people who had no knowledge to build on, how to awaken interest and promote further study. He made careful note of physical facilities, how lecture rooms were constructed, the extent and arrangement of mineral and chemical exhibits, and was fascinated by the system of boilers and pipes by means of which Count Rumford had attempted to install "central heating" in the Royal Institution—the first time such a thing had been attempted in England since Roman Britain. He described the theatre in detail:

The theatre is the room where the lectures are given. It is a superb apartment, and fitted up with great convenience. It is semicircular, and contains a pit and gallery, in which the seats rise row behind row. It is lighted from above, through a circular orifice, which, whenever the lecturer wishes to darken the room, can be shut at pleasure by a horizontal screen connected with a cord. This theatre has often contained a thousand persons. It is so fashionable a resort, that the ladies of Westminster are in the habit of coming to the Royal Institution to derive instruction from the rational-pursuits of philosophy. Surely every one would commend this preference, when the competition lies between routs and masquerades, and the delightful recreations of experimental science.

But, as one object of the institution has been to attract an audience, of course every thing has worn a popular air, and the amusing and the brilliant have been studiously pursued as well as the useful. The apparatus is by no means so extensive as I expected to find it.

Mr. Accum also introduced him to William Nicholson, Editor of the *Philosophical Journal* and one of the most prominent English chemists. Silliman said that "in preparing to decide what artist or artists to employ in constructing the philosophical apparatus for Yale College, I had frequent occasion to consult Mr. Nicholson, and he gave me the following wise advice: 'Seek for a man who has both skill and reputation, but one who is still ambitious of rising, and who still has, in some good degree, his fortune and name to acquire; with such a man, it will be a great object to serve you faithfully, and especially to gain a name abroad; but some of those who have already gained great celebrity and grown rich, are less careful that their articles should be excellent, than that they should be showy.' "

During the summer his scientific curiosity took him to the Royal Observatory at Greenwich, to Dr. John Hunter's museum—"probably the first in the world for the number and rarity of its anatomical preparations," and on a second visit to the British Museum where he found so much to interest him that he resented being hurried away at closing time. Again, as at Westminster Abbey, he was filled with a reverence for antiquity. "All these things serve to carry one back to the Roman ages, to identify the past with the present, and to produce a very pleasing impression when you reflect that a Roman hand once held the article which is now in yours." He persuaded the guide, although it was against the rules, to show him some of the royal correspondence and he was not a little awed to hold in his hand and see with his own eyes the clear and elegant Latin of Queen Elizabeth, and the scrawling, illegible hand of her father, Henry VIII.

He continued to lighten his visits to educational and scientific institutions with less serious occupations. The theatre attracted him often, though he was somewhat shocked at much of the entertainment offered him there. Thus he comments: "The dancing was very indecent; modesty seems not to be a necessary qualification in an actress." And at the Sadler Wells Theatre "the females laid aside the petticoat and appeared in loose muslin pantaloons, white silk stockings, and red slippers. They wore also, an open short frock, hanging loose like a coat. Such facts need no comment. I shall say nothing more than that they danced with much spirit and elegance." He visited also Old Bailey, Goldsmith's garret, the opera (which he did not like), the Royal Academy, and Hampton Court where he paused to contemplate the portraits of departed beauties—"notwithstanding the stiff drapery of the age, several of these belles were richly endowed by nature with those external charms, whose empire, if not as enduring as that of warlike conquest, is at least more extended."

THE WEST COUNTRY

On August 26th before he set forth on a brief journey to Windsor, Bath, Bristol, and the granite hills of Cornwall, he had the satisfaction of seeing Lord Nelson in the Strand, followed by an admiring crowd. "This is a distinction which great men are obliged to share in common with all wonderful exhibitions," he wrote, "—a dancing bear would immediately attract a throng in the streets of London, and this great admiral can do no more in the same circumstances."

At Windsor he called to see Sir William Herschel, the most eminent astronomer of his time. He was disappointed to find that Dr. Herschel was not at home but his sister, Miss Caroline

Lucretia Herschel, an astronomer in her own right, showed him the great telescope and explained its use. To one of his good friends at Yale he wrote: "I will thank you to tell Mr. Kingsley that the beautiful young lady whom his ardent imagination had painted as star-gazing through her father's magnificent tube, and discovering moons with eyes which might well have slain lovers, *is an ancient maiden lady, hard on three-score, and the sister, not the daughter, of the great astronomer.*"

The tin and copper mines of Cornwall, near Redruth, were of course the chief concern of his journey. To explore these mines it was necessary to descend vertically instead of walking down a path as at the Derbyshire mines, and since Humphry Davy had not yet invented his safety lamp for miners, he carried a lighted candle stuck in wet clay. "Although I was preparing, like Aeneas, to descend into the shades below, I could not boast of his epic dignity, for he bore a golden branch, while I carried only a tallow candle." After he had thoroughly explored the mines, he visited Penzance, ate breakfast at Land's End in the 'last house in England,' and then began a circuitous return journey to London, stopping at Stonehenge —grand temple of British Druids—and making a trip to the Isle of Wight whose chalky cliffs he recognized as similar to the white cliffs of Dover.

Back in London he went immediately about getting his papers in order for a trip to the Continent that was to be part of his official business. While awaiting his passports he came upon a sign in the Strand—"Bug Destroyer to His Majesty," and, much diverted, he promptly wrote his brother that he had seen all sorts of signs "but this knight of the bed bugs had escaped me till now; no doubt this bug destroyer takes good care that the royal slumbers shall not be disturbed by any of these rude vermin, which, alas for royalty! make no distinction between the king and the beggar."

TOURING THE LOW COUNTRIES

On September 29th he sailed for Holland, telling his brother that he did not feel it wise to continue his journal until
his return. Bad weather extended the journey to seven days,
during which they saw many signs of war and even witnessed
one slight exchange of volleys. On the 7th they arrived in Holland—a Holland which, Silliman observed, "is the mere cats-
paw of France. Sorely against her will, her claws are thrust into
the fire by her powerful mistress, while the humble and reluctant instrument gains no share of the nuts, but has the burning
entirely to herself." While exploring Rotterdam with an acquaintance, Silliman turned from admiring the statue of
Erasmus to look with disgust on a seventy-four-gun frigate
being built by the Dutch under French surveillance for the
war against England. Although warned to guard his tongue,
Silliman, thinking the shipbuilding useless since the English would only capture the vessel were it sent to sea, made
the unfortunate remark that they were "building for England." He scoffed at his companion's immediate concern over
the impropriety of saying this aloud, but his friend replied
that "Americans, who were accustomed in their own country
to utter whatever they thought, were not correct judges of
this subject, and that they were therefore constantly in danger
from their own imprudence, and their disposition to speak
their sentiments on all occasions."

And so it proved. Silliman's remark was overheard, inter-
preted as hostile to France, and he found, to his surprise and
vexation, that he would not be permitted to visit Paris. He
also discovered that the French in Holland made little distinction between the English and the Americans, since the
latter spoke English, and he was made somewhat uncomfortable by their suspicious hostility. For this reason he decided to return to England.

Before he was made aware of his doubtful welcome, however, he had visited Delft, Haarlem, The Hague, which "in point of beauty and magnificence far exceeds any place that I have ever seen; no part of London can be compared with it," and Leyden where he was disappointed in the appearance of the University but most interested in Boerhaave's botanical garden and in the library of "about forty thousand valuable books." The canals of course fascinated him; also the mode of travel on them. He liked the neat people, the mathematical precision of their gardens, and the gay lodges along the canal banks, but he did not feel at home as he had in England. He noted that gin was universally drunk by the common people who did not, however, appear intemperate —"they are probably saved from it by that profound national phlegm, which enables them to bear a considerable quantity of stimuli, without any remarkable excitement."

Delayed a day at Rotterdam on his return, he was pleased to find at a bookseller's many of the volumes he had hoped to buy at Paris. His guide, who was invaluable in translating bills of fare or dealing with the problems of transportation, was discovered to have limitations when it came to conversing of the classics. To their mutual delight Benjamin and the bookseller found a common language in Latin and they proceeded to carry on their business in that tongue, to the wonderment of the other customers. The bookseller's pronunciation, Silliman observed, was practically the same as that taught at Yale, and in the United States generally, "with the important exception of Harvard University." They parted good friends, Mynheer Van Spaan pressing his hand warmly with *"Vale! Vale Domine!"* and Benjamin re-echoing his adieu with a *"salutem sempiternam tibi domine!"* On October 24th he was once again in London sincerely blessing God for his safe return to a land of freedom and security. In the evening he attended Covent Garden to see the illustrious Mrs. Siddons make her last appearance on the stage.

While in Portsmouth before visiting Holland Silliman, with his customary luck, had on September 14th witnessed the embarkation of Lord Nelson. . . . "I thought myself happy to behold again, and under circumstances so peculiarly interesting, the man on whom the eyes of all Britain, and indeed of Europe and America, are at this moment fixed." He watched, with the rest of the huge crowd, as Lord Nelson walked down to the shore in "white underdress, with white silk hose, smallclothes and shoes; coat blue and elegantly illuminated with stars and ribbons, of which his lordship is said to be immoderately fond." As the boat pulled away an enormous ovation swelled from the throats of the watchers and Nelson acknowledged the salute with a wave of his hat.

This was the last time his countrymen saw him alive. After a tense summer of waiting the news had come that Pitt had succeeded in his negotiations with Russia and Austria, and Napoleon, "swift as an eagle and fierce as a lion robbed of his prey," had withdrawn the armies threatening England and rushed them to the banks of the Danube. At the time of Nelson's embarkation the British were not encouraged by Napoleon's successes, nor were they optimistic about the results of Nelson's inevitable encounter with the combined fleets of France and Spain. There was rejoicing, then, on the 6th of November when the news of the victory at Trafalgar on October 21st reached London—rejoicing mixed, however, with heavy sorrow, for the victory had cost England her greatest admiral. The stars and ribbons of Lord Nelson, the idol of the fleet and of the whole nation, had made him an easy target for the enemy.

Early in November Silliman had the honor of meeting Humphry Davy, then Professor Davy, who had been in Ireland during all of his residence in London. He wrote that Davy received him with "ease and affability; his manners are perfectly polite, easy and unassuming. He enquired concerning Dr. Woodhouse of Philadelphia, who visited London in 1802, and whose pupil I had since been. I was not less pleased with Professor Davy, as a man, than I had before been interested in him as a chemist and philosopher. We spent a short time in conversing on chemical topics and on his late tour in Ireland, and he shewed me a new article of apparatus which he had then recently invented. He is about twenty-five, and his appearance is even more youthful than would be expected from his years."

EDINBURGH

Silliman remained in London until the middle of the month when he started northward to spend the winter at the University of Edinburgh. He stopped for two days at Cambridge where he was put up at one of the colleges. Although he found the rooms very cold, he was impressed by their sumptuous appointments; he was horrified, however, that the fellows of Caius invited him to play at cards: "It struck me as unfortunate that the usual instruments of gambling should be found in the hands of the guardians of youth." He visited the principal sights of the University, including Trinity College Library and King's College Chapel, and he dined one night at high table at Caius College as the guest of one of the tutors. Although he thought well of the architecture of Cambridge, he concluded that it really could not compare with that of Oxford. Leaving Cambridge he journeyed on, stopping at York, Newcastle, and Alnwick. His fondness for castles made his journal covering this period read somewhat like a nineteenth-century Baedeker.

At Edinburgh, where he arrived on November 23d, he

spent the first week sightseeing and writing a long lamentation on the character of Mary, Queen of Scots, on the indelicate attentions of the unfortunate Rizzio, and on the birth of James VI of Scotland; he then settled down to more serious pursuits. To study the geology of the region surrounding Edinburgh he made frequent excursions to the top of Arthur's Seat, a hill overlooking the town, and on one occasion narrowly escaped serious injury from falling rock while climbing the Salisbury Craigs which lie to the northeast of Arthur's Seat. He was impressed by the close resemblance between the rock formation of the Craig and the ridge in New Haven forming East and West Rocks. As soon as he got home he eagerly investigated and found that it was the same kind of rock, *i.e.*, secondary trap. "Like Salisbury Craig and other similar eminences around Edinburgh both the East and West Rock at New Haven . . . repose upon sandstone, and there are other geological features in the structure of these districts that are extremely similar."

. While at Edinburgh he spent more time studying and less on social contacts than he had in London—he had used up much of his time and there was still such a lot to learn. His day, filled with lectures on chemistry and medicine, ran as follows:

I rise at seven o'clock and walk several miles before breakfast, which is over about nine o'clock. I then attend a lecture on the practice of medicine, by Dr. Gregory, till ten, and then one by Dr. Hope on chemistry till eleven. A walk succeeds and calls when necessary. Then study occupies the time till three o'clock P.M.; a lecture on materia medica by Mr. Murray succeeds till four o'clock. Dinner is served between four and five o'clock. At six o'clock I hear a lecture on anatomy by Dr. Barclay. At seven o'clock we have tea, and at eight o'clock I hear Mr. Murray on chemistry and mineralogy till nine o'clock. Then I have three hours at my books and pen, and my rule is to stop at midnight, but not unfrequently I am up till one o'clock A.M. Occasionally I hear other distinguished lecturers, as Professor Stewart, Dr. Thomson, Professor Playfair, &c. The severest part of my labour is in the composition of my own lectures [for Yale], about which I am employed all the time that I can redeem from the other objects of my pursuit.

Many of the men on the faculty of the University were known to him by reputation and he was glad to be able to meet the Alexander Monros, the foremost anatomists of that time. "The present professor, who is now far advanced in life [Alexander Monro *secundus*, 1737-1817] has been a very distinguished man, but he has almost relinquished the active duties of the station and has transferred them to his son [Monro *tertius*, 1773-1859]." Their fine anatomical museum was so similar to that of John Hunter in London that he saw no reason to comment on it.

He also met Professor Dugald Stewart—"the pride and ornament of the University, and of Scotland. With a countenance strongly marked with the lines of intellect; with an expression of thought, approaching almost to severity, but in conversation, softening with great benignity; and with manners, uniting every thing of dignity and ease, he, even at first sight, impresses a stranger forcibly with an idea of his superiority."

Silliman did not meet Walter Scott but he mentions that his *Marmion* was then in press. He also wrote one of his fellow tutors and good friends at Yale that he had learned that Robert Burns' dog was still in good health and he hoped to meet His Dogship before departing from Edinburgh. In this same letter he reported an amusing encounter with a Scottish lassie. Professing great interest in the language he begged her to say something to him, but of course he did not understand. He was greatly disappointed to find that his lack of knowledge had deprived him of the chance to further his education, for translated, her invitation had been: "Come my smart laddie and give me a kiss." This appears to be the only opportunity Silliman missed!

He was charmed by the kindliness and dignity of the hospitable Scotsmen. He enjoyed their "high intelligence" and
good conversation, he admired the fine complexions of the
pretty Scottish ladies, and at social gatherings he joined in
the merry singing and dancing with gusto. Only once was he
offered the national dish, the haggis, so highly praised by
Robert Burns. He thought it best described by Johnson as "a
mass of meat, made of the entrails of sheep, chopped small,
with herbs and onions, suet and spices, and enclosed in the
maw," and his only comment was that "its taste was fat and
heavy, nor did I feel any regret that the haggis was not an
American dish." But everything else delighted him and he
wrote that "the manners of the Scotch are full of affection
and cordiality;—on parting, after their little social interviews,
they all shake hands with each other, and with the strangers
who may be present; the ladies do it as well as the gentlemen,
nor is it a mere formality, but the frank and warm expression
of generous feelings; one hearty Scotch *good night* is worth
a thousand bows of ceremony."

Silliman could not leave Edinburgh without investigating
the *Edinburgh Review* and reported that he had "very good
opportunities of becoming acquainted with the origin and
plan of this work—a publication almost unrivalled in its way,
both for talent and learning." He enquired about the recom-
pense paid to writers, the editor's salary, the circulation, and
the details of publication. One wonders if it was at this time
that the idea of publishing a journal occurred to him. A
meeting with Dr. David Brewster, later editor of *Brewster's
Edinburgh Journal of Science,* developed through the years
into a friendship of great value to him when he started his
own journal.

After brief visits to Linlithgow and Glasgow, where he of
course visited the university, he boarded a ship homeward
bound. He had his last look at Britain as they slipped down

the Clyde on May 2, 1806. Twenty-five days later, after an uneventful crossing, Silliman was up at daybreak to catch his first glimpse of his native shores. He had left Britain with reluctance—it had been a happy, stimulating year he had spent there, full of interest and wonder—but he was now looking with eager anticipation toward New Haven and the challenge of the future.

CHAPTER IV

Meteors and Minerals
1806-1812

REFLECTING later in life upon his trip to England, Silliman set down his conviction that many of his life's accomplishments must be credited to his sojourn in Europe. "Had I remained at home," he wrote, "I should probably never have reached a high standard of attainment in geology, nor given whatever impulse has emanated from New Haven as one of the centers of scientific labor and influence."

The young man of twenty-six who went dutifully about his errands in New York probably was not troubled by thoughts of future fame. He called upon Oliver Wolcott, former Secretary of the Treasury under Washington and son of the signer of the Declaration of Independence, who had arranged the business details of his mission, and also on Colonel John Trumbull who had acted as his patron and friend in England. Then he and a friend proceeded to New Haven by packet sloop, embarking on Friday, May 30th. On Sunday, becalmed just twenty miles from home, they spent the day off Stratford, Connecticut, reading sermons and singing hymns. Late in the afternoon the capricious breeze returned and took them into port. Silliman went immediately to evening prayers at the College chapel, after which President Dwight, who had conducted the services, gave him a warm and paternal welcome. "I then realized that I was indeed at home again, and safe once more in my own town and institution." He was ready now to perform with zeal and energy the arduous responsibilities of his professorship.

His first duty was a visit to his mother in Wallingford. Although now seventy, she was in excellent health, and one can only guess with what relief she welcomed home her handsome youngest son. Since the summer semester had already begun at Yale, Silliman plunged immediately into teaching. This, and the hard physical labor involved in opening and unpacking all the boxes which had come from London, saved him from the 'let-down' that would have inevitably followed the strenuous exertion involved in his diverse activities abroad. He was pleased that the apparatus and books arrived in good condition with only a few unimportant pieces of glass broken. After his accounts were examined, the Prudential Committee gave him a vote of approbation as well as an honorary testimonial of entire satisfaction. His private commissions were also executed with fidelity, and he was able to balance his own account book—all of which allowed him a pleasant feeling of relief and a few modest comments on making expenditures correspond with his means.

When the summer semester was over, Silliman took a well-earned rest and he and his mother journeyed to Newport, Rhode Island, to visit his brother who had settled there to practise law after his marriage to Hepsa Ely in 1801. During the visit Selleck introduced him to the sister of Colonel George Gibbs, a wealthy gentleman who had brought over from Europe in 1805 a splendid collection of minerals to which he had made notable additions from time to time. Since Silliman's own collection consisted of some ores that he had brought from the mines of Derbyshire and Cornwall, a beautiful suite of Italian marbles purchased in Edinburgh, and some specimens of trap rock obtained in his excursions around Edinburgh, he was thrilled with Colonel Gibbs' treasures. The boxes were stored in a Newport warehouse and many had never been unpacked, but during the absence of her brother in Europe, Ruth Gibbs accompanied him to the warehouse several times while he examined the specimens. In fact, he was "even more delighted with the lady than with the minerals, although the latter were very instructive and gratifying." Miss Gibbs later married her cousin, Mr.

William E. Channing of Boston, but the story of the Gibbs cabinet of minerals did not end here; indeed it entered again and again into Silliman's life during the years when he was instituting the study of geology at Yale—the first course in geology to be given in America.

During the summer he had undertaken a study of the geological structure of the plains and hills around New Haven. On his excursions, usually on horseback, he was accompanied by several interested friends, one of the most enthusiastic being the distinguished philologist, Noah Webster. He was of invaluable assistance to Silliman, who wrote that "his large mind admitted every species of knowledge, and the fruits of his untiring industry in the prosecution of truth are garnered in his admirable Dictionary."

In the autumn of 1806 Silliman began teaching in earnest. He had before him a task challenging to any young man. He now possessed a solid foundation of contemporary scientific knowledge while his students had little conception of scientific thought, for their education had been chiefly classical and ecclesiastical. Few knew about science or were convinced of its value or even of its interest. Confronted with the problem of developing such interest, his imagination did not betray him into any theoretical flights of fancy. Rather it served to help him evolve a practical manner of presentation that proved both attractive and persuasive. His charm of manner and boyish enthusiasm did the rest. In his lectures, he tried to show the mutual relation between chemistry and geology where they existed, and he always used every means at his disposal to show illustrative material.

Silliman gave his first scientific communication before the Connecticut Academy of Arts and Sciences just two months after he had returned to New Haven. In this he made a comparison between the geological formations at Edinburgh and those of the terrain surrounding New Haven. Fifty-two years later he came upon this paper and was gratified to discover that there were no important errors, nor did he think that half a century had materially improved his style of writing.

Along with a number of other chemists of the time, Silliman was interested in mineral waters since at the turn of the century it had become fashionable to serve drinks diluted with carbonated water. Joseph Priestley had shown in 1772 that Pyrmont water, found at one of the more popular English spas, was nothing but ordinary spring water impregnated with "fixed air" (carbon dioxide). Various methods had been employed to secure the same effect and Silliman had available the John M. Nooth apparatus for achieving carbonation which he had purchased in Philadelphia. It is evident from some letters to Colonel Trumbull that he was called upon to produce considerable quantities of carbonated water to meet the demand in New Haven:

October 10, 1806.

Sir, I have been informed that you have been in the habit of importing soda water from London. I presume that the empty bottles may not be of much use to you and I should be glad to purchase all you have, as I am constantly called upon to manufacture soda water, and I cannot procure any glass bottles which will not burst, nor any stone ones which are impervious to the fixed air. I would thank you to inform me how many gross you have on hand—at what price they will come—and what steps I may take to procure them, if possible before you return to New York, or immediately after.

Finding it quite impossible with my present means to oblige as many as call upon me for soda water, I hence determined to undertake the manufacture of it on the large scale as it is done in London. . . .

Yale College, April 2, 1807.

Dear Sir—I have requested my particular friend, Mr. Twining of this city who is embarked with me in the soda water concern, to call upon you and apologize for my not having before this sent you a specimen. He will inform you that after succeeding perfectly in the construction of a complicated, difficult and expensive apparatus, and after having ascertained by two full trials that it would enable us to manufacture soda water of an excellent quality, we are thus far *completely foiled* by the very defective bottles which the potters have hitherto furnished us. They will not hold the fluid under such a pressure but weep copiously. The subject will not be abandoned and this is a principal object which now leads Mr. Twining to New York. Should it be in your power to afford him any information calculated to facilitate the object in view, you will greatly oblige, Your most afft. servt, B. Silliman.*

MINERAL CABINETS

When Colonel Gibbs returned from Europe in 1807 Silliman obtained an introduction to him, and through contact with Gibbs and familiarity with his splendid mineralogical collection he continued to broaden his horizons. With this same end in view he visited Boston in the autumn of that year and met other men with an interest in science, but he wrote that "at that period there was not much of a spirit of science in Boston. Literature was cultivated and flourished. In my visits to Cambridge I saw their small but beautiful collection of minerals, given them by the French Republic, which was followed by a similar donation from Dr. Lettsom of London. But mineralogy seems not then to have taken root at Cambridge; and neither mineralogy or geology entered into the plans of education in any of our seminaries." However, Salem, in its East India Museum founded by Dr. Nathaniel Bowditch, displayed to good advantage its large and instructive collections. As his interest in these museums grew, his desire to acquire a collection for Yale also took root, and he began to look about with a predatory eye. During his second year in college, Dr. Elisha Perkins of Plainfield, Connecticut, the father of a student at Yale, had introduced for therapeu-

* We are indebted to the Historical Society of Pennsylvania for permission to quote from these two letters to Colonel Trumbull. In Silliman's account book of this period there are many entries concerning his expenditures for the "soda water concern," but we have found no indication of what his receipts may have been.

tic purposes "something very curious called 'metallic tractors.'" These Silliman described as "tadpole-shaped pieces of
brass wire or steel—one of each—of about a finger's length,
and they were used by Dr. Perkins to remove pain in cases of
inflammation—rheumatism &c." The tractors were applied by
placing the two metals in contact, holding them between the
thumb and finger and thus pressing the points over the affected part. This new device became a storm center of controversy. Many people, Silliman said, attested to its efficacy,
but "how far imagination may have aided in such cases, it is
not easy to determine nor can we say that there may not have
been a galvanic influence, since two metals, especially those
so dissimilar as brass and iron, aided by perspirable matter of
the skin may have caused an electro-voltaic movement." However, he made no statement concerning the possible thera-
peutic value of the Perkins invention since he no doubt felt
that caution was indicated.

Dr. Perkins' son, Benjamin Douglass Perkins, went to England following his graduation from Yale to encourage there
the use of the tractors. His pretentions attracted wide notice
during his seven years' residence in London and he was encouraged to found a 'Perkinistic Institution' for further ex-
perimentation with the tractors. Since Mr. Perkins possessed
not only the self-assurance of a Yale education but also a certain plausibility of manner, he was able to enlist the support
of various influential members of the denomination of Friends
by treating them with tractors and by embracing their religion. Thereafter the "gay college student doffed his elegant
garments and appeared in Quaker Drab with large brimmed
hat and Quaker diction."

Silliman discovered in 1807, after Perkins' return to New
York, that during his sojourn abroad he had gathered together a very considerable collection of minerals, enough to
form a "cabinet"—which we would today designate a museum

collection. After calling upon him several times, Silliman was pleased to have Perkins express the wish that "thee might have this favorite collection to add to the attractions of thy lectures." He discovered that eight hundred dollars might be instrumental in persuading Mr. Perkins to present his collection to Yale and forthwith laid his request for its purchase before the Yale Corporation. Before the request had been acted upon, Mr. Perkins decided that one thousand dollars would be his price, but the Corporation authorized the purchase even at the increased figure, although the Treasurer, Mr. James Hillhouse, could not refrain from reproving Silliman somewhat caustically: "You are the gentleman who can open the College Treasury."

News of the arrival of the cabinet soon spread and many people came to view the exhibit which had been set up in Silliman's rooms. The interest thus aroused encouraged him to propose an independent and elective course in mineralogy. The classes were conducted around a table, seminar-fashion, and the minerals passed on trays so that each student could see and examine the material. A charge of five dollars was made for the course except to those who could not afford it. Twenty to twenty-five students immediately enrolled and their enthusiasm was such that the new elective became a regular part of the curriculum. Thus was the study of mineralogy—and the elective system—inaugurated at Yale College in 1807.

Meanwhile Silliman was also busy with other pursuits. He had discovered that he needed a textbook for his chemistry lectures and decided to publish an American edition of William Henry's *An Epitome of Chemistry,* because it was, he said, considered excellent among men of science. To this text, Silliman added some notes of his own to make it more adaptable to his own uses. The book, published in 1808, was recommended to the public (in a note signed by John Maclean and Silliman) "as the best Compendium of the Science with which we are acquainted."

Mr. Benjamin Perkins, having now forsaken the quixotic metallic tractors for the more sober profession of printing, was chosen as the publisher. Just as the proof sheets were beginning to come back, an event occurred which caused Silliman to drop everything he was doing and proceed to Weston, Connecticut. He wrote that on his return he found an accumulation of proofs from Mr. Perkins accompanied by reproofs, "as pointed as a Quaker and a newly converted one would presume to make." But Mr. Perkins was pacified when he heard of the phenomenon at Weston that startled all of New England and was deemed by Silliman so important to the cause of science that he immediately neglected all else to study it.

THE WESTON METEOR

In the early dawn of the 14th of December 1807 "a grand fireball passed over the town of Weston in the county of Fairfield apparently 2/3 as large as the moon . . . Several loud explosions took place near the zenith like heavy cannon with intermediate and subsequent discharges like those of musketry. There were three principal explosions during which stones fell to the earth—some of them very large, twelve and even thirty-six pounds in weight. One mass that was split to pieces upon a rock and ploughed its way into the earth might have weighed a hundred or two pounds." Silliman and his friend, Professor James Kingsley, examined the places where the particles of the meteor had fallen, questioned the witnesses of the phenomenon, and carried away with them a considerable number of specimens. They published a full account of the meteor in the *Connecticut Herald* (a New Haven paper), and after Silliman had made a chemical analysis of the specimens, he enlarged and revised their original paper and communicated it to the American Philosophical Society.

The Weston Meteor was considered of such importance in the scientific world that Silliman's account of it was read before the Philosophical Society of London and before the Academy of Sciences of Paris. Since it had been seen from Canada to New York and from Salem, Massachusetts, westward to the Delaware River, it was the considered opinion of Professor Day and of Dr. Nathaniel Bowditch, who studied the meteor separately, that it must have been several hundred feet in diameter, possibly a quarter of a mile. It was also decided that the meteorites did not come from the moon, nor from volcanoes on earth, but that their origin was celestial—that they came from "distant regions of space."

No scientific paper published in the United States had created so much interest and comment as that of Silliman and Kingsley on the Weston Meteor. Evidence of the limited knowledge of such phenomena even among educated persons is apparent in Thomas Jefferson's oft-quoted statement that "it is easier to believe that two Yankee professors could lie than to admit that stones could fall from heaven." But it is the chemical examination of the stones, published under a separate heading of the memoir, that is of greatest historical interest, for it was the earliest research of its kind of which any account is preserved. At that time there were few books on analytical chemistry and few laboratories equipped to make accurate analyses. Silliman found the composition of the meteorites to be as follows:

Silex	51.5	grains
Oxide of iron	38.0	
Magnesia	13.0	
Oxide of nickel	1.5	
Sulphur	1.0	

"Silex is the principal thing in the meteorites," he wrote, "combined with magnesia, a silicate of magnesia. Iron varies

in quantity. It is chiefly metallic iron alloyed with nickel."
Many years later Silliman's son wrote that his father appeared
to have followed "the memoirs of Vaquelin and Howard in
their analyses of the meteoric stone of Benares, and beyond
this to have been guided by his own sagacity."

Early in 1808 Timothy Dwight, Jr., son of President Dwight
and then a tutor at Yale, suggested that Silliman give a course
in chemistry for laymen that both ladies and gentlemen might
attend in the evening. Silliman records that "the proposition
was pleasing to me, as it placed me, professionally, in a new
position, responsible indeed, but promising to secure additional favor for the science then so new in Yale College." To
these lectures he invited a guest of the Hillhouse family, Miss
Harriet Trumbull, daughter of the second Governor Trumbull, whose acquaintance he had made a short time before.
Whether it was the fascination of the new science or the personality of its teacher, we cannot know, but Harriet Trumbull's parents announced her engagement to young Silliman
in August of that year. They were married on the 17th of
September of the year following (1809), their happiness
clouded only by the fact that Governor Trumbull did not
live to attend the wedding.

In the autumn of 1808, Silliman had been honored by a
visit from the man who later became known as the "founder
of American geology." William Maclure was a Scotsman who
had come to this country at nineteen to enter upon a business
career; he was forty before he became interested in geology.
He learned his geology in the school of Abraham Gottlob Werner, whose theories on the formation of the earth, in direct
opposition to those of the Englishman, Hutton, were creating
great controversy, and he became so fired with enthusiasm that
he returned to America and with hammer in hand went out
to study the valleys, mountains, and plateaus of eastern North
America. This resulted in the publication (in 1809, the year

after he visited Silliman) of his now classic *Observations on the Geology of the United States* containing the first geological map attempted for the eastern states.

It is indicative of the name Silliman had already made for himself that Maclure, a field geologist, should seek him out. He arrived in New Haven with a servant and a horse Silliman described as "lean from transporting stones," and he and Silliman spent several days exploring together the surrounding terrain. This visit was the beginning of a long professional and friendly association. When Silliman was instrumental in founding the American Geological Society in 1819, Maclure became its first president. Although Maclure gave the larger portion of his books and collections to the Academy of Natural Sciences of Philadelphia, which he served as president for twenty-two years, he also gave generously of both books and money to Yale because of his friendship with Silliman and his interest in the projects he sponsored.

Silliman himself was beginning to acquire a local reputation as a geologist, and in May of 1810 he was asked to survey a lead mine at Southampton, Massachusetts. For this he received his first professional fee—fifty dollars in gold. When he made a second survey of this mine a year later, he discovered that his advice had not been followed and in consequence the mining operations had been both costly and unsuccessful.

Domestic felicity was now added to the satisfaction of his increasing professional responsibilities. The limitations of bachelor quarters in the College had been replaced by a gracious house on Hillhouse Avenue* where the young Sillimans were exceedingly happy.

During the first year of his marriage, Silliman prepared for publication the journal of his European travels. In an indirect way, the journal had led him to his bride, for Mr. Daniel

---

* The house is still standing, but is now turned around to face Trumbull Street (No. 87).

Wadsworth, who was married to Harriet's oldest sister, Faith, had been so impressed with the diary when it came into his hands while Silliman was still in England, that he invited its author to his home as soon as he returned. During his first visit Silliman was asked to deliver a letter at the Trumbull residence at Lebanon on his way to Newport, and thus the romance began. Mr. Wadsworth further indicated his high opinion of the journal by urging Silliman to publish it so that others might enjoy it, and this suggestion was accompanied by a generous offer to underwrite the expense of publication. Urged by other friends also, Silliman reluctantly agreed to edit the material. He felt that much of it was too personal and that he had included too many details which, though interesting to his brother and his family, would not be particularly appropriate for the general public. He realized, however, if he expunged personal views and reactions from the material that much of its freshness and spontaneity would be lost. In the end he omitted very little and the journal was published in two volumes in 1810 under the title of *A Journal of Travels in England, Holland and Scotland, and of Two Passages over the Atlantic, in the Years 1805 and 1806.*

Mr. G. P. Fisher, Silliman's first biographer, states that "probably no book of European travel, by an American, has been so much read or so generally admired. A great many persons derived from it their first distinct impressions of England and English society." The distinguished jurist, Chancellor James Kent, of Albany, New York, wrote Silliman: "I have just finished your 'Journal of Travels,' and I feel a propensity too strong to be resisted of making known to you the pleasure I have received from the perusal, and the lively impression of respect and esteem which it has given me for your character. The volumes were read by me with minute attention and unceasing interest. By the aid of excellent maps I followed your steps over every part of the town and the country, and I feel proud that an American, and more so that a professor of the College to which I once belonged and for which I still feel a filial veneration, should have given to the world one of the most instructive and interesting views of England that any single traveller has ever presented." Silliman was further gratified to receive a warm letter of appreciation from William Wilberforce to whom he had sent a copy of the book.

After reading the journal Benjamin Rush of Philadelphia on June 8, 1810 wrote a letter to his son James, who had gone to England to study, advising him how profitably to spend his time. Dr. Rush apparently felt that his former pupil, Silliman, had made the most of his opportunities, for he advised his son to follow a similar course: " 'Be all eye, all ear, all grasp' in your intercourse with the citizens of London of all descriptions." He continued:

Mr. Silliman's travels through England and Scotland are read with great avidity in our Country. They are an excellent model for a journal. I presume they are or will be reprinted in London. Mr. James West carried a copy of them with him to England. While I thus wish to direct your attention to everything that can improve the gentleman, the philosopher, and the man of the world, so as to qualify you to mix with all those classes of people who are to be your patients to advantage, always recollect that your first duties will be to the sick, and that the physician and surgeon should predominate over all other human attainments in your character. For which purpose let the anatomical theatre, the dissecting room, and hospitals, together with such lectures upon medicine as are valuable, occupy your first attention. A short course of natural philosophy with experiments would be useful to you. I formerly advised you against buying books. But this is not to prevent your stepping now and then into a second-hand book store, or stopping at a stall in the street, and picking up at a *low price* a rare and valuable book. Could you obtain a complete copy of Bacon's Works or of Baxter's in theology in this way, they would be a great acquisition to our library.*

* We are indebted to The Library Company of Philadelphia, Ridgway Branch, for permission to quote from this letter and to Mr. L. H. Butterfield of the Princeton University Library for bringing it to our attention.

In the midst of the many expressions of pleasure and congratulation evoked by the journal, the Sillimans were happy on June 16, 1810 to announce the birth of a daughter. They named their firstborn, Maria Trumbull Silliman, and her arrival "sent joy to many hearts and grateful thanks to Heaven." With this additional incentive to succeed in his work, Silliman applied himself with renewed vigor.

THE GIBBS CABINET

Still with an eye to increasing illustrative material for his teaching, he asked Colonel Gibbs during the winter of 1809-10 what he intended to do with his superb collection of minerals. It developed that the collection had been offered to the government to be displayed at the military academy at West Point or at Washington, but the government officials had not been receptive to the idea, nor had Boston, Cambridge, New York, or Philadelphia. Silliman was overjoyed, therefore, to have Colonel Gibbs reply to his question: "I will open it here in Yale College if you will fit up rooms for its reception."

There was probably no more unoccupied room around the Yale College of that time than there is at Yale today, but Silliman hastily conceived a bold plan and lost no time in presenting it to the President. Dwight without hesitation warmly endorsed the suggestion that the walls between several of the rooms on the second floor of South Middle College be knocked out to provide one large room for the display of the cabinet. Colonel Gibbs was satisfied that the space would be adequate, and the work of preparing cases was commenced. "They [the cases] were to be glazed throughout and narrow receding shelves constructed to receive the minerals—these shelves were to recede and at the same time, rise like stairs, so that the minerals might not hide each other, but all be visible at one view. . . . They were carefully and skillfully made by Mr.

HARRIET TRUMBULL

From a crayon sketch by her uncle, John Trumbull

THE SILLIMAN HOUSE

On the corner of Hillhouse Avenue and Trumbull Street in New Haven

HILLHOUSE AVENUE ABOUT 1850

The Silliman house is at the extreme left

James Chaplin, an English workman who was in the employ of the College."

Silliman recounts an amusing incident that occurred while the work was in progress. He received a call one day from the Reverend Dr. Ely, one of the most active and efficient members of the Corporation and of its Prudential Committee. After inspecting the progress they had made, he said to Silliman: "Why Domine, is there not danger that with these physical attractions you will overtop the Latin and the Greek?" Silliman replied: "Sir, let the literary gentlemen push and sustain their departments; it is my duty to give full effect to the sciences committed to my care."

While the preparations were still in progress Silliman received a letter from Dr. Benjamin Waterhouse, Professor of Physic at the Harvard Medical School. Although Dr. Waterhouse was best known for his pioneer efforts to introduce Edward Jenner's method of vaccination in America, it was a mutual interest in mineralogy that drew the two men together. Silliman had seen the mineral collection given by Dr. Lettsom to Harvard when he visited Cambridge in 1807, but he did not meet Dr. Waterhouse on that occasion; indeed, it will be remembered that he was disappointed to find that "mineralogy seems not to have taken root at Cambridge."

Boston, Octr 11,

1811.

Dear Sir—I write this expressly to thank you for your polite attention to my son. Had I known that he contemplated visiting New Haven, I should have given him a line to you. I am very glad he visited you while my townsman Col. Gibbs was with you, because he has gained thereby a double advantage. From his description, I do not wonder that he is enraptured with your fine collection. He is now arranging anew his own, at my house in Boston. Should you visit this place, my son's collection of Insects, Plants, Fishes & Fungi might possibly afford you some amusement. The collecting these things, during the three last years of his college life, & without neglecting his collegiate exercises, has been rather too strong a draught on his health; but he is so deeply immersed in natural history that it has become his ruling passion, & will doubtless mark his future life.

When I consider my first efforts in Mineralogy, and my first lectures upon it, three & twenty years ago, and when I reflect on what has been done since, I am, in a degree, astonished at the rapid progress of that branch of knowledge. Hill & Cronstadt were my oracles. I began the collection, which you may have seen at Cambridge, with about as many minerals as you gave my son. As this was the first cabinet that was formed, as far as I know, in the United States (?) I shall publish an account of its origin & gradual increase, together with some particulars which may possibly give you, and every other liberally-minded man, pain. Dr. Lettsom sent me almost all the European specimens which we possess. . . . Is your mineralogical premium to be confined to the students of your own college, or extended to the sons of others? Do you consider an *ad euxdem* scholar as one of your own?

I have recently changed my residence from Cambridge to Boston, and should you travel hither, none would be more glad to see you than Your humble Serv[t] Benjamin Waterhouse.

P.S. My son wishes me to present you his thanks for your attentions, & a proffer of his services in transmitting you specimens of anything in the mineralogical department, as in that respect he leaves no stone unturned in this neighborhood.*

When the cases were finished, Silliman and Colonel Gibbs' servant placed the specimens on the shelves under the Colonel's direction and Silliman said that when they turned out something really superb, they could hardly restrain their admiration. Before the work was completed he had an unfortunate accident in the laboratory when preparing some "fulminating silver" which involved the use of corrosive materials. As he was stirring the mixture, it exploded in his face and blinded him. In his Reminiscences, he describes the accident as follows:

My face and eyes being directly over the dish, they received the full force of a violent explosion which threw me back upon the wall behind

* We are indebted to the New-York Historical Society for permission to quote this letter.

and produced intense pain both from the concussion and from the corrosive materials—alcohol, nitric acid, and lunar caustic—blown forcibly into my eyes. I was stunned but not deprived of my consciousness and I fully comprehended my perilous condition.

I was entirely alone, my assistant, Lyman Foot, having gone away on an errand. I made my way in the horror of deep darkness—for my eyes were involuntarily shut—to the pneumatic cistern, the only water that I could hope to reach. It was covered with drawers full of minerals but I managed to throw some of them aside and thus reached the water with which I washed my face and especially my eyes abundantly. My first anxiety was to ascertain whether fragments of the porcelain dish had hit and penetrated the balls of the eyes. With intense anxiety I passed my fingers carefully over the blind orbs and to my inexpressible relief ascertained that the eyes were there and not lacerated. I then pulled the lids apart one after the other on both eyes and to my great and grateful satisfaction found that the objects in the room could be dimly discerned as if through a thick and yellow haze. I had now done everything for myself that I could possibly do alone, and sat down to await the arrival of my assistant.

It was an hour of dismay as well as intense pain, as he contemplated the possibility of never being able to see the face of his beloved wife and little daughter again. He prayed that such a disaster should not befall him so early in their life together and at the beginning of his career, for of what use was a blind chemist?

The two months he spent in a darkened room were filled with anxiety, not only for Silliman himself, but for Harriet Silliman and for their physician, Dr. Eli Ives, for it was the first case of the sort that he had been called upon to treat. Even baby Maria, then thirteen months, seemed to feel uneasy about the bandages on her father's eyes as she played in the room beside him. When his sight was finally restored, completely, and he was able to return to the laboratory and to the arrangement of the Gibbs minerals, they looked particularly beautiful to him.

The opening day itself was sharply etched on Silliman's

memory. Mr. Mills Day, a tutor in the College and the brother of Professor (later President) Day had died and the College was in mourning; Colonel Gibbs had arrived for the formal opening, when on Sunday morning, June 18, 1812, tidings came of the declaration of war with England. "A thrill of painful excitement—an electrical stroke vibrated through the continent—it was a thrill of horror to all good minds that were not paralyzed by party, for fraternal blood, after a peace of almost thirty years, was now to be shed again."

In spite of the confusion, it was decided to proceed with the plans, and with appropriate ceremonies the Gibbs Cabinet was opened to the public. Silliman recorded that "nothing had been before seen in this country, as regards mineralogy, which could be compared with this cabinet. It kindled the enthusiasm of the students and excited the admiration of intelligent strangers. It was visited by many travellers and New Haven was then the focus of travel between the North and the South. Railroads were unknown and navigation by steam had hardly begun. The comparatively slow-moving coaches conveyed the passengers who were generally willing to pass a little time in New Haven, and the cabinet of Colonel Gibbs afforded a powerful attraction while it afforded also a high gratification."

It is perhaps difficult in our day to appreciate the profound impression that the collection made on those who came from near and far to see it, but it was a time when scientific collections were few, and therefore novel, and when specimens from Europe were rarely seen. It was also a time when visiting such an exhibit was a form of recreation as well as instruction. Among the distinguished guests who came to New Haven were the Honorable Josiah Quincy, later to be President of Harvard, the Honorable Harrison Gray Otis, prominent leader of the Federalist party, the Honorable Daniel Webster, and Colonel David Humphreys, statesman, diplomat, and aide-decamp to Washington. Silliman wrote that "trains of ladies also graced this Hall of Science and thus, mute and animated nature acted in unison in making the Cabinet a delightful resort." Some understanding of the prestige and recognition that the collection brought to Yale College may be gained from a contemporary account of its extent and history:

The great cabinet of Col. Gibbs, which consisted of about ten thousand specimens, was formed by that gentleman during a residence of several years in different parts of Europe. The catalogues and papers which accompany this collection show that it was formed almost exclusively by three separate purchases: one, made at Lausanne in Switzerland, another at Paris, and the third in London.

The collection purchased in Switzerland was made by Count Razamousky, a Russian nobleman, who had lived for many years in retirement at Lausanne, where he devoted himself to mineralogical pursuits, in the society of the celebrated Prof. Struve and other mineralogists of that neighborhood. At length, however, being desirous of returning to his country, he offered his cabinet for sale, and Col. Gibbs became the purchaser. This collection, from its richness in Russian and Siberian minerals, formed a very precious part of the Gibbs cabinet. It was also well furnished with the mineral productions of Saxony and Dauphiny, and embraced a valuable suite of volcanic specimens from the environs of Padua in Italy, and the borders of the Rhine in Germany.

The French collection, however, constituted by far the most valuable portion of this cabinet. It was made by M. Gigot d'Orcy, one of the Farmers-General under Louis XVI, a man of great opulence, who fell a victim to the guillotine during the French revolution. Its formation occupied him for forty years, and was the result of great expense, numerous travels, and an extensive correspondence. The number of pieces in the collection was rising of four thousand, the majority of which were obtained in France and the neighboring countries. It embraced also a valuable collection of rocks and fossils from Egypt, Franconia, Maestricht, Grignon, and Courtagnon. The mineralogical part of the collection was well arranged, and scientifically and minutely described. In this condition, the entire cabinet was purchased of the brother of M. Gigot d'Orcy by Col. Gibbs.

The third division of the Gibbs cabinet was furnished by the Count de Bournon, which consisted chiefly of English minerals and of gems from the East Indies; the latter derived, for the most part, from the duplicates of the celebrated Greville collection, afterwards bought by the British Museum.

An added attraction for the visitor was the catalogue of the collection. Although Silliman prepared it for the use of those who knew nothing of mineralogy, he discovered that it served to clarify and fix his own knowledge of the science.

With the acquisition of the Gibbs Cabinet, at least under Yale's roof if not in her possession, Silliman proposed that he teach a separate course in geology, combining it with the course in mineralogy already begun. Previously he had taught geology only when he could integrate it with his lectures on chemistry. The new course was instituted as soon as the Perkins Cabinet had been moved over into the room with the Gibbs collections. His early efforts are well described fifty years later when his son-in-law, Professor James Dwight Dana, succeeded to his chair of geology:

In entering upon the duties of this place, my thoughts turn rather to the past, than to the subject of the present hour. I feel that it is an honored place, honored by the labors of one who has been the guardian of American Science from its childhood; who here first opened to the country the wonderful records of Geology. . . . Just fifty years since, Professor Silliman took his station at the head of chemical and geological science in this college. Geology was then hardly known by name in the land outside these walls. Two years before, previous to his tour in Europe, the whole Cabinet of Yale was a half bushel of unlabeled stones. On visiting England, he found even in London no school, public or private, for geological instruction, and the science was not named in the English Universities. To the mines, quarries and cliffs of England, the crags of Scotland, and the meadows of Holland, he looked for knowledge, and from these and the teachings of Jameson, Hall, Hope, and Playfair, at Edinburgh, Professor Silliman returned, equipped for duty—albeit a great duty—that of laying the foundation, and creating almost out of nothing, a department not before recognized in any institution in America.

He began his work in 1806. The Science was without books—and too without system, except such as its few cultivators had each for himself in his conceptions. It was the age of the first beginnings of Geology, when Wernerians and Huttonians were arrayed in contest. The disciples of Werner believed that all rocks had been deposited from aqueous solutions—from a foul chaotic ocean that fermented and settled, and so produced the succession of strata. The disciples of Hutton had no faith in water, and would not take it even half and half with their more potent agency, but were for fire, and fire alone. Thus, as when the earth itself was evolved from chaos, fire and water were in violent conflict: and out of the conflict emerged the noble science.

Professor Silliman when at Edinburgh witnessed the strife, and while, as he says, his earliest predilections were for the more peaceful mode of rock making, these soon yielded to the accumulating evidence, and both views became combined in his mind in one harmonious whole. The science, thus evolved, grew with him and by him; for his own labors contributed to its extension. . . .

And while the science of geology was growing "with him and by him," Silliman became involved in the foundation of another new department in Yale College—he was asked to serve on a committee to investigate the feasibility of establishing a medical school in New Haven.

CHAPTER V

Founding a Medical School
1810-1813

IN 1810, when the Medical Institution of Yale College was formally authorized by act of the General Assembly at Hartford, only five medical schools existed in the United States. The earliest was the Medical College at Philadelphia (1765), and John Morgan's celebrated *Discourse on the Institution of Medical Schools in America,* which led to its founding, is remarkable for its vision and stands as the first important document in the history of American medical education. The school which Morgan organized, although modelled after European medical institutions (particularly Edinburgh), was well adapted to conditions existing in the Colonies. Another medical school, following the Philadelphia model, soon grew up at King's (later Columbia) College in New York (1767). This was merged in 1813 with the College of Physicians and Surgeons, which had been founded in 1807, leaving the latter the only New York school. In the intervening period medical schools also appeared at Harvard (1783), Dartmouth (1797), and Maryland (1807).

COLONIAL MEDICINE

In his illuminating study, *Medical Education in the United States Before the Civil War* (1944), Norwood estimates that at the time of the Revolution there were 3,500 persons practising medicine in the United States. Of these, not more than 400 had received an M.D. degree from a reputable college and only 51 of the degrees had been granted in America. According to N. S. Davis, whose report on *Medical Education and Medical Institutions in the United States* (1877) is the source of much factual knowledge concerning the early schools, the total number of medical degrees conferred in the States prior to 1810 by the five medical schools did not exceed 600.

The early colonists were therefore largely at the mercy of untrained practitioners, among whom were many charlatans. Prior to the Revolution, if a student in a community outside of Philadelphia or New York wished to study medicine and could not be admitted to one of these two schools (whose capacity was limited), he had either to apprentice himself to an older physician or betake himself to Europe.

The situation in Connecticut before 1810 was far from salutary. The apprentice system obtained and despite the fact that Connecticut physicians had succeeded in 1792 in forming a state medical society, there was an insufficient number of well trained physicians and insufficient regulation of medical practice. Earlier, in 1763, a group of physicians in Norwich, Connecticut, being aware that their own interests would be better served could the public be protected from malpractice, applied to the state legislature for the privilege of meeting quarterly and of selecting annually a committee of three physicians who would examine candidates for the practice of physic and would grant certificates to those found qualified. Unfortunately, this petition was defeated.

EARLY NEGOTIATIONS

In December of 1777, six months before Ezra Stiles accepted the presidency of Yale College, he had prepared a memorandum at the request of the Corporation which revealed that he was well aware of the acute need for medical education for the young men of Connecticut. In this document, Stiles showed both vision and sagacity by proposing a plan for the development of a university at Yale—as opposed to the college then existing—a university which, to discharge its responsibility to the public, would sponsor professorships both in Law and in

Physic. There were at that time two hundred physicians in Connecticut, and Stiles maintained that "to circulate and increase medical knowledge must be an object worthy the attention of every well regulated state." He even went so deeply into the question as to outline the subject matter that might be covered in the three lecture series that he proposed, the last to include material on the nature of diseases and the art of medicine and surgery as taught by Hippocrates, Boerhaave, van Swieten, Sydenham, and Mead.

This interesting document has never been published, nor was Dr. Stiles able to implement his cherished plan when he became president, for the College had been plunged into acute financial difficulties by the Revolutionary War. For this reason, Stiles' successor, Timothy Dwight (the elder), has been more often credited with the distinction of suggesting a medical school at Yale. Whether or not Dwight knew of Stiles' memorandum, he pursued the idea of a medical school with patient persistence. Thwarted at first by lack of funds and the skepticism of the physicians he approached, he for a time laid aside his plan and worked on the establishment of science in the College, an effort which resulted in Silliman's appointment. In 1806, through the cooperation of his classmate and close friend, Reverend Nathan Strong of Hartford, Dwight succeeded in having presented to the Corporation a resolution asking for the appointment of a committee to enquire into the feasibility of establishing a professorship in medicine.

The selection of this committee was important. Its membership must be forward-looking, wise, and have a thorough understanding of the issues involved. Silliman's study of anatomy, surgery, materia medica, obstetrics, and other medical specialties, in Philadelphia, London, and Edinburgh was now to bear fruit. He was appointed to the committee to serve with Nathan Strong and President Dwight. Although he had not taken a formal medical degree, he had studied in medical schools and he, more than any member of the Yale faculty, understood the needs of medical education and was also able to visualize the particular requirements of his own state.

The committee moved cautiously. The unusual charter which the State Medical Society had finally secured gave it power to confer medical degrees as well as to examine and license physicians. By 1807 the Society occupied a position of unusual strength and had assumed leadership in the formation of regulations governing medical education. The special committee at Yale College wisely recognized that any attempt to establish a school of medicine in Connecticut must necessarily be on a cooperative basis, and they accordingly made a formal overture that was presented to the State Medical Society on May 20, 1807.

Subsequently a committee composed of the Yale representatives and selected members of the Society met frequently in Silliman's rooms in the Lyceum at the College under President Dwight's chairmanship. Silliman reported that conciliation was necessary, as was to be expected, for there was considerable skepticism on the part of the practising physician of the theoretical ideas of the college professor. The physicians were fearful, too, lest they lose their control of medical practice. It was in resolving these difficulties that Silliman's particular talents were brought into full play. Although he was not yet thirty, he had already developed an adroitness in handling people and this, together with his enthusiasm and firm belief from the start that there was no reason why the two committees could not establish rapport, was responsible for the successful outcome.

Some of the medical men expressed concern lest promising candidates should be excluded from the proposed institution because of inability to pay fees then individually collected by the professors. Since Silliman anticipated that his course in chemistry would be given at the Medical Institution, he proposed: "That one medical student from each county recommended by the Medical Society should be admitted gratis to the lectures, eight persons in all—they being selected for their intelligence, worth and poverty." This proposal satisfactorily disposed of the objections and eventually "the prejudices with which some of the medical men appeared to have come to the meeting were removed and harmonious action ensued." He came to regret the arrangement, however, and wrote: "It has, we believe, been sometimes abused as men have come to claim the privilege who were unworthy of it and the physicians became reluctant, on account of the crowded state of the profession, to offer a premium for students of medicine."

In the autumn of 1807 the committee from the Medical Society announced its willingness to form a union with the College for the purpose of establishing a medical institution. Again a joint committee worked to formulate a constitution that would combine the purposes of both the College and the Society. In October 1810 the Act of Incorporation, representing the united efforts of the two committees, was passed by the General Assembly. This later formed the basis for the first charter of Yale's Medical Institution—the first, and for a long time the only, school to be formed under the joint auspices of a college and a state medical society.

SELECTING A MEDICAL FACULTY

The necessity for securing a medical faculty was the next consideration, and in this Silliman also played a leading rôle. The most desirable candidate for an appointment was Nathan Smith of Dartmouth College. Throughout New England his preëminence in the field of medicine, his driving force and originality as an administrator, teacher, and scientific investigator were widely recognized. At Dartmouth he had built up, singlehanded, a thriving medical school, but he had had to bear so much of the responsibility himself that it was rumored he might be willing to consider a less strenuous post. There was, however, one insurmountable difficulty that prevented the Yale Corporation (and Silliman of course concurred in this opinion) from inviting Nathan Smith to head the new Medical Institution—Dr. Smith's religious views were scarcely orthodox. Silliman wrote to Jonathan Knight, who was in Philadelphia studying for a possible position in the new school: "The talents & reputation of Dr. Smith of Hanover are doubtless known to you in common with the intelligent people of New England generally. Ever since a medical school has been projected here Dr. Smith's name has been much mentioned as a candidate for one of the places. In the opinion of many his claims were such that his repeated infidelity ought not to debar him; but our Corporation and President never countenanced the idea because they believe him an infidel & would not reconcile it with their duty to appoint any man of this description to a station in the College, whatever might be his talents, reputation & learning."

The Corporation therefore approached Dr. Mason F. Cogswell of Hartford who somewhat reluctantly, because of the demands of his large practice, consented to be Professor of Surgery, provided there be an assistant professor who would assume the burden of the work. For this assistant professorship they placed their confidence in young Jonathan Knight, a promising graduate of the Class of 1808 whom Silliman had selected from among the Yale tutors and sent to Philadelphia to study for his new assignment, even as he himself had done.

Shortly after Knight had made his decision to study medicine he received an enthusiastic letter from a former classmate, Timothy L. Gridley, aged twenty-two, who was then studying medicine at Dartmouth College under Dr. Smith. Gridley began his letter: "I was informed a few months since, that you had resolved to pursue the study of physic. I had long before

been convinced of your talents as a scholar. I was then convinced of the correctness of your taste. I shall not however
devote this letter to the purpose of descanting on the intrinsic,
or comparative merits of our profession. Suffice it to say, that
the intricate wonders of anatomy, in addition to those of
Chemistry & Botany, together with the extensive field that is
opened to the Physician for the exercise of fortitude, patience,
humanity & benevolence in discharging the duties of his profession, will afford abundant employment, as well as entertainment to the feeble powers which Nature has bestowed upon
me."

After this digression he came to the point by saying he had
heard that a medical school was being formed in connection
with Yale College and that the only obstacle to the commencement of lectures was the appointment of instructors. He then
proceeded to describe at length Dr. Smith's excellent qualifications for a professorship—his reputation as a lecturer and the
inestimable value to his teaching of his original work and improvements in operative surgery. "But his qualifications as a
Surgeon or Physician do not constitute the sum of his excel-
lences," Gridley continued. "He is a man of general information, of an easy, familiar but dignified deportment, communi-
cative, agreeable in conversation, of equable temper, and of a
charitable disposition. In short, wherever he is known, he is
admired & beloved. He has an extensive medical Library and a
very respectable anatomical Museum, in which there are one
or two preparations which he brought from Europe."

Before writing this long letter to Knight, Gridley had
broached the subject of the Yale Medical Institution to Dr.
Smith and without hesitation the latter had replied that in the
course of a few years it would undoubtedly excel any medical
school this side of Philadelphia. "He observed," wrote Gridley,
"that Yale College was the first institution in the U. S., had the
ablest Professors, and was under the best regulations. He en-

tertains a high opinion of Prof. Silliman, who is held in such estimation at this place that my having attended a course of Lectures under him was a sufficient guarantee for admission into the Court of Hippocrates, a kind of medical *Phi Beta.*" Dr. Smith had gone on to say that he would accept without hesitation any offer that might be made to him from New Haven. Gridley concluded: "But the consideration of the greatest importance relative to Dr. Smith's admission to a professorship is that it would not only facilitate the acquisition of medical knowledge, but give the school an immediate and extensive reputation. He has now 60 students. In case of his removal, they would most of them attend him. For the opportunity of attending Mr. Silliman's lectures in addition to Dr. Smith's would collect students from all parts of N. England." Whether or not Jonathan Knight showed this wholehearted recommendation to those in authority is not known, but had he done so it would have had little effect, for no offer would have been made from New Haven while the ministers of the Corporation were still convinced of Smith's heresy.

In the meantime Silliman was sending Knight, throughout his two years of study, letters of advice and encouragement revealing not only his interest in the young medical student, but the thoroughness with which he himself approached every matter that came within his sphere of influence. On January 29, 1812 he sent him a grant of $200 which he had procured for specimens for the new school, that Knight was preparing in one of his classes, with specific suggestions as to what might be needed.

I should suppose that three skeletons would be desirable; one with the bones connected by wires to be suspended by a cord & pully in the anatomical room in full view of the class for constant reference; one similarly put together but capable of having the bones unhooked & taken apart so as to be shown in pieces when necessary & one with the bones connected by the natural ligaments dried & varnished. It would be well to have great boxes with lids & hinges & locks made for them as will answer to keep them in after they arrive. Besides these it would be well to have plenty of separate bones of various ages & sizes—several crania & parts &c &c—and one of the skeletons should be a female. A good blood vessel subject would be desirable—several prepared hearts—[illegible] wax-injected preparations of the liver &c with some specimens of injected lymphaticks &c. Excuse these hints. I am sensible however that you cannot do as much as I have here suggested in one season but perhaps you can in two, if you should spend next winter also in Philadelphia. If you can obtain any serious advantage in remaining after the lectures are finished I think you had better do so & take as much money from the fund as may be necessary for your support. I will justify it to the Committee. I heard the President tell the Committee that sooner or later we must spend $2000 on the anatomical department; so you see there is a spirit of enterprise & liberality.

You have heard correctly as to Col. Gibbs cabinet. I trust you will see it all arranged when you return. More college buildings will no doubt be created if the means can be obtained. Our members rise—300. . . . With much regard, I am, truly your friend, B. Silliman.

In May, Silliman wrote again, giving further advice and some information about Yale's financial condition. During the uncertain years following the Revolution Ezra Stiles had barely been able to keep the College going; he was not able even to keep the buildings in repair, much less to build new ones or to create new departments. Timothy Dwight had had to wait four years before funds were available for the appointment of a Professor of Chemistry, and it is nothing short of miraculous that he was able to raise the $9,000 with which they sent Silliman abroad to secure books and apparatus. With the need for a new building now increasingly urgent and with the new school to finance, the Corporation was about to approach the state legislature for an appropriation. In any case, funds for the education of Jonathan Knight were not available as they had been for Silliman; nevertheless Silliman was urging him to spend another year in Philadelphia if possible. Since his letters were usually more fatherly than official, he added a conscientious postscript: "This communication is from *me in my private* capacity and intended merely for your information."

Benjamin Silliman to Jonathan Knight   New Haven, May 18, 1812.

My dear Sir— . . . I trust you will make your arrangements, if practicable, so as to spend another winter in Phil[a], and to begin as soon as possible to digest the heads of lectures. As to pecuniary aid from the corporation I think it would not be safe to calculate upon it; their funds will be pretty much pushed by their efforts to build a new College; they are now making an application to the Legislature for aid on that subject. By & by we must try them (the Legislature) on the subject of aiding the medical school, but you must be contented to begin in a small way & as *you* grow I trust your means will. Can you not spend a few weeks with Dr. Post in New York before you go again to Phil[a]? It is of vast importance that you become a good operator as well as anatomist; a good surgeon is extremely wanted here & would not fail to be supported, if prudent. . . .

Everything, my dear Sir, will depend upon your own exertion & let me add the success of the School will depend in a great measure upon you; the thing must be done ably & prudently & it will go. Yours sincerely,

B. Silliman.

Although Knight was developing in a manner most satisfactory to those interested in his welfare and the future success of the medical school, he had been taken on promise rather than performance, and the desirability of having someone of Nathan Smith's reputation on the faculty whose name would lend prestige to the school was still keenly felt. It was therefore with great satisfaction that the Corporation received the news that Dr. Smith's religious sentiments had undergone a complete change. Silliman wrote Knight that since "those who know him best believe him too frank & high minded a man to allow them to credit the idea that he would be willing to practice duplicity to carry a point," the conversion was believed to be genuine, and since Cogswell was very happy to yield his appointment, the Corporation had forthwith decided to invite Nathan Smith to become the Professor of Surgery.

Lest Knight be disappointed in the decision, Silliman wrote: "Dr. Smith's reputation in surgery & midwifery is unrivalled in New England—in these he could be of vast advantage to you both by instruction & practice. . . . In the meantime you can be growing up to take his place by & by. . . . Dr. Cogswell, Dr. Dwight, Dr. Ives & myself all agree in opinion that Dr. Smith, far from standing in your way, would be of great advantage to you in the ways mentioned above and also by causing the school at once to rise to a point which it would probably otherwise take years to attain."

At Commencement in 1813 it was announced that Nathan Smith had been appointed Professor of the Theory and Practice of Physic, Surgery and Obstetricks; Eneas Munson and Eli Ives, both New Haven physicians of the highest reputation, had been appointed Professor of Materia Medica and Botany and Adjunct Professor of Materia Medica and Botany respectively; Benjamin Silliman, Professor of Chemistry and Pharmacy; and Jonathan Knight, Professor of Anatomy. In the autumn of that year thirty-seven students, having produced "satisfactory evidence of a blameless life and conversation," assembled for instruction in a building rented from Mr. James Hillhouse, and the Medical Institution of Yale College was thus officially launched.

Simultaneously with the opening of the school, Silliman was beset with domestic worries, for Harriet Silliman, who had been seriously ill following the birth of a second daughter (Faith) in December 1812, now suffered a painful attack of acute rheumatism. Since dysentery prevailed in New Haven, Silliman entrusted their two little girls to the kind care of the Wadsworths while he remained at home with Mrs. Silliman. He wrote that Eli Ives, "as friend as well as physician, assisted me in lifting and moving her, as she was unable to move a limb, and the swollen muscles were very painfully sensitive to the touch." It was an anxious month, but finally, at the end of October, she was sufficiently recovered so that by stopping

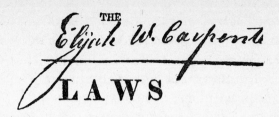

THE LAWS

OF THE

MEDICAL INSTITUTION

OF

𝔜𝔞𝔩𝔢 𝔆𝔬𝔩𝔩𝔢𝔤𝔢.

NEW-HAVEN,
PRINTED BY OLIVER STEELE.
1813.

TITLE PAGE OF THE FIRST EDITION OF THE
LAWS OF THE MEDICAL INSTITUTION

overnight at Wallingford she was able to go to Hartford where Faith Wadsworth spared no effort in bringing about her complete recovery.

For nearly forty years Silliman continued to teach chemistry and pharmacy to the medical students at Yale. The original faculty worked together for sixteen years (until Dr. Smith's death in 1829) and built up the Medical Institution into a flourishing school. Nathan Smith's prestige and leadership soon increased the enrollment to approximately ninety students. Dr. Knight completely justified the confidence which Silliman and the Corporation had placed in him and became one of the most distinguished professors in New England. He and Silliman were the last surviving members of the original faculty.

President Hadley, speaking at the hundredth anniversary of the founding of the Yale School of Medicine, made this pertinent observation: "Among the many great things which the elder President Dwight accomplished for Yale, perhaps the most striking was the establishment of an active interest in chemistry, mineralogy, and geology, under the leadership of Benjamin Silliman. But the practical applications of chemistry and geology to the problems of industrial life were in these early days hardly recognized; and the interest thus created by Professor Silliman would have rested on a purely theoretical and therefore rather precarious basis, had it not been for the establishment of the Yale Medical School a few years later. I doubt if any of us today recognize how dependent the scientific courses in the College and the practical courses in the Medical School were upon one another in those early days or how much each did for the other."

Silliman undoubtedly contributed much through his long years of lecturing, but his first and perhaps most valuable service to the Medical Institution was his part in bringing together the representatives of the College and the State Medical Society into a harmonious working group. It was an unusual situation requiring exceptional tact and compromises on both sides. The success of their joint undertaking was a tribute to all those concerned in this farsighted enterprise.

CHAPTER VI

War Years and Family Problems
1812-1818

T H E spring following the establishment of the Medical Institution (1814) found Silliman and other officers of the College working with the students and townspeople, spade and
shovel in hand, in a hurried effort to fortify the city of New
Haven against possible attack by the British. The War of 1812
was unpopular in the United States with all save the western
and southern pressure groups in Congress that looked with
envious eyes upon Canada as the most likely territory for their
next aggression. The New England states, particularly those
along the coast, were flatly opposed to the war because it in-
terfered seriously with their whaling and Pacific East India
trade, in fact with all trade. They particularly resented it since
the war had been declared supposedly to protect these very
interests. The British Admiralty had been impressing American seamen into service for the Crown, but these incidents
were minor compared with the interference and insults of
Napoleon. Feeling in the New England states was therefore
bitter—if there must be war, it was felt it should have been
against the French. Silliman, from his residence in England
and his thwarted attempt to visit France, knew from first-hand
experience that it was the Napoleonic regime which had made
things difficult. He shared President Dwight's view (and that
of many other New Englanders) that Great Britain and the
United States were natural friends, bound together by the
strong ties of common origin, language, laws, religion, and
interests. Along with the rest of New England they deemed the
War of 1812 unnatural and causeless. Indeed, it is hard to
comprehend how President Madison and those who precipi-
tated the war could have played quite so naïvely into the hands

of their real enemy, Napoleon, or how they could have been so stupidly blind as to enter into a costly war on such a trumped-up excuse—to protect a section of the country to which such a war could only spell economic ruin. As a matter of fact, it forced New England to turn from seafaring to manufacturing, a change inevitable in the long run, but New Englanders at that time could see nothing favorable in the situation.

The warfare along the Canadian border and the Great Lakes (where the real objective of the conflict was to have been gained) resulted in disaster, due to poor generalship and half-hearted fighting on the part of the inadequately trained American soldiers. The British took every fort and won every engagement with disconcerting ease. Along the East coast the British squadrons worried the populace, destroyed thousands of dollars worth of property, made off with supplies, and kept American shipping successfully bottled up in the harbors. The government sent no troops to protect the coast, indeed the troops available were inadequate even for the war with Canada, for in some states the war was so unpopular that militia refused to respond to the call.

Only at sea did the Americans meet with any success at all. The Navy's three oldest frigates, the *Constitution, United States,* and *President,* made several gallant attacks on formidable British forces, whose victories at Trafalgar and the Nile were still of recent memory. Their success created "amazement and indignation in England, and rejoicing in the United States." But while these gains raised the morale of the American people, their military value was slight, and most of the American men-of-war were blockaded in their harbors during the remainder of the war.

Professor Parker Cleaveland wrote to Silliman from Bowdoin College in 1814 where, midst the alarums of war, he was trying to finish his *Elementary Treatise on Mineralogy and Geology* :*

> . . . I have long been wishing to write you, and among other things, to thank you for the politeness, &c., of your last favor. I need not attempt to describe to *you* the state of alarm in which we have lived during a great proportion of the last summer; for I perceive you must have participated in similar troubles. . . . It has been supposed that Brunswick is in very considerable danger of an attack, as we have two large manufacturing establishments, and two iron furnaces, one of which is constantly bringing forth the *means of annoyance*—as Mr. Madison calls them—that is, cannonballs; and more especially, as we are so easily accessible from the sea.

Professor Cleaveland entertained the serene belief that college ground would be held sacred by the attacking British, but nevertheless he wrote that he had "found it difficult to avoid entirely the contagion of alarms, and have for some time kept my most valuable papers, &c., in trunks, ready to decamp when I see contiguous buildings in flames. So much,—and all to gratify the cursed democracy of this country. Can brother [Jeremiah] Day keep *cool,* even when breathing the sober atmosphere of mathematics? I confess I cannot,—and, when I reflect on the present state of our native country, and perceive *'Troja fuit'* [Troy was] written on all our greatness, my only relief is to sally forth with my hammer, and vent my feelings in the demolition of some rugged cliff of granite that rises on the banks of the Androscoggin. But I have insensibly gotten into the mineral kingdom, and will now endeavor to feel a little calmer, notwithstanding these turbulent times. I still go on, and suffer no day to pass *without a page or two.*"

But Brother Day could not keep cool breathing the "sober atmosphere of mathematics," nor Silliman the fumes of the chemistry laboratory when the British began to move closer

* A book which came to stand with Maclure's *Observations on the Geology of the United States* as one of the most important of the early publications on the subject.

to New Haven, threatening the safety of the town, the College, and their families. Groups of some fifty students with a professor in charge worked in relief parties with the townspeople strengthening the Revolutionary fort on Beacon Hill (later known as Fort Wooster), building a bulletproof shelter for powder, drawing up heavy artillery to guard the harbor, and throwing up redoubts for the protection of those who might have to defend the city. Since there were no troops and no army, citizens and military companies volunteered, and they drilled much as equally unprepared townsmen had drilled in the Revolutionary War. British depredations continued down the coast while the citizenry of New Haven anxiously waited. Then one morning the masts of three British ships could be seen from the hills of the city. A ship of the line, a frigate, and a sloop of war had anchored off Guilford, just sixteen miles away, bringing the war awkwardly close. That morning the troops paraded and James A. Hillhouse, son of the Treasurer of the College—"scholar and poet"—marched as a volunteer in the ranks with a musket on his shoulder even as had his father when New Haven was once before invaded by the British on July 3, 1779. Silliman, with heavy heart, saw another friend and neighbor, Captain Blake, embark in a sloop armed with only one piece of field artillery to investigate the rumor that there was a small British cruiser in the Sound. He knew that there was no possible chance that Blake would return if he did encounter the enemy. But fortunately the British did not attack, and the city and Yale College survived the war unharmed.

In February of this year (1814) Silliman had had another accident which kept him confined for a month or more. He had taken a shortcut across the campus in an attempt to maintain his record of always being punctual for classes and in climbing a fence, his foot slipped and he fell astride the fence inflicting a painful injury. He was helped to the medical school where he was treated by Dr. Smith and eventually went home on a cot borne by medical students. He was gratified to learn that the waiting class was not surprised when the report of his accident came to them because they had been certain that only something serious would have prevented him from appearing.

There were other domestic events which distracted some of his attention from his classes during this year. In the spring he bought for $4,500 the house on Hillhouse Avenue in which they had been living for five years, and although prices were high because of the war, they went about enlarging and altering it. Not only was their family growing but Mrs. Silliman's mother, Mrs. Jonathan Trumbull, had sold the family place at Lebanon and was to make her home with the Sillimans. Mrs. Trumbull had helped them buy the house, for a professor's salary did not reach far beyond the necessities; but even with this assistance, Silliman found that with his family increasing and the expense of Mrs. Silliman's two illnesses, he must secure money to do the rebuilding. He accordingly borrowed a thousand dollars from Yale College.

Late in the summer, on August 24th—the very day that the British were burning the Capitol in Washington—their first son was born. This, their third child, was christened Jonathan Trumbull after the late Governor Trumbull. Accompanying his joy in this first son was righteous indignation at the news from Washington. "The government was disgraced by permitting such an event," wrote Silliman, "and the British disgraced themselves, not by burning the ships and the munitions of naval warfare at the navy yard, for that was within the rules of war, but by destroying by fire the National Capitol, the Presidential Palace, the National Library and public offices."

He further commented with reference to the war that "nothing was gained on either side but military and naval renown—dearly bought. . . . On our side we gained not one of the points for which we contended. In the treaty of peace concluded at Ghent in December 1814 [although hostilities had not ceased and the decisive Battle of New Orleans was not won until January 1815], the principal alleged causes of the war—the right of search for the property of an enemy and the impressment of American seamen—are not even mentioned."

The war—the needless waste of men and material—troubled Silliman deeply, but he took no active part in protesting against it as did many other New Englanders. Indeed, the demands made upon his time by two courses in science in addition to his classes for the medical students, which he taught separately, kept him too busy to look far afield. In 1813 he had begun to teach in the rooms where the Gibbs Cabinet had been set up and the summer of 1815 found the cabinet fully arranged and the lectures well systematized and established. He gave elementary mineralogy in the spring in a course of twelve or fifteen lectures, with geology following in the summer. He also continued his class in geology for the public, as well as an elective course. In those days students paid each professor for his course rather than a general tuition fee to the College, and from the five-dollar charge for the elective course, Silliman had an average income of $190 a year for the seven years the course was given.

President Dwight's deep interest in the new science made him a regular attendant at the lectures on mineralogy and geology, and in the summer of 1815 Silliman welcomed a friend of former years. Robert Hare, who in 1804 and 1805 had helped him with chemistry, had now come to learn geology. Hare was preparing for a professorship at the College of William and Mary at Williamsburg, Virginia, but he stayed only one year in that position, transferring in 1819 to the University of Pennsylvania where for forty years his brilliant lectures made him one of the most distinguished of the early American scientists. The friendship that had been so firmly established in the basement laboratory of Mrs. Smith's Philadelphia boarding house was mutually gratifying and helpful to these two pioneering spirits.

A fever which prevailed in New Haven in the autumn made it necessary for Silliman to take Mrs. Silliman and the children to Wallingford. Almost simultaneously there was a terrific hurricane which devastated the seacoast and is said to have "salted the twigs and leaves as far inland as Worcester, Massachusetts" (much as did the September hurricane of 1938). Such was the damage, that Silliman and his brother-in-law, Mr. Wadsworth, journeyed by horse and carriage to Providence to view the results of the tempest.

The next two years were full of activity but without special significance in the advancement of science at Yale. A second son and fourth child was born to the Sillimans on December 4, 1816, making this a memorable year to Silliman personally, for he regarded his growing family with satisfaction and deep affection. The boy was named Benjamin Silliman, Jr.—very appropriately so it developed, for this child was to follow in his father's profession.

But happiness was offset by sadness caused by the death of his great and good friend, President Dwight, on January 11, 1817. Dwight was mentally alert until almost the end, despite intense suffering, and the evening before his death Silliman read to him the fourteenth, fifteenth, and sixteenth chapters of the Gospel according to St. John "which appeared to command his reverent attention." Silliman was asked by the Corporation to deliver the funeral oration in the Center Church and he was glad to have an opportunity to express once more his deep admiration and unfailing devotion to the man who had so largely determined his own destiny.

. . . President Dwight embraced the whole circle of human knowledge within his views; and gave every science its just estimation. Although his principal occupations, as an instructor, had been in studies of a different character, no man appreciated more highly than he the importance of mathematical and physical science. While he greatly extended the courses of instruction in his own peculiar branches and procured the addition of a distinct professorship of languages and ecclesiastical history, and another of law, he promoted with all his might the increase of the means of teaching the physical and experimental sciences. The library of the College and the apparatus of natural Philosophy and Astronomy were very greatly enlarged; and Chemistry and Mineralogy, constituting a distinct Professorship, were introduced, with extensive means of experiment and illustration. In these he took much delight, and he dwelt with particular pleasure on the splendid deposit for the illustration of mineralogy with which Col. Gibbs' liberality has honoured the Institution. . . .

He early conceived the plan of a Medical Institution, and his classmate and friend, the late venerable and distinguished Dr. Strong of Hartford, brought forward the first distinct proposition for that purpose. . . . Under his auspices the number of the academical instructors was doubled; besides the entire addition of the Medical faculty . . . he anxiously desired, and hoped soon to see a professorship of eloquence, and he aspired to such an enlargement of the whole plan of the Institution as fully to entitle it to the character of a university.

Death again brought sadness the following year when his mother, then eighty-two years old, failed to recover from an attack of pneumonia. This happened during the summer of 1818 when the Sillimans were also worried over the illness of their son Trumbull (Jonathan Trumbull, now four years old). He had developed into a most attractive child, with a bright and happy disposition and a "pensiveness" that especially endeared him to his father. His unfavorable symptoms of fever and coughing were aggravated during the winter and Silliman after long and busy days at the College would come home to sit by the boy's bedside during the night, cheering the child by singing hymns. Mrs. Silliman at this time was helpless with another acute attack of rheumatism.

In the spring Silliman and a faithful nurse took the boy to Monte Video, the estate of Mr. and Mrs. Wadsworth outside Hartford, in the hope that a change of climate might prove

efficacious and that Mrs. Silliman, who was soon to bear
another child, might not be distressed by the sight of his suf-
ferings. They knew then that he could not live so his every
whim was satisfied, and since he loved to ride, Silliman on
every pleasant day drove with him around the countryside in
the carriage which the Wadsworths placed constantly at his
command. The slowly unfolding beauty of a New England
April this year wrenched his heart, but at times the child, re-
sponding to his surroundings, rallied to such an extent that
Silliman dared to hope that he would survive. Finally, dis-
heartened, he took him back to New Haven—Mrs. Silliman's
confinement was approaching and she longed to see her son.
Silliman arranged a swing for Trumbull's amusement and
continued to take him on daily rides, but the child lived only
a short time longer. "The evening before his death his little
brother Benjamin came into the room and although Trumbull
was panting with cough and fever, on seeing his little friend
waddling into the room, he smiled and uttered his favorite expression, 'O funny little Bunny!' " The next day he was gone.

On the 18th of June (1819), the day before Trumbull died,
another daughter, whom they named Harriet Trumbull, was
born to the Sillimans. She "gave us much consolation under
the loss of our darling son," but she could not take his place,
and Silliman's deep sorrow began to undermine his health.
When they lost the baby daughter also, in just two months, he
became so distraught that he was advised to go away for a rest
and change of surroundings. His devoted brother-in-law,
Daniel Wadsworth, accordingly accompanied him on a tour
of Canada. They went by way of Albany, Lake George, Fort
William Henry, and Ticonderoga to Quebec and Montreal,
and the remarkably full diary which Silliman kept indicated
that he was reading widely at the time, both in the history of
the period and in general literature. Wadsworth made sketches
of various landmarks (Lake George, the approach to Quebec,

etc.) which were subsequently included with the diary when Silliman issued it in 1822. The book was so popular that a second edition was published in 1824. There were included, of course, many minute observations on local geological formations, and while the text does not have quite the freshness of his English diary of 1805-1806, it suggests that the trip had pulled him out of the depths of his depression.

But he and Mrs. Silliman had not yet reached the end of their sorrows. Two more children—Charles, born on July 6, 1820, and Edward, born on October 4, 1821—died a few months after birth. "Thus, four children had been removed from us within three years," Silliman wrote, "and anxiety, watching and sorrow had worn upon the health of both parents."

During the spring of 1821 he had barely escaped pneumonia, and a severe cough that subsequently persisted wore upon his strength. In May, in company with Samuel F. B. Morse (a former student of the Class of 1810, artist and inventor-to-be of the telegraph), he went on a trip to Albany, Fort Ticonderoga, etc. He discovered that he should have gone south instead of travelling north, for the journey did little to help him throw off his cough.

During the summer Silliman applied to the Prudential Committee for a professional assistant in addition to his man of all work. The Prudential Committee granted this request, and Sherlock J. Andrews of Wallingford was engaged at a salary of $200 a year in addition to board and room. Although Andrews knew no chemistry, he proved quick to learn, and his enthusiasm, warm heart, and genial temperament were good medicine for Silliman, whose state of mind and health was still uncertain. In addition to his general debility, concern over Mrs. Silliman's health after losing three babies in close succession and worry over money matters in connection with the professional journal he had started in 1818 kept him in a prolonged state of anxiety.

ILLNESS

In the autumn of 1822 symptoms of insomnia and gastric distress became acute and were scarcely surprising in a man of his sensitive and introspective nature. His doctor seemed unable to relieve the condition, and a journey to New York and Philadelphia in May and June of 1823 with Mr. Wadsworth, although it diverted his mind, did not ameliorate his pain and discomfort. On this trip, Daniel Wadsworth suggested that as a last resource he try a bland diet. Silliman's careful and detailed description of his symptoms is a nice bit of self-diagnosis showing considerable medical perception:

When my health began to fail in 1821 and 1822, I was under the common delusion that debility and functional derangement must be overcome by a moderate use of stimulants. I had used the oxide of bismuth as an anti-dyspeptic remedy, but with no serious benefit. The muscular system was enfeebled along with the digestive, the nervous power was thrown out of healthy action, an indescribable discomfort deprived me in a great degree of physical enjoyment, and the mind became unequal to much intellectual effort. My spirits were, however, cheerful; and even when I was unable to sustain a conversation with a calling stranger, I still believed that I should recover, for my physicians, after careful examination, could find no proof of any organic disease, but only of functional derangement. I yielded for a time to the popular belief that good wine and cordials were the lever which would raise my depressed power; but the relief was only temporary; a flash of nervous excitement produced an illusive appearance of increased vigor with which the mind sympathized; the transient brightness was soon clouded again, and no permanent benefit followed; but often disturbed slumbers, with nocturnal spasms and undefined terrors in dreams, proved that all was wrong.

No medical man informed me that I was pursuing a wrong course; but the same wise and good friend, to whom I have been already so much indebted, Mr. Daniel Wadsworth, convinced me, after much effort, that

SILLIMAN IN 1825

By S. F. B. Morse. Silliman is shown lecturing, with West Rock in the distance
and specimens from the Gibbs Collection in his hand and before him. The
portrait was given to Yale by Bartlett Arkell, '86, and hangs in the Common
Room of Silliman College

TRUMBULL GALLERY OF PAINTINGS:

YALE COLLEGE.

By agreement between the College and Colonel TRUMBULL, this valuable collection of Paintings became the property of the Institution, on the death of the venerable artist,—which occurred in November, 1843. This agreement requires that the income of the Gallery, after paying his annuity, be forever applied towards the education of needy and meritorious students in Yale College.

The Gallery is contained in a stone edifice, built expressly for the object; and comprises two rooms each 30 feet square, 24 feet high, and lighted from above.

The TRUMBULL GALLERY *proper* occupies the North Room, and contains 53 Paintings from the pencil of Col. T., including all his original historical pictures of Scenes of the American Revolution. The following is a summary of the collection.

Battle of Bunker's Hill.
Death of Gen. Montgomery, at Quebec.
Death of Gen. Mercer, at battle of Princeton.
Resignation of Gen. Washington.
Our Savior with little children.
Our Savior bearing the cross.
Holy Family.
Communion of St. Jerome.
Madonna della Sedia.
Transfiguration, (copy from Raphael.)
Earl of Angus, conferring Knightood on De Wilton.
Lauders and Gelchossa.
Joshua at the battle of Ai.
"I was in prison and ye visited me."
Portrait of Mrs. Trumbull.
    Timothy Dwight.
    Stephen Van Rensselaer.
    Christopher Gore.

Declaration of Independence.
Capture of the Hessians at Trenton.
Surrender of General Burgoyne.
Surrender of Lord Cornwallis.
Preparing the body of our Savior for the tomb.
Infant Savior and St. John.
St. John and Lamb.
St. Jerome, (copy from Correggio.)
Madonna au corset rouge.
Woman accused of adultery.
Peter the Great at the capture of Narva.
Death of Paulus, Emilius.
Last Family which perished in the Deluge.
Portrait of Duke of Wellington.
    Gov. Trumbull, sen.
    Gen. Washington.
    Rufus King.
    Alexander Hamilton.
12 Groups, comprising 58 portraits.

The South Room comprises a collection of portraits of the past and present officers and benefactors of the College, besides many other paintings of historic interest, the whole number being about fifty. It also includes the celebrated group in marble of *Jephthah and his Daughter* by AUGUR, several busts of distinguished persons,—ancient coins, medals, and other memorials of antiquity.

The Gallery is open for visitors generally throughout the day, except the hour from 1 to 2 P. M. *Price of admission,* 25 cts. Access to the *Cabinet of Minerals,* the *Library,* and the other public Rooms of the College, is *without charge.* Directions for finding these rooms may be obtained by visitors, on inquiry at the Treasurer's Office under the Trumbull Gallery.

N. B. *Visitors are earnestly requested not to touch the paintings or the statuary. Canes, whips, umbrellas, fruit, tobacco and dogs are excluded.*

B. SILLIMAN, *Curator.*

Courtesy of Yale University Art Gallery

TRUMBULL GALLERY BROADSIDE

my best chance for recovery was to abandon all stimulants and adopt a very simple diet, and in such quantities, however moderate, as the stomach might be able to digest and assimilate. I took my resolution in 1823, in the lowest depression of health. I abandoned wine and every other stimulant, including, for the time, even coffee and tea. Tobacco had always been my abhorrence, and opium, except medically, when wounded, I had never used. With constant exercise abroad, I adopted a diet of boiled rice, bread and milk—and milk usually boiled and diluted with water—plain animal muscle in small quantity, varied by fowl and fish, avoiding rich gravies and pastry, and occasionally using soups and various farinaceous preparations. I persevered a year in this strict regimen, and after a few weeks my unpleasant symptoms abated, my strength gradually increased, and health, imperceptibly in its daily progress but manifest in its results, stole upon me unawares. . . .

I record these facts, not with any feeling of vanity or pride, but with deep gratitude to God; and I am influenced more than all by the wish to warn my children, and my children's children, to obey God's physical as well as moral laws, and so remember, if they would enjoy health and long life, that they must not waste their physical powers upon extraneous indulgences, but must be satisfied with nutritious food, water, or watery fluids and milk for drink, regular and sufficient sleep, and a due regulation of all propensities, physical, moral, and intellectual. With a good conscience and a faithful discharge of duty, which will naturally result from the course which I have sketched, they will pass on agreeably and usefully through life, and may expect, under the influence of religious principles and the hopes which they inspire, to meet death without dismay.

Silliman thus settled down to a life of somewhat self-righteous sobriety. On his innocuous diet, avoiding highly seasoned foods and stimulants of all sorts (except cambric tea), the gastric pain diminished, and there can be little doubt that in this way he successfully cured a gastric ulcer of psychogenic origin. He was also cheered and encouraged by the fact that two daughters, Henrietta Frances, born April 30, 1823, and Julia, born May 26, 1826, were both thriving. Maria, their eldest child, was now an attractive young lady of sixteen and Faith was almost fourteen; Benjamin Jr. was in his tenth year. It was a close family group, and with Silliman returned to health, the future became brighter.

Silliman went back to his laboratory with much of his old enthusiasm. During these years of sadness and uncertainty he had carried on as best he could with the aid of assistants; Sherlock Andrews had been particularly helpful to him in his effort to keep up his newest venture—the regular publication of the *American Journal of Science and Arts,* the journal he had started in 1818.

CHAPTER VII

Launching a Journal of Science
1818

IN 1918 on the occasion of the centenary of the *American Journal of Science,* Edward S. Dana pointed out that: "the establishment of a scientific journal in this country in 1818 was a pioneering undertaking requiring of its founder a rare degree of energy, courage, and confidence in the future. It was necessary not only to obtain the material to fill its pages and the money to carry on the enterprise but before the latter end could be accomplished, an audience must be found among those who had hitherto felt little or no interest in the sciences." Such were the problems that confronted Silliman in the undertaking which was judged by many to be his most significant contribution to the advancement of science.

Always quick to see the worth of an idea and to project his mind into the future, Silliman had pondered deeply the suggestion made by Colonel Gibbs in the autumn of 1817 that he found a journal as a clearing-house for scientific studies. At this time he was thirty-nine years of age. "Energy, courage, and confidence in the future" he possessed in full measure. His concept of the value of science was utilitarian and broad. He foresaw its practical application to the development of the rich resources of the country, he visualized it as the handmaiden of the arts, he saw it as a tool in the hands of historians. He was never an advocate of the study of "pure" science confined within the walls of a laboratory—science for science's sake— he wanted to put the knowledge in the hands of all who could do anything to promote its growth and usefulness.

Through his published travel diaries, his museum collections that were visited by many from far and wide, and through his voluminous correspondence, Silliman had become recognized throughout the country as one of the most powerful protagonists of science. And no one knew better than he that science needed a channel of publication in America. At that time scientific papers had either to be sent abroad or to be published in journals of learned societies such as the *Transactions of the American Philosophical Society,* the *Memoirs of the American Academy of Arts and Sciences* (or the more local *Memoirs of the Connecticut Academy of Arts and Sciences),* or in the New York *Medical Repository.* This latter, as its name implies, was not designed for the publication of papers of a geological or mineralogical nature, but Samuel Latham Mitchill, its editor, himself a versatile scientific writer, was deeply interested in both sciences and he often extended the hospitality of its pages for studies in these fields. Since in the latter part of the eighteenth century there were few like Silliman who made science a career, much of the early work in geology was done by men of the learned professions who were interested in natural history, geology, etc., as an adjunct to their chosen profession; but their discoveries received limited notice, for the academic journals as well as the *Medical Repository* appeared irregularly and had small circulation. When Silliman and Professor James Kingsley wished to publish their account of the Weston meteorite, Silliman wrote to Kingsley from Philadelphia, where he had presented the paper before the Philosophical Society: "Both Mitchill's and Coxe's journals are out, so that our piece cannot appear under two or three months in either of them." *

In 1810 Professor Archibald Bruce, a physician, established the first American journal published primarily for geologists and mineralogists—the *American Mineralogical Journal.* But due to the ill health of its founder, this journal, too, appeared spasmodically and by 1814, when the last issue was published,

---

* Coxe's "Journal" was the *Emporium of Arts and Sciences* founded by John Redman Coxe, Professor of Chemistry at the University of Pennsylvania. This journal was later taken over for a time by Thomas Cooper, then Professor of Chemistry and Natural Philosophy at Dickinson College, Carlisle, Pennsylvania.

he had completed only one volume of four numbers. Mitchill, Silliman, and Colonel Gibbs had all been contributors to the journal during its short life, and when it was evident that Bruce would not revive it, Gibbs had then made his suggestion

THE

AMERICAN

JOURNAL OF SCIENCE,

MORE ESPECIALLY OF

MINERALOGY, GEOLOGY,

AND THE

OTHER BRANCHES OF NATURAL HISTORY;

INCLUDING ALSO

AGRICULTURE

AND THE

ORNAMENTAL AS WELL AS USEFUL

ARTS.

CONDUCTED BY

BENJAMIN SILLIMAN,

PROFESSOR OF CHEMISTRY, MINERALOGY, ETC. IN YALE COLLEGE: AUTHOR OF
TRAVELS IN ENGLAND, SCOTLAND, AND HOLLAND, ETC.

VOL. I.

New-York:

PUBLISHED BY J. EASTBURN AND CO. LITERARY ROOMS, BROADWAY.
AND BY HOWE AND SPALDING, NEW-HAVEN.

Abraham Paul, printer

1818.

TITLE PAGE OF THE FIRST VOLUME OF THE AMERICAN JOURNAL OF SCIENCE

to Silliman. After obtaining the approval and encouragement of Dr. Bruce prior to his premature death in February 1818, Silliman decided to go ahead with the idea and proceeded forthwith to collect materials for the first number.

The Journal was broadly conceived and was "intended to embrace the circle of the physical sciences with their applications to the arts and to every useful service." With characteristic forthrightness and simplicity Silliman took the public into his confidence in the "Plan of Work" set forth in the first number which appeared in July 1818. Within the plan were embraced "Natural History, in its three great departments of Mineralogy, Botany, and Zoology; Chemistry and Natural Philosophy, in their various branches; and Mathematics, pure and mixed. . . . While Science will be cherished *for its own sake,* and with a due respect for its own *inherent* dignity it will also be employed as the *handmaid to the Arts.* Its numerous applications to Agriculture, the earliest and most important of them: to our Manufactures, both mechanical and chemical; and to our Domestic Economy, will be carefully sought out, and faithfully made." The Journal also promised to receive communications on Music, Sculpture, Engraving, Painting, Comparative Anatomy, and Physiology, and would contain notices and analyses of new scientific works, inventions, etc., and book reviews. While it was intended primarily as a repository for original American communications, selections would also be made from foreign journals, and an attempt would be made to include current information about scientific advances in other countries.

If this seems like a most ambitious program, it must be remembered that there was no other journal in the country devoted exclusively to science and its application to the arts; also that scientific activity in all the various arts and sciences listed was still so limited that it was not impossible to cover them all.

In the first number of the Journal the leading article was a technical essay on "musical temperament," by Professor Alexander M. Fisher, a young member of the Yale faculty. Under mineralogy and geology were covered such varied subjects as the native copper near New Haven, petrified wood from Antigua, native sulphur from Java, and the mineralogy and geology of Virginia and Tennessee. There were articles on botany, on zoology, and on physics and chemistry, with two miscellaneous contributions, one of which was a symposium of foreign presentations on the "Northwest Passage, the North Pole, and the Greenland Ice." Silliman made this editorial comment: "If Horace thought that man almost impiously daring who first adventured upon the open sea, what shall we say of the hardihood of the attempt to visit THE POLE?" It was an exciting age—there was so much to discover.

But while interest in the new Journal was great, it was not yet widespread, and there were only 350 subscribers when the first volume of four numbers (totalling 448 pages) was completed in June of 1819. The publishers, the J. E. Eastburn Company of New York, accordingly abandoned the venture as unprofitable. Nearly a year elapsed before Silliman was able to make satisfactory arrangements with another printer. This time he and the printer assumed equal responsibility for the costs.

The financial difficulties that plagued the Journal during many of its early years were ever a source of concern to Silliman and he was forced to contribute a considerable sum from his own slender earnings to keep it going—this at a time when there was illness in his own family and when he still owed money to Yale for the repairs on his house.

After nearly five years of uncertainty, during which he carried no small part of the financial burden, he succeeded in placing it on a secure basis, and in the number dated September 25, 1822 he made this editorial comment: "A trial of four years has decided the point that the American public will sup-. port this Journal. Its pecuniary patronage is now such that while not a lucrative, it is no longer a hazardous enterprise. It is now also decided that the intellectual resources of the country are sufficient to afford an unfailing supply of valuable, original communications and that nothing but perseverance and effort are necessary to give perpetuity to the undertaking."

In an early history of Yale there was high praise for the new venture:

Before closing this chapter, intended to illustrate the facilities and advantages for literary pursuits at New Haven arising from the long established influence of the College and other incidental circumstances, it would be unpardonable to omit a notice of the 'American Journal of Science and Arts': a periodical work of the highest merit, and which, under the able editorship of its projector, Professor Silliman, has exercised for several years a powerful and salutary influence on American literature. This ably conducted Journal was commenced in July, 1818, and may be fairly considered, although not subject to its control, as having received its birth in the generating influence of the University. As a valuable repository of facts and speculations, in regard to the arts and sciences, it has attracted greater attention than any periodical work of the kind has ever received in our country.

But while Yale was thus glad to claim a modest degree of credit for the Journal, it did not allow its approbation to extend to the point of giving it subsidy. The following may indicate that they even considered it a bit indelicate of Silliman to advertise this fact by seeking funds outside of the College, as he was forced to do some ten years later when the Journal was again floundering financially: "It were to be wished that the pecuniary profits of this excellent work bore some nearer proportion to the value of its contents, and that the learned Editor might be saved from the painful necessity of making any further appeals to his fellow citizens for additional patronage to a Journal which is honorable to the science of our common country."

Encouragement was not lacking, however. Robert Bakewell sent him a heartening letter and the *English Mining Review* published the following announcement:

We are induced to notice this volume [the *American Journal of Science*], which our want of space would have otherwise compelled us to defer until a future opportunity, from the circumstances of its containing an address to the Friends of science and knowledge by the Editor, from which we are given to understand that the patronage bestowed on the work is insufficient for its support. The talents of Professor Silliman, and the character of the Journal, are too highly appreciated on this side of the Atlantic to need our testimony, and it is with feelings of deep regret and astonishment we learn that a nation professing a regard for literature and philosophy should have been so indifferent to the success of a periodical which has materially conducted to raise America to the rank it now holds in the scientific world. The appeal is addressed to his own countrymen, but Professor Silliman is entitled in the highest degree to be considered as a Citizen of the World, there being few parts to which his reputation has not extended and if by quoting the following extract from his address we can promote his views, it will afford us sincere gratification. [There followed the address of Professor Silliman alluded to above.]

Historians of science will continue to pay tribute to Silliman for the herculean task he accomplished during the twenty years (1818 to 1838) when he carried the responsibility of the Journal alone, constantly extending its invaluable contributions to scientific knowledge. The onerous burden of correspondence, all by his own hand, he carried in addition to his expanding activities. His letters went to almost everyone of consequence in the scientific world in this country and abroad and the replies, which he frequently published in the Journal, gave a personal, unique flavor to its pages. Often these personal communications contained more of interest in the way of new studies and discoveries than was to be found in the formal papers. So thoroughly was Silliman identified with the undertaking that it came to be known simply as "Silliman's Journal."

Joseph Henry, an outstanding American scientist who became the secretary and first director of the Smithsonian Institution, wrote with understanding of what is involved in such a publication. It is almost impossible, without actual experience, he said, to form an adequate idea of the amount of labor and absorption of thought required properly to conduct a journal of this character. Essential for its success is its regular appearance on the day fixed for its publication, and to ensure this, a supply of suitable material must always be in preparation in advance. An enormous amount of correspondence is entailed in each issue between the editor and the authors—to urge them to send their material on time, in the correction of errors, the possible modification of controversial statements or opinions, the elucidation of certain points, etc.

Since the editor is responsible for the scientific character of the articles admitted, diplomacy is frequently required to avoid wounding the feelings of sensitive authors. "In reply to some remarks on an article of less scientific merit than the general standard of the Journal, Professor Silliman once said to me," Henry wrote, " 'Could you see what I reject, and the amount of correspondence which such rejection involves, you would not be surprised that I should occasionally suffer an article to appear not strictly in accordance with my own views. I try, however, to express disagreeable truths in language as little offensive as possible; to encourage beginners, and to elicit observations of natural phenomena even from those who make no pretensions to science.' "

Silliman himself contributed comparatively few signed articles through the years, but his pen was nearly always evident in the editorial comments. His talents went into the selection of material, for soon there was more than he could publish even though he enlarged the Journal to a fat quarterly with two volumes a year. During the first twenty-five years there were approximately 600 contributors and some 1,800 original articles. In addition to some of the most important scientific communications of the time, there appeared articles on a wide range of topics, including essays on "gypsies" by J. Griscom, on "mystery" by Mark Hopkins, on the Trumbull paintings, and on "Arabic words in English" by J. W. Gibbs.

Applied science occupied a prominent place, as Silliman had promised in the first number, and one finds Eli Whitney's account of his cotton gin in 1832, applications of the steam engine and early developments of the steamboat, letters on steam navigation, etc. Charles Griswold's important description of David Bushnell's submarine, first used in the Revolutionary War in August 1776, appeared in the second volume; in 1826 there was an account of a dirigible, the forerunner of the Zeppelin; and in 1834 a prolonged discussion of aerial navigation by H. Strait. Amos Eaton, Edward Hitchcock, Parker Cleaveland, and others whose names are a part of the early history of American science likewise appeared in its pages.

In 1947, the centennial year of Simpson's discovery of the anesthetic properties of chloroform, it is particularly interesting to find that two papers—one by Samuel Guthrie announcing his discovery of chloroform ("chloric ether"), the other a note by Eli Ives on its medicinal effects—were published in 1832, fifteen years before it was recognized as an anodyne and made available to the world. A statement in the second volume of Silliman's own text on the *Elements of Chemistry* had started Guthrie on his experiments: "Its medicinal powers have not been ascertained, but from its constitution and properties, it is highly probable that it would be an active diffusive stimulant." The simultaneous discovery of chloroform by two European chemists, Liebig at Giessen and Soubeiran at Paris, seems to have received no notice in the Journal.

Two years later Silliman published his account of the chemical analyses that he had carried out at the request of Dr. William Beaumont on the gastric juice of Beaumont's celebrated patient, the fistulous Alexis St. Martin who had a permanent aperture leading into his stomach (from an accidental gunshot wound of his chest) through which Beaumont made his famous observations on the processes of digestion. Indeed, there was little of scientific interest or importance in the nineteenth century that was not either presented in the Journal or commented upon in its pages. The impetus which it gave to American science cannot be too strongly emphasized. Charles Schuchert (for many years Professor of Paleontology and Historical Geology at Yale) in a paper on "A century of geology," published in the centennial number of the Journal, called it "one of the greatest influences in American geology." He further said that "Editor Silliman was not only the founder of the Journal, but the generating center for the making of geologists and promoting geology during the rise of this science in America." Although not officially sponsored by the College, the Journal brought enormous prestige not only to Silliman but to Yale, and did much to increase an interest in science among the lay public, to encourage its applications among industrialists and manufacturers, and to stimulate the many technologies which have contributed so notably to the development of the unparalleled natural resources of the United States.

At the end of the first ten years Silliman reviewed the accomplishments and concluded with an explanation of his policy for the selection of material:

It is believed that a strict examination of its contents will prove that its character has been decidedly scientific. . . . Still, the editor has been frequently solicited, both in public and private, to make it more miscellaneous, that it might be more acceptable to the intelligent and well educated man who does not cultivate science; but he has never lost sight of his great object, which was to produce and concentrate original American effort in science, and thus he has foregone pecuniary returns, which by pursuing the other course, might have been rendered important. Others would not have him admit anything that is not strictly and technically scientific; and would make this journal for mere professors and amateurs. . . . But our savants, unless they would be, not only the exclusive admirers but the sole purchasers of their own works, must permit a little of the graceful drapery of general literature to flow around the cold statues of science. The editor of this Journal, strongly inclined both from opinion and habit to gratify the cultivators of science, will still do everything in his power to promote its high interests, and as he hopes in a better manner than heretofore; but these respectable gentlemen will have the courtesy to yield something to the reading literary, as well as scientific public, and will not, we trust, be disgusted, if now and then an *Oasis* relieves the eye, and a living stream refreshes the traveller. Not being inclined to renew the abortive experiment to please every body, which has been so long renowned in fable; the editor will endeavor to pursue the even tenor of his way; altogether inclined to be courteous and useful to his fellow travellers, and hoping for their kindness and services in return.

His middle-of-the-road policy came in for some criticism of course, for, as he said, it was impossible to please everyone. Amos Eaton, a field geologist and lecturer who had been one of his special students (See Chapter IX, p. 150), was outspoken about the Journal in a letter he wrote (not to Silliman) refusing to contribute to the *Annals* of the New York Lyceum. Although Eaton was known to be an egotist who was quick and often unreasonable in his criticisms, he was a practical geologist of considerable repute and behind his tirade there was doubtless something of the feeling shared by those who wanted none of the "graceful drapery of general literature flowing around the cold statues of science."

I would write frequently to your Lyceum. But I see no object in it. My pieces are all, *necessarily,* on practical parts of Science, which, according to my views of the present rapid progress of Natural Science in our country, ought to be immediately given to teachers, etc. Well, you publish nothing, excepting now and then a piece, entirely for the benefit of the *Author's Vanity.* . . . To be *emphatically* serious, the Journal of Silliman, the N. York Magazine etc. have admitted such puerile wretched trash, that I am heartily sick of American periodical works. Silliman's last number contained something, but he studies to please fools. . . .

I am prepared with the best article on Geology I ever wrote. But I know not what to do with it. Silliman will not know whether it is worth printing or not. He will print it to be sure if I send it. But he would prefer a long dull mess of trash about Music, or William's toad.*

But despite the criticisms (there were not many as outspoken as this), Silliman through his Journal was a powerful influence in stimulating and molding the scientific thought of the century not only through his own period of editorship, but much longer—when the Journal was ably carried on by his son, Benjamin, Jr., by his son-in-law, James Dwight Dana, and by his grandson, Edward S. Dana. In the preface to the fiftieth volume (1847), which marked the close of the "First Series," Silliman again summed up the progress that had been made. "Comparing 1817 with 1847, we mark on this subject a very gratifying change. The cultivators of science in the United States were then few—now they are numerous. Societies and associations of various names, for the cultivation of natural history, have been instituted in very many of our cities and towns, and several of them have been active and efficient in making original observations and forming collections." After touching briefly on the advancement in the various sciences, Silliman continued with pardonable pride:

. . . We only give single examples by way of illustration, for the history of the progress of science in the United States, and of institutions for its promotion during the present generation, would demand a volume. It is enough for our purpose that science is understood and valued, and the right methods of prosecuting it are known, and the time is at hand when its moral and intellectual use will be as obvious as its physical applications. Nor is it to be forgotten that we have awakened an European interest in our researches: general science has been illustrated by treasures of facts drawn from this country, and our discoveries are eagerly sought for and published abroad.

While with our co-workers in many parts of our broad land, we rejoice in this auspicious change, we are far from arrogating it to ourselves. Multiplied labors of many hands have produced the great results. In

* Amos Eaton to John Torrey, August 15, 1820.

the place which we have occupied, we have persevered despite of all discouragements, and may, with our numerous coadjutors, claim some share in the honors of the day. We do not say that our work might not have been better done—but we may declare with truth that we have done all in our power, and it is something to have excited many others to effort and to have chronicled their deeds in our annals. Let those that follow us labor with like zeal and perseverance, and the good cause will continue to advance and prosper. It is the cause of truth—science is only embodied and sympathized truth and in the beautiful conception of our noble Agassiz—'it tells the thought of God.'

The Journal, the oldest scientific publication which has been continued without a break since its inception, is still issued from Yale University under the able editorship of Richard S. Lull, Professor Emeritus of Paleontology.

CHAPTER VIII

Geology and Genesis

LITTLE had been known about the structure of the earth's crust until early in the eighteenth century when there appeared a number of men whose pioneer work in the field, although often stumbling and erroneous in the light of later knowledge, nevertheless gave rise to the modern science of geology. We shall pass quickly over Jean Étienne Guettard (1715-1796) who made the first attempt at geological maps, who made known the existence of extinct volcanoes in France, and recognized the value of organic remains in reconstructing geological history. Guettard's observations revealed remarkable acumen, but he was severely criticized by his brilliant countryman, Nicolas Desmarest (1725-1815) who carried the knowledge of geology still further, and he was almost entirely ignored by the English geologists so that he was lost sight of until late in the nineteenth century.

While the original observations of Desmarest were marking a new era in geological thought, a man by the name of Horace Benedict de Saussure (1740-1799) was climbing the mountains of his native Switzerland and studying the geology of the Alps. Although de Saussure did not add much in the way of new knowledge, he collected invaluable data to confirm existing facts and to him is credited the adoption (in 1779) of the terms "geology" and "geologists."

A few early attempts were made to draw conclusions about the geological order of the various strata, but it was Abraham Gottlob Werner (1749-1817) who made the world listen to his theories. To the School of Mines at Freiburg (where he became a professor in 1775), he attracted students from far and wide, and through the force of his personality and the persuasiveness of his lectures his ideas took firm root until he became the most outstanding figure in the field. He had never studied geology outside his native Saxony but he rejected the evidence of volcanic action found by both Guettard and Desmarest and built up, by theory alone, a system of geology based on the belief that the earth had been formed through the precipitates of a vast ocean that had once covered its entire surface. He had a powerful influence on geological thought even after some of his own pupils, especially d'Aubuisson and von Buch, published contradictory reports when they had gone away from the spell of his teaching and had observed the facts for themselves.

WERNER VERSUS HUTTON

Werner detested writing and did not publish his theories but they were carried all over Europe by his devoted pupils. In the meantime a Scotsman, James Hutton (1726-1797) read a memoir to the Royal Society of Edinburgh in 1785 entitled "Theory of the Earth; or an Investigation of the Laws Observable in the Composition, Dissolution, and Restoration of Land upon the Globe." Written tersely, in a quiet, logical manner, this paper in no way indicated that it marked a turning-point in the history of geology. It lay buried in the *Transactions* of the Society, attracting neither friend nor foe until 1793 when Richard Kirwan, a well-known Irish chemist, came forth with a strenuous attack which prompted Hutton immediately to set about the revision of his paper postponed because of illness. In 1795 it was published under the title of *Theory of the Earth with Proofs and Illustrations*. In this he took exception to Werner's views—the rocks which Werner believed were the chemical precipitate of a primeval ocean were judged by Hutton to be instead of igneous origin—a conclusion based on thirty years of study in Scotland and far afield. Two friends, who had accompanied him on his field trips, carried forward his work after his death in 1797. These were Sir James Hall and

John Playfair, the latter publishing in 1802 his now classic *Illustrations of the Huttonian Theory.*

Two years later another Scotsman, Robert Jameson, returned from Werner's school to Edinburgh to assume the professorship of natural history at the University. Conflict was inevitable, and Silliman described in his Reminiscences the situation as he found it when he arrived there in 1805:

There was no distinct course of geology in Edinburgh in 1805-6. Some dissatisfaction was indeed expressed regarding Professor Jameson—who had then recently returned from Werner's celebrated school of geology at Freiburg, in Saxony, and who was fully imbued with the doctrines of his great master—that he did not commence his course of instruction. He had, however, an able substitute in Dr. Murray, who was a well-instructed and zealous advocate of the Wernerian theory on the agency of water; while Dr. [Thomas] Hope [Professor of Chemistry], on the other hand, was an ardent and powerful supporter of the Huttonian or igneous theory. The discussions on these subjects were held in the midst of the chemical lectures, being introduced in connection with the elementary and proximate constitution of rocks and minerals. . . .

The discussions of Dr. Hope and Dr. Murray afforded me a rich entertainment, and a wide range of instruction. Dr. Murray would solve most geological phenomena by the agency of water. Even granite, and of course the members of that family, were a crystalline deposit from the primeval chaotic ocean; and this being granted, the Wernerians would fain give an aqueous origin even to porphyry and basalt and all the traps. As far as I had any leaning, it was towards the Wernerian system. Water is always active upon the surface of the earth, and it flows also from its interior; and atmospheric waters are ever descending upon the earth in rain, snow, and hail, as well as in the gentle dews, not only to refresh the surface and to sustain life in all its various forms, but to replenish the fountains themselves. Then again it reascends by evaporation to form the clouds, those exhaustless storehouses of rain, snow, and hail. But in the progress of this endless circulation it is everywhere obvious that water produces extensive and highly important geological results, in the transportation and deposition of solid as well as of dissolved materials, in the formation and disintegration of strata, and especially in the ceaseless wear of rivers and torrents, and in the never-ending motions of the oceans and seas in tidal waves and storm billows and currents.

It is not wonderful, then, that the powerful mind of Werner should appreciate, and even exaggerate, these agencies. He had not travelled far away from his own (geologically) peaceful Saxony, and knew little from personal observations of the agencies of internal fire. He founded his system, therefore, upon a partial and imperfect view of evidence; but his zeal and eloquence captivated his numerous pupils, whose delight it was to blazon the system of their great teacher; and for many years few were bold enough to question its entire truth.

But a change of opinion had been for some years going on. The philosophy of fire as regards its agencies in the earth—not entirely new indeed—had been revived and greatly extended by the researches of Dr. Hutton of Edinburgh, aided by his enthusiastic followers, Playfair, Hall, Hope, Seymour and others. The followers of Hutton were now organized into a geological phalanx, and my residence in Edinburgh occurred at the fortunate crisis, when the combatants on both sides were in the field; and I, although a non-combatant, was within the wind of battle, and prepared, like victory, to join the strongest side. When Dr. Hope came out with his array of facts in support of the Huttonian theory, I was in a state of mind to yield to evidence. Being a young man, uncommitted to either theory, I was a deeply interested listener to the discussions of both the Wernerian and Huttonian hypothesis. From the fierce central heat of the philosophers of fire and its destructive heavings and eruptions and overflows, I went to bathe in the cool ocean of Werner; and as both views were ably and eloquently sustained, the exercise was to me a delightful recreation and a most instructive study. I found time, also, to read Playfair's illustrations of the Huttonian theory, and Murray's comparative view of both the conflicting theories; and I was not long in coming to the conclusion that both theories were founded in truth, and that the crust of the earth had been formed and greatly modified by the combined, or sometimes antagonistic and conflicting powers of fire and water.

Following his return to New Haven and in the early years of his professorship Silliman watched closely the advancements being made in geological knowledge. William Maclure and Parker Cleaveland were studying the American continent while Georges Cuvier and Alexandre Brongniart were classifying the geological structure of the country around Paris. In Great Britain William Smith from Oxfordshire, called by

Adam Sedgwick the "Father of English Geology," in August 1815 published *A Geological Map of England and Wales, with Part of Scotland*, the first to portray the distribution and the stratigraphy of the formations of an entire country.

Roderick I. Murchison and Adam Sedgwick were adding new chapters—the Devonian, Silurian, and Cambrian layers— to the geological record. William Buckland, one of the most popular professors at Oxford (who had earlier guided Murchison), was starting another geologist on his way. This was Charles Lyell (1797-1875), son of a Scottish laird from Forfarshire, who came to believe and expound the startling theory that nothing cataclysmic had formed the earth, but rather thousands of years of everyday effects of rain, earthquakes, volcanic eruptions, and floods that were still occurring under the eyes of man. His first edition of the *Principles of Geology* stated this in mild form but he brought out revised editions as his knowledge increased. Other geologists, among them Robert Bakewell and Gideon A. Mantell who became Silliman's particular friends, were adding the results of specialized research to the total picture. Silliman followed the advances carefully not only because of his great interest, but because he must keep his teaching abreast of the new discoveries.

CONFLICT WITH HOLY WRIT

While the geologists themselves were still presenting conflicting theories, they were attacked from without by religious groups for preaching doctrines contrary to the Scriptural account of the creation, and in his early efforts to establish the science of geology in America Silliman discovered that creating an interest in the science was the least of his difficulties. In the words of James Dwight Dana: "Geology from the first encountered opposition. Its very essence, indeed the very existence of the Science, involved the idea of Secondary causes in the progress of the creation of the world—whilst Moses had seemingly reduced each step of progress to a *fiat,* a word of command. The champions of the Bible seemed called upon, therefore, to defend it against scientific innovations; and they labored zealously and honestly, not knowing that Science may also be of God. Professor Silliman being an example of Christian character beyond reproach, personal attacks were not often made. But thousands of regrets that his influence was given over to the dissemination of error were privately, and sometimes publicly expressed. An equal interest was exhibited by the lecturer in the welfare of his opponents, and the progress of what he believed to be the truth; and with boldness and power he stood by both the Bible and the Science, until now there were few to question his faith."

From Britain as late as 1836 came a letter from Robert Bakewell which showed that the controversy was still being waged.

. . . Geology is in a rather strange state in England at present; the rich clergy begin to tremble for their incomes, and seek to avert their fate by a revived zeal for orthodoxy, and are making a great clamor against geology as opposed to Genesis. I have no doubt this is the prime cause why Buckland's Bridgewater treatise, though announced and reviewed in the 'Quarterly' last May, has not yet appeared. . . . The reviewer brought forward all those points which Buckland would have been glad to pass *sub silentio*—namely, that B. has now given up the Noachian deluge, so far as it was to explain any geological phenomena, and also stating how much he differed from the literal account of creation in Genesis. . . . In England the attempt to introduce new names and new theories is sinking geology in the opinion of well-judging people. The Eocene, Miocene, and Pliocene, these names, as Sedgwick says, with Greek heads and French tails, are absurdly introduced, as they assume the truth of a theory that cannot be proved—that the age of tertiary strata can be determined by the proportions of recent and extinct shells. . . .

Silliman himself had been able to reconcile the opposing views of the Neptunists and the Plutonists, as led by Werner and Hutton, and to combine them amicably with the teachings of the Pentateuch. And if it should seem strange that he could accept so easily what many men of his religious background found difficult to understand, President Woolsey has suggested a plausible explanation:

> . . . The grandeur of the subject-matter [of geology] seemed especially fitted to kindle and exalt his fervor. The mighty agencies that have moulded the earth over and over, as clay is moulded in the hands of the potter, the immense ages which almost appall the imagination, this vast framework of the earth, the theatre of such sublime displays, and over all, before the eye of faith, the Divine Architect carrying the great building forward, until it had become a fit dwelling-place for his immortal creature, man—these grand objects inspired him, and he threw the inspiration into his audiences, wherever they were gathered.

This was the secret of Silliman's ability to stimulate interest, for if it had not been known that he was a deeply religious man, it seems probable that he could never have secured such solid support for his undertakings. That he could reconcile the Mosaic account of the creation and the latest findings of the geologists carried so much weight among his contemporaries that many were won over who might otherwise have remained hostile toward the new science.

Silliman in his early publications on the "Mineralogy of New Haven," first presented in 1806, and on the Weston Meteor, published with Professor Kingsley in 1808, had not been obliged to touch upon the controversial issues, but he faced the problem squarely when he published a syllabus of his geological lectures at Yale in an appendix to his first American edition of Robert Bakewell's *Introduction to Geology* (1829). In his supplement to the second American edition (1833), entitled *Consistency of the Discoveries of Modern Geology, with the Sacred History of the Creation and the Deluge,* he outdid all others in his effort to harmonize conflicting ideas, and some thought, as Huxley remarked, that he wrote "with one eye on fact and the other on Genesis." Under "Statement of the Subject" one finds the following:

In this country, the cultivation of scientific geology is of so recent a date that many of our most intelligent and well educated people are strangers even to its elements, are unacquainted with its amazing store of facts, and are startled when any other geological epochs are spoken of than the creation and the deluge, recorded in the pentateuch. But it is beyond a doubt that there are innumerable and decisive proofs of successive revolutions, and of a gradual progress in the course of geological events, implying, on the whole, a regular order in the formation of the crust of the planet, interrupted by occasional disorder and convulsion. These events necessarily imply much time, and cannot be referred, exclusively, to any course of diluvial action. . . .

In this country, where the moral feeling of the people is identified with reverence for the scriptures, the questions are often agitated: When did the great series of geological events happen? If the six days of the creation were insufficient in time, and the events cannot all be referred to a deluge, to what period and to what state of things shall we assign them? This is a fair topic of enquiry, and demands a satisfactory answer. This answer is given by the whole series of geological facts, and the question will never remain of doubtful issue in the mind of any one who has fully studied and mastered them. The subject of geology is possessed of such high interest that it will not be permitted to slumber; it will proceed with increasing energy and success; a great number of powerful minds and immense research are now employed upon it, and many collateral branches of science are made tributary to its progress. Its conclusions have been supposed to jar with the scripture history: this is contemplated with alarm and displeasure by some, and with satisfaction by a few; but there is no cause for either state of feeling: the supposed disagreement is not real; it is only apparent. It is founded upon the popular mistake, that, excepting the action of a deluge and of ordinary causes still in operation, this world was formed as we now see it, and that all its immense and various deposits were made in a very short period of time. Both these are fundamental errors, which have misled both the learned and the unlearned, and are still extensively prevalent. Although the materials were created by almighty power, they were evidently left to the operation of physical laws, which laws also affected, more or less, the fate of the various races of plants and animals that were successively called into existence. But, there is no reason to believe that any part of the crust of the earth, reaching even to a fathomless depth, is now in the condition in which it was originally made; every portion has been worked over and brought into new forms, and these changes have arisen from the action of those physical laws which the Creator established, and which are as truly his work as the materials upon which they operate. The amount of time is the only difficulty, and this will vanish before an enlarged and reasonable view of the whole subject, taken both in its geological and historical bearings.

These views were bitterly resented by Professor Thomas Cooper, then President of South Carolina College at Columbia, who maintained that Silliman's religious interpretations beclouded his evaluation of geological facts. Cooper, or "Old Coot" as he was called, was a brilliant liberal, Oxford bred, who throughout his stormy career had encountered opposition to his views, so in advance of his time that they were often radical; indeed, he had left England with Priestley to seek a more enlightened and free atmosphere. Interested in science through Priestley, he had turned to the teaching of chemistry in this country and occupied chairs at Dickinson College, the University of Pennsylvania, the University of Virginia, and finally at South Carolina College which he served as president from 1821-1834. Although not a geologist, he played an influential part in the early educational movements relating to the introduction of this science into universities, and at South Carolina he was instrumental in founding a chair in geology, the only one in the country at that time outside of Yale College. His keen, direct mind was affronted by Silliman's attitude of compromise, and the latter's acceptance of the Mosaic theory called forth a vigorous expression of opinion which Cooper published in a sixty-four-page pamphlet entitled *On the Connection Between Geology and the Pentateuch*. He concluded that: "It is well for Professor Silliman that his useful services to science have placed his reputation on a more stable foundation than his absolute unconditional surrender of his common sense to clerical orthodoxy."

Silliman's reaction to this was dignified silence. He recorded that when Cooper had visited him in New Haven with William Maclure his manners were mild and conciliating and his appearance patriarchal and venerable, "very different from what I imagined from what I had heard," and that in their correspondence over the years Cooper had "always exhibited a vigorous and discriminating mind," but of their opposing views concerning geological concepts he wrote: "In an appendix I had endeavored to reconcile the Mosaic history with geology but this gave great offence to Dr. Cooper who in a letter to me protested against my views both scientific and moral and even wrote a considerable book primarily in opposition, to *me* indeed, but still more to vituperate *Moses,* or the author of the *Pentateuch,* whoever he might be. In the last letter which I received from him he reviled the Scripture, especially of the Old Testament, pronouncing it in all respects an unsupported and in some respects a most detestable book. To this letter I made no reply, feeling that it was such a violation of gentlemanly courtesy when writing to one whose sentiments he knew to be so opposed to his own, that I thought it better to drop the correspondence and I never heard from him again."

It is somewhat ironic that when Dr. Cooper, openly an infidel, found it politic to resign because of divided public opinion, Silliman was offered the presidency of the college—whether through the influence of Cooper's opponents or through John C. Calhoun, Silliman's former pupil at Yale, it is not known. But Silliman had no wish to leave Yale and the matter was dropped.

GEOLOGICAL SURVEYS

During these years he was doing much to foster geological surveys of specific areas and many of his students going out from Yale, men such as Denison Olmsted, Amos Eaton, and Edward Hitchcock, conducted some of the first state geological surveys. Silliman himself had studied the rocks in the region of Edinburgh and around New Haven when he returned, and in 1817 he made a geological tour of the counties of New Haven and Litchfield, publishing a detailed account of his findings in the second volume of the *American Journal of Science and Arts*. He discovered that the valley of the Housatonic was, according to the earlier language of geology, highly primitive. He found the territory rich in marble and iron ores and other valuable minerals. When he looked over the report of his geological tour forty years later he had the satisfaction of finding that his early labors were, as he wrote, "faithfully performed . . . I do not perceive that I could conduct the geological examination more correctly or describe the parts more lucidly. I was then thirty-eight years of age . . . and I must confess it is an honest satisfaction that age is not mortified by the errors of youth." However, he added: "The classification is that of Werner which is no longer in vogue. Although at Edinburgh I had espoused igneous agency as the great power that had governed the physical globe I had not abandoned water, nor do I abandon it now. . . . If I were to write this essay again I should modify some sentences and perhaps insist less upon the Wernerian distinctions between primitive and secondary."

In 1819, on the last page of the first volume of the *American Journal of Science,* it was announced that an American Geological Society "has been recently organized by an association of gentlemen residing in various parts of the United States." In May Silliman had obtained a charter for the new society from the Legislature at Hartford—easily, he said, because no money was requested—and in the second volume of the Journal the text of the charter is published with the list of officers. William Maclure was elected president; Gibbs, Silliman, Hare, and others were named vice-presidents. This society was the first American society devoted to geological and allied subjects. Although it remained in existence only until the end of 1828, it did much to stimulate geologists throughout the country.

A similar venture, of more local interest, was the formation of the Yale Institute of Natural Science, which later became the Yale Natural History Society. The society, established "for the promotion of natural history," named a fee of five dollars for admission, and made ambitious plans for a $20,000 library. William Maclure promptly sent them $400 toward this end and the Reverend Dr. Peter Parker, a graduate of the Medical Institution then in China, sent them a splendid collection of Oriental birds which arrived in good condition. But despite the early enthusiasm, the society languished and was not revived until 1857.

THE GIBBS CABINET

In 1819 the College, having recovered somewhat from the financial strain of the disturbed national economy during the War of 1812, decided to build a new commons for the students. It was to be a single-story affair, 83 feet long, with basement kitchens. Silliman, who had long felt that his mineral collection, and particularly the Gibbs Cabinet, could be more advantageously displayed, looked upon this as a heaven-sent opportunity. He was certain that the building would not make a good appearance unless it were more elevated. "I proposed for this reason," he wrote, "and for another of more importance, namely the better accommodation of the Gibbs Cabinet, that another story should be added, to receive that very valuable collection. President Dwight, my noble counsellor and patron, was no longer with us, but President Day, his excellent successor, who was also a man of large mind and liberal views, approved of the plan and it was affirmed by the Prudential Committee. But there was a point of delicacy to be attended to before proceeding to carry it into effect. The cabinet being left with us only on loan, it was proper to consult Colonel Gibbs as the contemplated removal might imply that we counted on the cabinet as a permanency. I therefore submitted the matter to his consideration and he approved of the design."

Silliman rearranged his specimens personally and when the task was completed "the spectacle was now splendid; a room 84 feet by 40 and nearly 12 feet high presented its walls, the spaces for the windows excepted, entirely covered by cases brilliant with glass and still more brilliant from the effect of the minerals which they contained. The fixtures for the lectures were also transferred to the new room and here the lectures on mineralogy and geology were given for a series of years. The cabinet became an object of greater interest than ever. Being now in a well-lighted upper room with sufficient space for visiting parties, it became a favorite resort." A short time later he succeeded in obtaining from the Corporation an appropriation of $150 annually for its support. The only difficulty about the new situation was the fire hazard from the kitchens below which caused Silliman considerable anxiety until 1842 when the building was no longer used as a commons.

In May 1825 Colonel Gibbs informed Silliman that he had decided to sell his cabinet for $20,000 and that Yale could have the first refusal. This announcement filled many with dismay. Was Yale to lose the collection of which it was so proud? Silliman recorded that "we were startled indeed by this letter and taken by surprise, although we had no right . . . to entertain any other sentiments than those of grateful acknowledgment for the long continued loan of such a treasure." He went on to say that "the cabinet had rested with us from thirteen to fifteen years. From it the owner had derived no pecuniary advantage whatever . . . and at his own expense and without the College knowing it [until it was moved to the Commons where fire hazard existed] kept the cabinet insured."

Although he secretly hoped, without doubt, that Colonel Gibbs might see his way clear eventually to present the cabinet to Yale, Silliman said nothing of this and set about the stern task of raising what in those days was a sum of great magnitude. It is a particular credit to the judgment of the Yale Corporation that they concurred in the unanimous opinion of Silliman, President Day, and Professor Kingsley that the cabinet "long our pride and ornament, must not be removed from Yale College." The College, of course, did not have the funds available and "our only resource appeared to be to call again— as had always been done from the founding of the College —upon the loyalty of our alumni and the liberality of the friends of Science and of the College—a resource which had never failed in previous exigencies." The Corporation authorized Silliman to proceed with the solicitation of funds.

The first attempt was made at a public meeting for which a handbill stating the case "concisely, clearly, and forcibly" was prepared. Members of the faculty and prominent citizens addressed the meeting, among them the Reverend Dr. Crosswell, Rector of Trinity, who although not an alumnus, nor sympathizing with the religious organization of the College addressed the assembly with powerful arguments. He subtly appealed to the civic pride of the people of New Haven by intimating that if they did not "come forward and secure the Gibbs Cabinet, Hartford might obtain it, as the people of Hartford were always prompt and liberal in cases where their local interests were concerned and they too had a college." This effort was augmented by a house-to-house canvass. "President Day zealously led in the canvass and all the gentlemen put forth such efforts as were convenient to them. It is obvious, however, that no one could be expected to labor so much as the head of the department." Professor Chauncey A. Goodrich, who was always zealous and efficient in every good cause, was of especial aid to Silliman, indeed he would have been invaluable on any money-raising committee, for "he worked with all his might and he had uncommon tact in approaching people— he could put the pressure both upon the right man and in the right place, and was not only successful with the willing, but with the unwilling!"

By these means, some $10,000 was raised in New Haven, but this was only half of the amount needed. Among the loyal alumni who contributed was the Honorable John C. Calhoun. In a letter to Silliman he wrote: "You do not mistake my feelings in supposing that I take deep interest in the prosperity of Yale College. . . . I regret that my contribution must fall so much short of my inclination. I had the misfortune last year to lose by fire my cotton crop and gin-house, which for the present has greatly limited my means. You will place me among the subscribers, and affix one hundred dollars to my name. . . . Should there be any difficulty in making out the necessary sum to buy the collection, and thereby a greater effort becomes necessary on the part of the friends of Yale, I trust that you will not be backward in informing me, as I would, in that event, very cheerfully increase my contribution."

In New York, during May and June, Silliman and Professor Goodrich conducted a canvass similar to the one in New Haven, though not as extensive. Silliman recorded that, working on foot to save the expense of a conveyance, they suffered considerably from the intense heat, with an occasional chilly reception to cool them off. Since he had but recently recovered his health, Silliman found the task particularly arduous, but they raised approximately $3,000 which, added to the sum raised in New Haven and through solicitation by letter, amounted to nearly $15,000 by the end of the summer. The Corporation made up the balance, and the Gibbs Cabinet, to Silliman's infinite satisfaction, became the permanent property of Yale College. The Corporation had thus taken one of the early steps toward transforming Yale College into a university.

Through the formation of societies, local and national, through his textbooks and articles, through the Journal, and through his untiring efforts to enlarge the collections at Yale College, Silliman's influence spread. But during these years he was advancing the cause of science in yet another way —the pupils he had trained were going out to other academic centers imbued with his enthusiasm and thoroughly grounded in the methods by which they could carry his work forward.

CHAPTER IX

Widening Sphere of Influence
1819-1833

IN 1809 a farmer's son from Farmington, Connecticut, entered Yale College. He had received his preliminary education in a district school, learning arithmetic (which was not a part of the school curriculum) from Governor John Treadwell in exchange for such offices as a boy could do for his board. After leaving school he had worked for a time as a clerk in a store, but being dissatisfied with this narrow existence he proceeded to New Haven to extend his education.

In his senior year he elected a course in mineralogy taught by Professor Silliman. Up to this point he had not known what direction his life would take—henceforth there was no doubt in his mind, for a whole new world was opened to him as the professor passed around for the class to see and handle the wonders of which he spoke. There were rock crystals magnificent in size, perfection, and variety of form from Switzerland, Dauphiny, Piedmont, and Savoy; a rolled pebble from Madagascar; smoky quartz and dark violet-blue amethyst from Siberia; quartz shading in color from deep purple to light rose from Hungary and Bohemia; blue chalcedony, crystallized, from Tresztyan in Transylvania, also white chalcedony from Iceland, the Faroe Islands, Hungary, and Cornwall, red from India, and applegreen from Silesia; woodstones and agates of every variety from all over the world; opal from Hungary. The names of these faraway places, the beauty of the specimens, and the impelling enthusiasm of the teacher were all magic to Denison Olmsted, the farmer's son, and he, like many others who attended Silliman's classes, decided to make science his career.

The professor who exercised such a profound influence on his pupils was himself young—barely in his thirties—and tall,

146

with dark hair and serene brown eyes. He had a kindly face and gracious manners and there was an air of common sense and dependability about him that sometimes made him appear older than he really was. When he became engrossed in his subject, his face would light up with enthusiasm and his speech would quicken so that those who had no understanding of the material would be hard put to follow him. What he taught was not all theory; he passed around specimens and stressed the practical applications of science in a way that caught the imagination of many an eager student pondering his future.

Years later, after the professor had retired and was writing his reminiscences of those early, exciting days when science was new in the young country and Yale was a center from which interest was spreading far and wide, he made a list of his pupils whose names came to be writ large in the early history of science in the United States. Many, of course, had remained with him after they had graduated to further their knowledge by acting as his assistant, some had come with degrees from other colleges; a few had already achieved notice—Robert Hare as an original investigator in chemistry, and Amos Eaton, who had for several years been practising at law. Silliman set down their names with modest pride, classifying them according to his own lights:

REGULAR ASSISTANTS

Who became Professors of Science

Edward Hitchcock	Amherst College
George T. Bowen	Nashville University
Charles U. Shepard	Yale College and Medical College, Charleston, South Carolina
James Dwight Dana	Yale College
Denison Olmsted	College of North Carolina and Yale College

| Oliver P. Hubbard | Dartmouth College |
| Benjamin Silliman, Jr. | Medical College, Louisville, and Yale College |

Eminent Lawyers
| Sherlock J. Andrews | Cleveland |
| B. D. Silliman | New York |

Physicians
| Lyman Foot | Surgeon in the Army of the United States |
| Burr Noyes | Physician at Chester, Saybrook, Connecticut |

Scientific Editor
| Mason Cogswell Weld | Editor of *The Homestead*, Hartford |

VOLUNTARY ASSISTANTS

Who achieved eminence
Reverend Sereno Edwards Dwight
William C. Leffingwell
Edward H. Leffingwell, M.D.

Chester Dewey	Williams College and Berkshire Medical Institution, Pittsfield, Massachusetts
Robert Hare	University of Pennsylvania Medical School
William C. Fowler	Amherst College
Gamaliel Olds	Burlington College, Vermont
Prof. Avery	Hamilton College, Clinton, New York
Ormond Beattie	Kentucky

Learner to become a Lecturer
| Amos Eaton | [Founder of Rensselaer School, later Rensselaer Polytechnic Institute] |

Learners for Chemical Arts
  George Spalding
  John S. Parkin

Distinguished pupils who acted sometimes as assistants
  William P. Blake
  George J. Brush   [Sheffield Scientific School]
  William H. Brewer   [Sheffield Scientific School]
  Mr. Vigus   Montgomery, Alabama

Of these men, Lyman Foot had come to him first. He was twelve years old when he arrived from Wallingford and he served him well for nine years, becoming intensely interested and highly skillful in aiding with the experiments that Silliman performed to illustrate his lectures. Foot showed such promise that in 1813, with Silliman's backing, he entered the first class of the Medical Institution. He continued to serve in the laboratory throughout his medical course and in 1815, on the recommendation of Silliman, President Dwight, and other faculty members, he was appointed surgeon in the Medical Department of the Army by Mr. John C. Calhoun, then Secretary of War. His services came to be widely recognized and when he retired at the age of fifty, he was second surgeon in the Medical Department.

Denison Olmsted followed Foot in the laboratory, having served as tutor following his graduation in 1813. He had lost none of his early determination to continue in mineralogy and geology; indeed he had already accepted a professorship at the University of North Carolina. He spent three years (1815-1818) preparing for this post, and Silliman wrote in his Reminiscences years later: "When he left he feelingly expressed to me his sense of the advantages which he had enjoyed in the course of preparatory labor and instruction through which he had passed, without which he said he could not have dared to enter upon the duties of his station. In that station, during the seven years of his professorship at Chapel Hill he bestowed important advantage upon the college there and acquired deserved honor for himself." Olmsted also served as state geologist and mineralogist, making the first survey report on the state's natural resources.

Yale and his former professor were not forgotten, for Olmsted sent a duplicate set of all the minerals he collected to help build up Silliman's American mineral cabinet (the Gibbs Cabinet contained only European minerals). After returning to New Haven in 1825 as Professor of Mathematics and Natural History he became interested in astronomy and showed his versatility by writing much-needed textbooks in both fields. Like Silliman, he was not primarily an investigator, believing it his function to teach and stimulate an interest in science more than to cultivate it. He did much to support Silliman's efforts along these lines and became well known through his teaching and writing. He was ever loyal in carrying forward the traditions of the professor who had set him on his course and encouraged him throughout his career. Some forty of his articles appeared in the *American Journal of Science and Arts,* including those which brought him scientific acclaim—his papers on meteoric showers and zodiacal light.

AMOS EATON

During Olmsted's apprenticeship there came to Silliman in 1816 a man whom he later set down under the heading: "Learner to become a lecturer." This man, Amos Eaton—a colorful figure and something of a storm center in his time—was destined to have a career in science which in many respects paralleled Silliman's own. Born at almost the same time (Eaton in 1776, Silliman in 1779), they had both studied law, Silliman commencing in 1798 and Eaton in 1799 when he graduated from Williams College. Both were admirers of Timothy

Dwight, Eaton naming his third son, born in 1807, after
Dwight.* Both passed their bar examinations in 1802, but here
their paths went in different directions. Silliman was diverted
to science, but Eaton began working as a land agent and lawyer.

In 1811, just as Silliman was making plans for displaying the
Gibbs Cabinet at Yale, Amos Eaton was convicted of forgery
on a trumped-up charge by an unscrupulous counsellor-at-law,
Nathaniel Pendleton (who had been Alexander Hamilton's
second in his duel with Aaron Burr). Although entirely inno-
cent, Eaton was sentenced to life imprisonment at hard labor
and served for nearly four years in the Newgate Prison located
in the section of Manhattan later known as Greenwich Village.

A dormant interest in science had caused him in 1810 to
open the Catskill Botanical School where he taught mathematics and botany on Mondays and Saturdays to "all persons
of both sexes, from twelve years old to sixty." His trial and
imprisonment put a stop to this, but in prison his mathematical ability soon changed his assignment to clerk rather than
laborer. In his spare time he began the study of geology and
completed a manuscript of 342 pages.

As soon as the friends he made while in prison—especially
John Torrey and DeWitt Clinton—had secured him a pardon
in November 1815, Samuel Latham Mitchill supplied him
with letters of recommendation that made it possible for him
to rebuild his life, although he was now forty, along the lines
of his chief interest—science. Eaton now went to New Haven
to study with Silliman, arriving in the spring of 1816 fresh
from prison. He attended the lectures in chemistry every morning and mineralogy on Wednesdays and Saturdays; he also
studied botany with Eli Ives.

After a year of intensive study he accepted an invitation to

---

* His devotion to science caused him to name other children after great scientists; thus Charles Linnaeus Eaton, Cuvier Eaton, Buckland Eaton, and Johnson
Humboldt Eaton.

lecture at his alma mater, Williams College. For seven years
Eaton continued to give public lectures on science throughout
New York State and New England. He possessed a strong and
dynamic personality and had the same practical desire to make
science work for the development of the country that prompted
Silliman to go before lay audiences. Since he was not restricted
by an academic attachment, he went about securing lecture-
ships with more method and with a more conscious effort at
showmanship than did Silliman, and although he did not acquire a reputation and prestige equal to that of his teacher, he
was nevertheless highly successful.

Inspired by Silliman to do original work, he published a
small textbook in 1818 called *An Index to the Geology of the
Northern States.* In 1820 under the sponsorship of Stephen
Van Rensselaer, he made a geological and agricultural survey
of Albany County and later of the country along the then new
Erie Canal. When Van Rensselaer suggested that he secure the
help in the canal survey of a geologist known to the public, he
turned to Silliman. In the gracious letter he wrote him * there
was no hint of the scathing criticism contained in an earlier
letter to his friend, John Torrey. It was the sort of criticism he
frequently dealt out with a free hand to fellow scientists, now
directly, now indirectly. At the same time, he could be equally
vehement in their support.

By your letter I presume you know Silliman personally by this time. I
can tell you the good and the bad of him in a few words. He is an excellent practical chemist and a good *cabinet* mineralogist. With very little
knowledge of geology, he affects much. He is impatient when his opinions
are questioned, and has very lofty conceptions attached to the stupendous
title of Professor of Yale College; and expects us to be ever mindful of his
honorable marriage into the family of Governor Trumbull. Still he is a
pretty good fellow; though quite too formal for a man of science.

* Although Silliman agreed to assist Eaton, his illness during the early 1820's
prevented him from taking an active part.

Eaton during this period was making the first attempt at a systematic arrangement of American rock strata. In his *Geological Text-book* published in 1830, he wrote: "The progress of geology in America may be divided into two eras. First Maclure's surveys for establishing our Geographical Geology. Second, Van Rensselaer's surveys for establishing our Stratiographical Geology." George P. Merrill, in his *First One Hundred Years of American Geology* (1924) stated: "According to Amos Eaton, 1820 marked the close of the first era of American geology. Accepting this, it may well be called the Maclurean era. The second, including the decade 1820-1829, may with equal propriety be called the Eatonian era, since Eaton was the most prominent worker as well as most profuse writer of the decade."

Silliman and Eaton, though not always in agreement, kept up a lively correspondence for many years. Silliman was glad to give Eaton's articles a prominent place in the Journal, but he sometimes admonished him as follows: "I will thank you to take care that the handwriting be fair & technical terms particularly distinct." Eaton on the other hand, in his forthright way, wrote Silliman concerning the Journal: "David Thomas, the scientific Quaker of the west, says you have an unnecessary proportion of typographical errors. . . . D. Thomas, however, considers the Journal next to his bible in point of merit."

Perhaps the last parallel between the work of Eaton and Silliman lies in their establishment of schools where the practical approach to science was emphasized. Eaton in 1824 founded a school at Troy, New York, now the Rensselaer Polytechnic Institute (after Stephen Van Rensselaer who virtually supported the school in its early years), and to it dedicated all his tremendous energies until his death in 1842. Silliman in 1846 was influential in founding a scientific school at Yale, but unlike the school at Troy, this was in the beginning on a graduate level.

OTHER PUPILS

Eaton had left New Haven in 1817, and when Olmsted departed in 1818 he was followed by Edward Hitchcock, who had first engaged Silliman's attention when as a young instructor at Deerfield Academy he had asked that a box of minerals be identified. Silliman, pleased by the request, asked for further specimens and eventually invited him to come to New Haven. This Hitchcock did in 1819 and although he entered to study theology, he attended Silliman's lectures regularly and became so interested that he decided to follow science as a career.

Hitchcock was a most prolific writer and, beginning with a paper in the first volume, he contributed over the years some sixty titles to Silliman's Journal. He accepted the chair of chemistry at Amherst College and later served as president for ten years. In 1830 he conducted a geological survey of Massachusetts, the first work of its kind in America to be completed at state expense. His *Elementary Geology,* published in 1847, passed through thirty editions and was then revised.

Silliman followed his career with the interest of both teacher and friend and kept in close touch with him throughout the rest of their lives. In 1863, when they were both old men and Hitchcock was ill, he wrote Silliman as follows:

When I opened your letter, my eyes fell first upon the photograph, and it is so very perfect, and gives the expression of your face so exactly like what it was when more than forty years ago I first heard you lecture, and a hundred times afterwards, that a crowd of reminiscences came over me, and I had quite a crying spell before reading the letter. This shows the weakness of my nerves; but it also shows how powerful was the influence of your eloquence and your kindness upon me in those early days when I was bashful and uncultivated, poor and without scientific friends. Certain it is that your instruction and encouragement and example have had more influence upon me to make me what I have been than those of any other man, and if I have not been grateful, God forgive me!

When Hitchcock left in 1821, his place was taken by George T. Bowen of Providence who made a special request to work in the laboratory during his junior and senior years. Since there was already some feeling on the part of the classicists about the popularity of the chemistry laboratory, Silliman declined to receive Bowen until he could obtain special permission from the President. Though contrary to all precedent, the indulgence was granted—on the express condition that he should perform all his college duties with fidelity.

Silliman was highly gratified with his performance and several of his original observations and analyses found their way into the Journal. In 1817 an unknown mineral was discovered in Saybrook, Connecticut. Silliman set Bowen to examining it. He eventually concluded that it was a new series, which he named Sillimanite. In 1824 an account of it was published in the Journal with the following editorial comment signed 'B.S.':

. . . Had the name, *originally* proposed for it at New-Haven, or *any other* than the one which it now bears, been given to it, I could have had no objection to its appearance in this Journal, and as the present name was bestowed entirely without my privity and was already placed beyond my control [the paper had been read before the Academy of Natural Sciences and had appeared in their journal] before I was informed of the design, I have reluctantly yielded to Mr. Bowen's request, supposing that a refusal under such circumstances would bear less the appearance of a proper feeling than of an over scrupulous delicacy.

From Yale, Bowen went in 1822 to Philadelphia to work with Robert Hare and from there to Tennessee as Professor of Chemistry in the University of Nashville. Unhappily he died prematurely in 1828 at the age of twenty-six, evidently of tuberculosis, and Silliman recorded that on his deathbed he sent him an affectionate farewell accompanied by an aerolite that had fallen in Tennessee.

Now came the period of Silliman's ill health and the appointment of Sherlock J. Andrews as his assistant. Andrews was a recent graduate of Union College and although he knew no chemistry, as mentioned previously, he was quick to adapt himself and to become invaluable. He was frequently in the Silliman house and was a favorite of all. Silliman recorded with a deep sense of gratitude that he could not have retained his place in the College had it not been for Andrews' faithful and efficient assistance.

On his side, Andrews wrote many years later: "It was my privilege to be connected with Mr. Silliman as his assistant from the fall of 1821 until the winter of 1823 and for a considerable part of that time to be a member of his family. It was when his health was broken down by care, excessive labor, and domestic affliction and when if ever any infirmities of temper or character were likely to be revealed to one intimately associated with him. . . . [But] though his cheerfulness was occasionally abated, he was never irritable, never impatient, never unmindful of the claims or comfort of others." Despite his devotion to Silliman, Andrews' heart was in the law, and he finally resigned to take up a law practice in Cleveland, Ohio. Thereafter a series of men served for a year each—first Selleck's son, Benjamin D. Silliman, a graduate of the Class of 1824, and then another relative, Burr D. Noyes. A career in science did not tempt them, however, and Benjamin became a lawyer and Noyes a physician.

In 1826 the position of assistant to Silliman was offered to Charles Shepard. A contemporary account runs thus: "In addition to the preceding appointments, Mr. Charles Upham Shepard has been elected an assistant [to the] Professor in the Chemical Department, the growing importance of that Professorship having satisfied the Corporation that the indefatigable exertions of an individual would be inadequate to the labor of all its duties, and that the addition of a scientific assistant would greatly promote the interests of the College."

Shepard, a graduate of Amherst College, was already indoc-
trinated with a love of science through having attended the
lectures of Amos Eaton and he had brought together a substantial collection of minerals that Eaton had used to illustrate
his Amherst lectures. In New Haven Shepard continued his
field trips to collect minerals and fossils, and Silliman, under
the stimulus of his enthusiasm, resumed the geological lectures based on his cabinet which had been given up during
the period of his ill health. Shepard remained with Silliman
for five years, resigning in 1831 to become Lecturer in Botany.
In 1833 he was appointed Lecturer in Natural History at
Yale College. He remained in this position until 1847, although from 1834 on he simultaneously held a part-time appointment at the Medical College in Charleston, South Carolina, as Professor of Chemistry. After Silliman's death he set
down some impressions of his preceptor during the years he
was in the laboratory:

. . . For easy, sprightly, instructive conversation, he surpassed any
man I have known. He was the charm of the social circle, and one in
whose solitary companionship you never tired. His correspondence was
equally entertaining and reminded one of some of the best models of
the old English letter-writers. His charity towards his fellow-men was a
striking feature in his character. . . .

He was neither elated by success or depressed by disappointment. His
cheerfulness of mind and bodily elasticity were wonderful. I never saw
him out of humor, or apparently fatigued. He was never idle, never in a
hurry. His temperance was remarkable. The pleasure he derived from
the table could only be seen in the agreeable flow of conversation attending the meal, for I never heard him remark upon a dish, nor did I
ever see him drink wine. His health was perfect. During our entire acquaintance he never complained of an uneasiness in my hearing. He required the least amount of sleep for the preservation of all this vigor and
freshness of any man of whom I have read. . . . Had the energies of his
life, instead of being devoted to the diffusion of science in a new country,
been concentrated upon a single department of knowledge, his claims to
scientific éclat would be more easily established.

Overlapping Shepard was Oliver Payson Hubbard of the Class of 1828, whom Silliman took on immediately after his graduation (also for a five-year period) at the recommendation of Denison Olmsted. Hubbard, as had Shepard, proved a particularly agreeable associate and Silliman came to lean on him heavily in connection with his chemical and geological demonstrations. During his years at Yale, Hubbard found his way into the good graces of the Silliman family and married Faith Wadsworth, Professor Silliman's second daughter, on May 17, 1837. He had meanwhile received many invitations to lecture outside New Haven and in 1836 he had accepted the chair of chemistry, mineralogy, and geology at Dartmouth College where he had a long and productive career.

The story of Silliman's next two assistants is told in a later chapter. In 1835 it was James Dwight Dana, just back from an assignment with the Navy in the Mediterranean, who received the appointment, and he was followed in 1837 by Silliman's own son, Benjamin, Jr. In his Reminiscences Silliman wrote: "I have found occasion to confess myself a partial judge in the case of Mr. Hubbard and Mr. Dana—what shall I say when my own son is the subject of my remarks? I might indeed name him as the successor of Mr. Dana and do no more. But if it would be weak and foolish to laud him because he is a part of myself, it would be unjust were I, for that reason, to withhold from him his just due. I shall therefore treat him with Roman impartiality."

Another student who figured subsequently in Silliman's life was John Pitkin Norton whom he did not mention in the list but who studied with him in 1840-41 and again in 1842-44. He, George J. Brush, and William H. Brewer all became identified with science at Yale.

COLLEGE OFFICER

While this succession of men was assisting in the work of the laboratory, Silliman's responsibilities in connection with the College as a whole were increasing, and students, tutors, associates, and President Woolsey himself have written of his activities during the 1820's and '30's. One of his duties was to serve on the committee that examined students for entrance. His kindness and tolerance made a deep impression on the candidates, but they soon learned that he could be quick to reprove when discipline was indicated. One, Thomas A. Thacher, later Professor of the Latin Language and Literature at Yale, remembered how Silliman smilingly passed over the embarrassing fact that he had forgotten his credentials, but during the session firmly reprimanded a tutor for spitting from one of the windows of the chapel where the examination was being held. The tutor's assurance that he had carefully looked beforehand to see if anyone were below did not satisfy him, for it was the breach of manners he deplored as much as the danger to passersby.

Another student wrote: "My first knowledge of Professor Silliman was in 1827 when he examined me in Geography for admission to Yale College. He was then forty-eight years old, tall, erect . . . carefully and even elegantly dressed, very dignified, and yet very attractive in his manners. I was greatly impressed by the extent of his knowledge, the rapidity of the movements of his mind, the affability of his address, and the great kindness of his heart. He was the presiding officer of the Board of Examiners at that time and for many years, and there are doubtless hundreds of the graduates of the College who can recall similar impressions of his graceful dignity, his unaffected kindness on an occasion which is always memorable and trying."

Silliman was particularly considerate of the younger members of the faculty who had but recently been pupils. "He at once called them his colleagues in the grave business of the instruction and government of the College," one of his associates wrote, "and seemed disposed with unaffected sincerity to take them to a full equality with himself as such. Not that there was any want of this respect on the part of others toward the younger officers, but he was more carefully demonstrative."

He did not meet the students in classes until their junior and senior years, but the undergraduates knew him well since he and the other professors often conducted the nightly chapel services. He always spoke rapidly, the rich tones of his voice rising and falling in melodious and ofttimes extravagant oratory. However, he was particularly popular because he more than the others was accustomed to adapt his selections, both of hymns and Scripture, to the season of the year or to national and local events. His prayers, especially, showed the fertility of his mind, and his petitions were sometimes unusual.

Silliman was also called upon to "orient" the freshmen, speaking to them of personal habits, diet, sleep, methods of study, and the moral pitfalls to be encountered in college life. Professor Noah Porter (B.A. Yale 1831), for many years a member of the Divinity School faculty, remembered being summoned, in company with the rest of his class, to Silliman's laboratory—to the freshmen "a mysterious apartment, made impressive by the manifold and multiform arrangements of furnaces, retorts, and crucibles." He recalled that these lectures made a strong impression upon the class, not only in respect to the matters discussed but as to the kindness of the professor and his earnest desire to promote the welfare of the students.

Although no lecturer in the College was more popular, some criticized his delivery. He was guilty of frequent digressions, he spoke rapidly, assumed too much knowledge on the part of his listeners, and touched on many points so lightly that his lectures were sometimes devoid of value as a philosophical discipline. But his brilliant and attractive experiments so impressed the principles of chemical science on his audience that they were never forgotten. He stressed the practical applications of chemistry—in glass and pottery making and in other industries. His digressions were always interesting and stimulating and, when enriched by his contacts and correspondence with celebrated scientists, they doubtless served better to enlarge the minds of his hearers than if he had tended strictly to imparting information.

As a college officer, Silliman assumed his full share of responsibility. He was inclined to be lenient and to be impatient with petty rules, but he was full of spirit and when occasion demanded, no one was quicker than he to punish real offences or to strike out against meanness in any form. And because he was so even-tempered and just in all his dealings, his reprimands were unusually effective. President Woolsey described the special place he occupied both in the College and in representing it to the public:

His personal presence, his great popularity, his fine powers of persuasion caused him to be put forward whenever there were wants to be urged before the legislature or before private friends, whenever strangers of distinction were to be honored, whenever on academic festivals responses were due from the authorities of the Institution. There were, I believe, in the universities of the Middle Ages orators annually appointed who represented their communities on public occasions. He, in his prime, was our standing orator, the principal medium between those who dwelt in the academic shade and the great public.

A very important duty of Professor Silliman grew out of his function as a member of the College Faculty. For more than fifty years he sat and voted in that Faculty, aided in discipline as well as instruction, and being the senior Professor, had a prominent place in all Faculty measures. . . . When he took the Professor's chair, no especial part of the College discipline fell on him; he had no care of a division and hence had less direct and intimate contact with the students than most of the other officers exercised. It was natural, therefore, that he should think less of rules than those whose business it was to enforce them. But his influence was all exerted in favor of discipline and order, and especially where insubordination and combination to resist law was rife—as happened more than once— . . . he was a tower of strength to the government. His influence as a man, upon those students whom he knew or who were committed to his special care, was often exceedingly happy.

As a citizen of the town he was loved and respected. On the way home he would stop to chat with neighbors and townspeople and because he was especially fond of children, they would run to meet him when they saw him approaching. His happy, even gay, disposition at home made his own children adore him. So eager were they to please him that discipline was rarely necessary, and even then his firmness was clothed in gentleness.

Lessons they took to him unhesitatingly because he was so kind in his correction and instruction that they never feared him as many children feared their parents in those days of stern discipline. Maria, the eldest, could remember being allowed to play in the room with him while he worked on his lectures or on his Journal correspondence, but he would always say to her: "My little girl will not trouble papa." Later, when the children were old enough, he made a habit of telling them of his activities so that they could feel a part of all he did. He would include them with their mother in the audience on which he tried out his papers and speeches. On such occasions the opinions of even the youngest were given respectful attention and consideration. He also let them help him read proof on the Journal, an opportunity to be useful that they particularly enjoyed.

His children were enormously proud of the deference shown him on all sides and laughed at the timidity of their mother who always feared that he would break down when speaking in public. On one occasion the girls went with their father to a lecture for which the lecturer did not appear. Silliman was appealed to and proceeded to hold the interest of the audience for two hours in an impromptu discourse on atmosphere. The girls could hardly wait to reach home and tell their mother.

It was this unfailing composure combined with his deep interest in the subjects he taught that made him popular with his assistants, the student body, and later with his lay audiences. One who attended his early public lectures wrote to a friend: "Prof. Silliman has a few days since finished his Mineralogical-Geological lectures which I have had the pleasure of hearing. . . . Perfectly at home among the wreck and ruins of a former world, in either hand balancing a flood of waters & a lake of fire, before his respectable and attentive auditors of both sexes, he stands, like some kind but mighty spirit sent to instil into the minds of the rising generation the sublime and awful mysteries of the past creation, himself 'filled to bursting nigh' with the majesty and grandeur of the subject; occasionally among other veterans making honorable mention of Prof. Eaton's name and services, yet not infrequently dissenting to his opinions and more frequently adopting the opinions of his trans-atlantic brethern, yet professing to be a genuine eclectic and unfettered by theories."

In 1833 Silliman started to give lectures in science outside of Yale College. It was a venture which began in a small way but shortly developed into one of the most interesting and important phases of his career.

CHAPTER X

The First College Gallery of Art
1830-1832

SILLIMAN'S friends were now accustomed to find him in the vanguard of any progressive movement in science, but to some it may have come as a surprise to discover him as the moving spirit in the foundation at Yale of the first college art gallery in the country. It came about because circumstances were once more in favorable conjunction, and Silliman never missed an opportunity once it was apparent to him.

His acquaintance with Colonel John Trumbull, the founder of the new gallery, began when he was a tutor at Yale College. "As I came into early manhood I heard his praise from eminent men—President Dwight, the Honorable James Hillhouse and others; for his country was proud of him, and his fame as a soldier of the Revolution and a friend and aide of Washington and his celebrity as an artist were cherished at home, and especially in his native state of Connecticut. It was therefore no small gratification to me, and was felt to be an honor, to form his personal acquaintance. . . . This was in one of the public rooms of Yale College in which Institution I was then a tutor. It was, I believe, in October, 1801, during the autumnal session of the legislature, when his distinguished brother Jonathan Trumbull Esq was in attendance, as Governor of the State. He came to the College with Col. and Mrs. Trumbull, and I was introduced in the old Philosophical Hall over the former Chapel now the Athenaeum. The brothers were elegant, graceful gentlemen of winning manners & their familiarity with each other manifested in little sallies of wit was pleasing to me, who had regarded them only as grave, dignified men. A picture of their father and mother was hanging on the wall—the original painted by Col. Trumbull. . . . It soon caught the attention of the brothers and the artist said, referring to

the wig & curls on his father's head, 'Aye—that looks like a
Governor, not like this little queue of yours,' at the same moment playfully taking it up, and shaking it between his fingers,
much to the Governor's amusement & to my surprise."

Silliman further records that "ever after my introduction
to this distinguished man he treated me as a friend. He was soon
established in New York, and when, in 1804, I was preparing
to visit England, he gave me valuable letters of introduction,
and still more valuable written instructions as to life in England and especially in London, embodying the results of his
own long experience of 20 years."

John Trumbull was born at Lebanon, Connecticut, in
1756. At Harvard, although he distinguished himself in Latin
and Greek, he continued to show the propensity for drawing
manifested in early youth when he had painted in oil on the
inside of a closet door a spirited female figure brandishing
aloft a naked dagger. After entering the American Army in
1773, serving as Deputy Adjutant General of the Northern
Army under Major General Gates at Ticonderoga (at the age
of twenty), as aide to General Washington at the opening of
the campaign at Cambridge in 1775, and as aide to General
Sullivan in the attack upon the British in Rhode Island, he
resigned his commission and in 1778 went to England to study
painting with Benjamin West. Silliman writes: "Until the
period just before the American Revolution this country had
produced no painter of eminence, and Copley in Boston had
stood forth almost alone as a model for young artists, while
West shone in England. . . . When he began to paint, the
colonies, commencing an arduous struggle with the mother
country, were comparatively poor, and for many years the
Revolutionary War and subsequently the difficulty of establishing a reliable government turned the American mind to the
stern realities with which it was necessary to grapple and left

little disposition and still less ability to cultivate and patronize the beautiful art of painting. . . ."

But it was natural that Trumbull, having served in the Revolution with all the ardor of youthful patriotism, should cherish the idea of devoting his talents to commemorating some of its great events. He conceived the plan, therefore, of doing a series of twelve historical paintings, only eight of which he completed. He travelled extensively in this country and abroad in an effort to execute true portraits of the men he represented in the "Battle of Bunker's Hill," the "Surrender of General Burgoyne," the "Surrender of Lord Cornwallis," etc. His brilliant interpretation of the "Declaration of Independence," which occupied him eight years, "remains the most important visual record of the heroic period of American history, although not historically accurate in every detail." * At great expense Colonel Trumbull had engravings made of these paintings in order that they might be widely distributed, but the effort was unappreciated at that time [now they are known to every schoolboy] and he "often expressed, in strong terms, his disappointment and chagrin that the prints were not sold, and that they still rested with him until new generations had arisen to whom the Revolution was history merely; while in the meantime, the patriotic ardor of that period had, in a great measure died out, and the pursuit of wealth and the spirit of party reigned in its stead."

It was in a similar mood that Silliman found Colonel Trumbull in 1830 when he called on him at his apartment in New York. They had been in close touch through the years, since in addition to the friendship formed in 1801, there was the further tie of kinship, Mrs. Silliman being Colonel Trumbull's niece. Although one of the best portrait painters in America and surrounded by a fortune in paintings, Colonel

* Sizer, Theodore. Account of Trumbull in the *Dictionary of American Biography.*

Trumbull, now seventy-four years old, found himself without ready means of support. Silliman therefore broached the subject of the ultimate disposition of his art treasures, to which Colonel Trumbull promptly replied that he would give them to Yale to "be exhibited forever for the benefit of poor students" [admission fees were to provide scholarships] if Yale would grant him an annuity of one thousand dollars a year for the rest of his life.

Once more Silliman was able to offer thanks that "our President, the Revd Jeremiah Day, and my immediate colleagues among the older members of the College Faculty as well as the officers of the fiscal department were men of liberal minds, and I found no difficulty in exciting in them a lively interest and a strong desire to obtain the prize that was thus unexpectedly offered to us." Colonel Trumbull first contemplated dividing his collection between Hartford and New Haven, for Daniel Wadsworth, one of the leading citizens of Hartford, had also married a niece of his. Silliman waited in anxious silence for his decision because, although he thought it a great shame to break up the collection, he, too, was very fond of Mr. Wadsworth, and he was therefore in a delicate position. Trumbull finally decided that the pictures should remain together,* so Silliman set about to raise the money for the annuity.

Although Mr. Wadsworth was not to be a direct benefactor, he generously pledged a considerable proportion of the annual sum required. Jeremiah Day, Professor Goodrich, Stephen Twining, and Silliman made up the balance. They pledged the amount for six years believing that this term "upon the ordinary valuation of human life might be presumed sufficient for a man who had already numbered seventy-six years and might not pass beyond eighty-two." However, they were willing

* Copies of five of the paintings were eventually purchased from Trumbull's estate by Mr. Wadsworth to be hung in the Wadsworth Athenaeum which he founded in Hartford.

to continue after that time if necessary, or if the College was not in a position to take over the responsibility. Reimbursement was to be made them in some measure from the proceeds of the gallery. As it happened, their calculations proved somewhat optimistic, for Colonel Trumbull, relieved of his financial worries, relaxed and enjoyed life to the goodly age of eighty-seven.

The next step was to secure funds for the erection of a suitable gallery, and to accomplish this Silliman became a lobbyist at the state legislature. He wrote that his chief aim was to obtain sufficient means to erect a building for the Trumbull paintings and more if possible. Although many prophesied failure, his cogent arguments were ably supported by two Yale alumni, the Honorable Truman Smith and Judge Romeo Lowry, both members of the Legislature, and he went triumphantly back to New Haven with $7,000.

The erection of the building was commenced immediately on a site at the north end of the old Yale campus. The original estimate of the building cost was $2,500, but Silliman recorded that "it rose to $3,000 and by movement of the Corporation themselves to $3,500. Our worthy and vigilant friend Mr. Twining [the Steward], always laudably anxious to the most economical applications of the funds of the College, was much annoyed that the charges ran up to $5,000, but I felt differently. My only regret on that subject is that the entire sum of $7,000 which I earned by my own efforts, aided by my friends in the legislature, had not been expended upon the building." Mr. Theodore Sizer, Director of the Yale University Art Gallery (formerly the Trumbull Gallery), in 1940 described this first building:

. . . The early museums of Germany and Britain were ponderously classical and correspondingly unfunctional. One of the earliest examples to be built in these United States was the little temple-like Trumbull Gallery at Yale. . . . Designed by a romantically-inclined, bellicose ex-army officer, whose dramatic ideas were tempered by a serene-minded professor [Silliman], the Gallery was chastely classical but eminently practical. Patriotism, opportunism, didacticism, and a newly-awakened social consciousness were all ingredients that went into its making. The justly proportioned, prim little building only served its original purpose of an art museum for thirty-five years. It was an administrative office for thirty-four more, and was then obliterated, leaving only a memory.

The walls of the new building were lined with pine plank, for greatest facility and security in hanging the paintings, and covered with coarse red woolen moreen. Green carpeting and settees and chairs of yellow curled maple with cane seats added to the attractive appearance. Colonel Trumbull selected the furnishings, as well as guiding the design of the building, and he came to New Haven to supervise the last details of the arrangements, particularly the hanging of the paintings. To quote again from Mr. Sizer: "The red moreen covering was in place the first week in October, 1832, and the 'numerous boxes containing the Paintings arrived, under the safe conduct of the artist himself, who came to New Haven in the same Steamer which brought his treasures.' The steamboat line between New York and New Haven 'generously tendered a free passage to Col. Trumbull & all his effects, and this was only in accordance with that gentleman's considerate & habitual benevolence as exhibited on many occasions'—those were gentler days! The Colonel brought an experienced man for the hanging of the pictures and all was ready for the opening of the earliest art museum connected with an educational institution in America, we may hazard, on Saturday, October 29, 1832, ten months after the signing of the Indenture, in which it was specified 'that the building shall be finished on or before the first day of October, in the year of our Lord one thousand eight hundred and thirty-two.' The 'Connecticut Herald' noted on October 30th that 'this institution is now open for the reception of visitors.' New Haven was then a city of some ten thousand souls."

Since Colonel Trumbull regarded it as his finest painting, prominence was given to his full-length portrait of George Washington executed for the city of Charleston but refused by them because they preferred him in civil dress. In addition to the eight historical paintings of the Revolution, there were forty others on various subjects and a few by other artists, that had been presented to the College previously, including a portrait of Elihu Yale. Silliman records that the stairs were not carpeted until President Andrew Jackson visited New Haven in 1833. "As in the ceremonial of that day it fell to me to accompany him as President of the United States from the reception room in the State House to the College, I took care to have the stairs carpeted that very morning, and the Hero of New Orleans was the first public dignitary who ascended them in their improved condition." Since the building was not completely fireproof because of these wooden stairs, Silliman had had constructed in the floor of each room a slit, twelve feet long and fifteen inches wide, through which the pictures could be dropped to the room below, if it were not on fire, and speedily removed from the building. The slits were concealed by a movable board covered by the carpet.

Silliman became the first curator of the gallery and with characteristic thoroughness he later issued a broadside describing the history of the collection and listing the more important holdings. This, one of the earliest official publications, carried at the bottom the amusing admonition: "N.B. Visitors are earnestly requested not to touch the paintings or the statuary. Canes, whips, umbrellas, fruit, tobacco, and dogs are excluded. B. Silliman, Curator." It is still invoked in 1947!

It was Colonel Trumbull's wish that he and Mrs. Trumbull be buried under the gallery. After his death on the 10th of November 1843, this and his other requests were faithfully carried out by Silliman, his executor, and "the relatives and particular friends of the deceased, the College Faculty, professional students, undergraduates, and citizens went through College to Chapel and High Street to the Trumbull Gallery and on a bleak, blowing evening in November deposited the body in its last resting place." * Trumbull had lived long enough to see the stimulating effect of his benefaction on the cultural life of Yale College.

Some of his activities during his last years are recounted in a letter of Silliman's to C. Edwards Lester, Esq.: †

He retained his love of his art almost to the last. The gallery contains several very good pictures painted after he was 78 years old & some after he was 80. The copies of the "Transfiguration" and of "The Death of St. Jerome" were the last, the latter the very last and he found some difficulty in following out the minutiae of the drapery owing to the decay of his vision, but both these pictures are surprising productions for an artist of 82 to 83 years of age with only one useful eye. The social feelings of Col. T. were vivid and his conversational powers extraordinary. His long and varied life abounding in changes & passed among the great men of the age furnished him with a rich fund of historical anecdote which he was accustomed to communicate to his friends in his familiar conversation. With these he could had he chosen to do so enriched his autobiography and probably many of his readers would have preferred them to the grave details of important events. He used to mention that in the composition of the "Sortie of Gibraltar" he wanted a subject for his dying Spanish cavalier, Don Jos. Barbosa who appears fallen in the front of the picture with the hilt of his broken sword still grasped in his hand & refusing the succor offered him by Genl Elliott. At this crisis of the picture who should come into the painting room but the afterwards celebrated Sir Thomas Lawrence then a rising young artist. Trumbull familiarly accosted him—"Come, Lawrence, lie down for my dying Spaniard," which he promptly did and this is the origin of that fine figure, not however intended for a portrait.

The gallery furnished the impetus for the founding of the Yale School of the Fine Arts (1866), made possible by the generosity of Augustus R. Street. Its object was "to promote the

---

* The remains of Colonel and Mrs. Trumbull have been twice moved; in 1866 they were placed beneath the new Street Hall and in 1928, when the present gallery was dedicated, they were once again moved.
† Recently presented to Yale University by Mr. Henry Schuman of New York.

appreciation and cultivation of art in the community and more particularly to bring the refining and elevating influence of art culture to bear upon college students during the formative period of their academic life." The teaching of art, a new feature in the college curriculum in this country, was now inaugurated at Yale College.

Silliman, who had occupied the first chair in chemistry at Yale College and the Medical Institution, who established the first course in geology in the country, who founded the first successful journal of science, was the driving spirit behind another "first" in American education.

CHAPTER XI

Presenting Science to the Public
1834-1857

BY 1834 Silliman, now in his fifty-fifth year, had become something of a national figure. His two-volume *Elements of Chemistry*, published in 1830, had added to the reputation already achieved through his previous writings and his *Journal*. He was in demand as a consultant in technological problems and for mining surveys and these, together with the public lectures which he was soon called upon to give over an extensive area, were added to his professorial duties at Yale. It was a strenuous existence, especially since travelling was slow and often entailed hardship. Even before his lecture tours began to absorb a great deal of his time, he was accustomed to returning to the laboratory every evening after supper and working until ten or eleven o'clock in order to keep abreast of his many activities.

The first series of lectures he gave outside of New Haven was presented in April and May of 1834 at Hartford, on the invitation of several prominent citizens. At this time popular lectures were a comparatively novel thing, particularly in the field of science, and Silliman probably did more than anyone to bring this mode of instruction into fashion in this country. Having studied the devices of Dalton and other popular lecturers in England and having had a long apprenticeship before his classes at Yale, he had developed an effective method of presentation which rarely failed to please. He always prepared a public lecture with the greatest care, generally writing out his major sections in longhand; he also rehearsed his scientific demonstrations prior to the lecture to be quite certain that every experiment would work, and it was said, particularly of his chemical demonstrations, that they never failed. His first biographer, Fisher, records that as a public speaker he was "dignified, animated, and fluent." Although his notes were always before him, he seldom referred to them since the process of writing them out in advance had fixed his material in his capacious memory.

He had employed Mr. Robert Bakewell (son of his friend of the same name who came to New Haven from England in 1828 and taught drawing at Yale for thirty years), to make geological drawings for him and "the advantage was so immediate and manifest," he wrote "that I was greatly gratified, because I found that, speaking to the mind through the eye was a very successful mode of imparting knowledge." Three or four pictures of primeval scenes, five feet square, were hung about the lecture room—one "of the coal era with hills, one of the Saurian period, one of the early animals, and one of the dawn of terrestrial life." These drawings, together with the mineral specimens and fossils which Silliman used to illustrate his lectures, offered a considerable problem in transportation, but this was readily solved. "My outfit of drawings and specimens was contained in a box fitted to the running part of my carriage, the body being removed. My faithful assistant Robert Park [his negro servant] took it to Hartford drawn by our noble old white horse—once Mr. Wadsworth's."

The lectures were highly successful and the Hartford invitation proved the first of many during the next two decades. From the admission fees at these lectures and those he gave in New Haven outside the College, he derived an income of $550, $220 of which he invested in drawings. In Lowell, Massachusetts, where he gave a course of lectures in September of the same year assisted by Benjamin, Jr., then eighteen, his drawings extended over 80 feet along the walls of the lecture room and aroused considerable interest. In this series he gave an introductory lecture and then three lectures a week for three weeks, plus two extra at the close of the series—one on meteors and the other on temperance. He recorded that both were well received. Between 400 and 500 people attended these lectures, for which men paid $1.50 and women $1.00. A large proportion of the audience was composed of young women who were "operatives in the manufactories."

One can only imagine what interest was created among these people by the white-haired lecturer who told them how the history of the earth could be read in rock—how successive strata represented a period in the earth's past, one layer of rock marking an epoch, groups of rocks, periods, and still larger groups, ages, geological time being reckoned in millions of years. He explained that in the successive layers, the history of the growth of life could be traced—from the first age, when little or no animal life existed, to the Age of Mollusks when the inhabitants were the already living corals, jelly fish, sea urchin, star fish, and others of their kind, followed by oysters, clams, snails, crabs, and other crustaceans. Fish followed the mollusks, then came the Age of Reptiles when creatures with twelve-foot legs walked the earth. From this the lecturer progressed to the Age of Mammals and the Age of Man, illustrating his points from time to time by references to the colored drawings on the wall or by showing geological specimens. His presentation was easy, his subject engrossing, his enthusiasm contagious. The Honorable Daniel Webster was in the audience when he discussed the formation of the earth—a favorite theme he entitled "Diluvial Action and the Deluge." When Silliman met him after the lecture "he entered into the subject with zeal, and discoursed upon it with energy and eloquence, showing that his great mind had not overlooked this subject."

In addition to the formal lectures, Silliman devoted an hour each morning to showing the minerals and other specimens to those who wished to examine them closely and to ask him questions. He discovered that interest was so great that he was occupying far more than an hour in this way, so he changed the time to six a.m. and, since everybody was ready for break-

fast at seven, there was no more lingering. Many were inspired
to go into the field to hunt specimens and frequently brought
in minerals and pieces of rocks for him to identify.

Silliman records that throughout the lectures "my son gave
me great satisfaction by his zealous and skilful assistance. The
occasion was very favorable to the expansion of his mind and
the enlargement of his knowledge and he was a general favorite
—the young ladies not excepted." In addition to the $350 re-
ceived from the lectures, Silliman was given several gifts, all
of which were manufactured in Lowell. Amongst these were a
soapstone pump, some cotton, broadcloth and kerseymere material, two "large and elegant" rugs, and an ivory-mounted
carriage whip.

THE LOWELL LECTURES

During the following year he had a second invitation to
lecture in Boston. The first, several years earlier, he had not
accepted because he felt unable to leave his college duties for
so long a time, but on this occasion he accepted the invitation,
"thinking that it presented a fair opportunity of introduction
to the Athens of New England." It was the first of six seasons
—in 1835 and 1836 he undertook the lectures at the invitation
of the Boston Society for Promoting Useful Knowledge, but
more or less on his own responsibility; in 1840, '41, '42, and '43
he lectured under the auspices of the Lowell Institute. "These
courses," he wrote, "were of the utmost importance to me both
as regards my reputation and my pecuniary resources. They
enabled me to repay money borrowed of Yale College for the
enlargement and improvement of my place and to aid my children in making their establishments."

Silliman journeyed to Boston for his first lecture by stagecoach, via Hartford and Worcester, the last lap of the journey
being accomplished in a heavy snowstorm. In all it took three
days (February 25-27). When he reached Boston he found that

his faithful Robert Park, who had travelled by water through
New York and Providence, had already arrived with the boxes.
He and Robert spent a morning preparing the lecture room in
the Masonic Temple on the southeast side of the Boston Common. It was characteristic of Silliman that since he had never
lectured in Boston before, he thought it, he said, "both fair
towards my audience and prudent as regards myself, to afford
the citizens an opportunity to hear me before any of them
should have been committed." Apparently many came to hear
the "sample" lecture before buying their tickets for the course.

I entered the lecture-hall through a private door leading from my
study. A large and brilliant audience was before me—much larger than
any one that I had ever addressed. I was awed but not abashed, and I
entered upon the duty with good courage and entire self-possession. The
room was more than full—alleys and all—the people filled the stairs and
were clustered around the door in crowds. My friend, Dr. Woodbridge
Strong, told me that those who went away because they could not gain
admittance were more than the actual audience. They were differently
estimated, by different persons, from 1000 to 1400; perhaps 1200 might
have been nearer to the truth. Such an audience of intelligent and attentive persons was sufficiently encouraging.

The subject of the lecture was Meteors. I spoke seventy minutes—giving
first an introductory view of luminous meteors, including lightning and
shooting stars—this being merely introductory to the meteoric fire-balls.
Then followed an historical sketch of the arrival in our atmosphere of
fire-balls throwing down stones and iron, preceded and accompanied by
violent explosions and cannon-like reports. The Weston Meteor of December 1807 was fully described. . . . Specimens of the meteorites were
then exhibited; their external characters and mechanical and chemical
compositions were explained.

The courses in Hartford and Lowell had gained him a reputation as a lecturer, but this course in Boston was, he records, his
first great success. People came to the lectures in droves, often
an hour or more beforehand in order to get good seats. "Not
to lose time while they are waiting," Silliman wrote, "individuals often bring their work—knitting, sewing, reading, and

proof-reading, not to mention newspapers." Because he felt
that the chemical constitution of the earth was little known
to people in general and, he recorded: "for the reason that experimental illustrations of the elements and their primary
combinations are very beautiful and very interesting, I prepared a series of experiments. With the assistance of Robert I
made oxygen and chlorine and preserved the gasses in stop-
pered bottles. . . . The experiments were entirely successful
and appeared to afford great satisfaction to the audience. Thus
they had before them an outline both of the mechanical and
chemical constitution of the world—the rocks, the waters, the
atmosphere, organic bodies, etc."

During the day he occupied himself with preparing for the
next lecture, with writing letters to his family and to his scientific colleagues at home and abroad, with sightseeing trips
around Boston, or "with ordering a cloak of blue broadcloth
—very handsome." He also sat for two portraits by the artist
Willard about which he made amusing comment: "As far as I
can judge, he is succeeding well with the second picture, which
is spirited; the first was too mild, even tame."

In the evening he was entertained by many of the prominent
people in Boston and Cambridge, not only by men of science
and scholars, but by many others. At a soirée at Dr. Jacob Bige-
low's he met President Quincy and former President Kirkland
of Harvard. He was a guest of Dr. Charles T. Jackson, the
geologist and chemist who, some ten years later, was involved
in the acrimonious controversy over the discovery of ether. He
dined with General William Sullivan under whom his wife's
uncle, Colonel John Trumbull, had served as aide; also with
Governor Winthrop—"a noble and perfect gentleman of the
old school—his person grand, being large and handsome, and
his locks white—manners dignified, but courteous and encouraging to strangers." He attended a dinner meeting of the Friday Evening Club and there met many of the professors from

Harvard College. In fact, his social engagements became almost more arduous than his lectures, but he seemed to enjoy every occasion keenly, preferring dinners, however, to functions where he had to stand all evening.

He returned to New Haven by steamer through New York, arriving on the 13th of April, which allowed him only twelve days to attend to his college affairs before he opened a course of lectures in Salem on May 1st. In a letter to Mrs. Silliman he wrote that "the house is at present full of wonders, there are in this hotel forty or more equestrians and theatricians and there is in the town a play or a circus every night—the caravan and menagerie will arrive today—and your husband and son the climax of wonders!"

He returned to New Haven the last week in May, taught his college course in geology from June first to the latter part of August, and in September gave a series of lectures at Nantucket, Massachusetts. During October, November, and December he completed his chemistry course at Yale, including his course for the medical students. In January he lectured in New York, and in March and April 1836 returned to Boston. Four days after the close of his Boston engagement he was lecturing again in New York.

Such a program must have been a considerable strain, especially when it required the transportation of extensive equipment of great value. For the Boston course in chemistry, he had had a deflagator constructed at a cost of $1,000—he could have used a smaller, less spectacular one, but he felt the people of Boston should be fully repaid for their enthusiastic support of his efforts. But despite the large sums which he invested in equipment he had enough left over from his outside activities to present each of his children with a thousand dollars, to buy some new furniture for Mrs. Silliman (the first in the twenty-seven years since their marriage), and to order from

England two gold watches—one costing forty guineas for himself and one at thirty guineas for Benjamin, Jr.

His reputation was now firmly established in New England and the following year he was approached by Mr. John A. Lowell of Boston in regard to opening the Lowell Institute, of which Lowell was the sole trustee. When Mr. Lowell's cousin, John Lowell, Jr., had died in far-off Bombay while yet a young man, he had left a will which said, in part: "As the prosperity of my native land, New England, which is sterile and unproductive, must depend hereafter, as it has heretofore depended, first on the moral qualities, and secondly on the intelligence and information of its inhabitants; I am desirous of trying to contribute . . . towards these objects." His contribution was $250,000 (in 1928 it amounted to $1,500,000) for the establishment of a foundation which would offer free lectures in science, literature, and the arts. No portion of the fund was to be used for a building, so Silliman opened the first Lowell Lecture in the Odeon on January 2, 1840, assisted by Benjamin, Jr. Silliman regarded these lectures, attended by "large and approving audiences," as the "crowning success of his professional life." When Governor Everett announced to the audience "the name of the individual who would have the honor of opening the Institution," he remarked thus:

The first course of lectures is now about to commence on the subject of Geology, to be delivered by a gentleman—Professor Silliman of Yale College—whose reputation is too well established in this department of science, both in Europe and America, and is too well known to the citizens of Boston to need an attestation on my part. It would be arrogant in me to speak farther of his qualifications as a lecturer on this foundation. The great crowd assembled this evening, consisting as it does of a moiety only of those who have received tickets of admission to the course, sufficiently evinces the desire which is felt by the citizens of Boston again to enjoy the advantages of his instruction, while it affords a new proof, if further proof were wanting, that our liberal founder did not mistake the disposition of the community to avail themselves of the benefit of an institution of this character. . . . The few sentences, penned with a tired hand by our fellow-citizen on the top of a palace of the Pharaohs, will do more for human improvement than, for aught that appears, was done by all of that gloomy dynasty that ever reigned.

Silliman was gratified by this introduction and he replied with his customary grace, making appropriate mention not only of the founder of the lectures, but of Mr. Lowell, the director, and the people of Boston. During the period of his stay he was again entertained handsomely and frequently, but somehow he found time to refresh his mind with Darwin's *Natural History and Geology of South America* after the "labors of the day and evening."

Following the close of the series he went to Philadelphia where he was named the first president of the "association of geologists formed for the purpose of promoting the progress of science and its applications in this country." This society, later called the American Association of Geologists and Naturalists, in 1848 became the American Association for the Advancement of Science, at the present time the largest scientific organization in the United States. In 1948 it will celebrate one hundred years (actually one hundred and five) of distinguished service—its purpose still "to promote the progress of science and its applications in this country."

In 1843 when Silliman completed the fourth of his Lowell Lectures, the *Boston Transcript* commented:

Professor Silliman, whom all the Bostonians love as a Christian and honor as a man of science, concluded his series of valuable and instructive lectures to one of his audiences and will complete this evening, before another audience, his engagements in the Lowell Institute, which, as is well known, have been continued for four years, and have diffused among our people much useful knowledge, exciting, as we do not doubt, many a dormant intellect, and compelling the awakened mind to renewed activity and investigation. Admiring as we do the perfection of science exhibited continually by the lecturer in all that he has undertaken to explain, we have yet a higher love and reverence for that beautiful exhibition of divine truth to which Mr. Silliman constantly alludes, as seen in the wonderful works which he has successfully presented as designed by the Almighty power, and made known to man by human intelligence. . . .

Silliman himself closed the account of his lectures thus:

In concluding my labors in Boston during the six anxious years—the most arduous scientific engagements of my life—I did not indulge, and have never felt any sentiment of pride or vanity. Deeply impressed with my responsibility for the honor of Yale College, and with still higher moral obligations, and being ably assisted by my excellent son and a devoted artist [Mr. Wightman, a Boston instrument maker] I labored earnestly to fulfil every duty. By God's blessing, to whom be all the honor, our efforts were crowned with glorious success, and I was satisfied.

Benjamin, Jr. took a darker view than did his father of the benefits the good people of Boston might derive from the lectures. In a candid letter to his sister he wrote: "Pa bears up under his labors wonderfully and I think sometimes less labor would do, but you know the character of his mind which will not stop short of the ultimate. It seems like casting pearls before swine to take so much pains for those who for the most part appreciate it so little."

He was now called farther afield and in 1843 he lectured on geology at Pittsburgh, in 1844 and 1846 at Baltimore, and in 1845 at New Orleans, Mobile, and several other places on the way home, for he found Yale friends in every town. During the next years there was no easing of his schedule and he was called upon for many lectures in New York State, Pennsylvania, and all over New England. In 1851 he gave two lectures at the Smithsonian Institution (then in its sixth year) to which he, together with his friend Robert Hare, Albert Gallatin, and Washington Irving, had been elected (1849) to honorary membership. These lectures were preliminary to a series of twelve that he gave the following year.

His last extended lecture tour was to St. Louis in 1855 when he was seventy-five years old. After this trip, when he had difficulty making himself heard in the vast hall provided for the lectures, he decided that the time had come for him to stop and he thereafter accepted only a few short engagements.

☞ *PLEASE PRESERVE THIS FOR THE LECTURES.* ☜

LECTURE COURSE

OF

Prof. B. SILLIMAN, Sen.,

BEFORE THE

YOUNG MEN'S CHRISTIAN UNION,

OF BUFFALO,

AT

KREMLIN HALL

On the Evenings of Nov. 5th, 9th & 12th, 1857.

SUBJECTS—FIRE AND WATER.

THE LECTURES WILL BE ILLUSTRATED BY DRAWINGS.

Tickets for the Course, 50 Cents; Single Tickets, 25 Cts., to be had at the DOOR AND BOOK STORES.

BUFFALO:
C. E. YOUNG, PRINTER.
1857.

STILL LECTURING IN 1857

CORRESPONDENCE WITH SCIENTISTS

During these years when he was so actively engaged in presenting science to the public, Silliman was able to keep abreast with scientific advancement (and great interest was thereby added to his lectures) through the letters, publications, and specimens he was constantly receiving from his correspondents abroad. As early as 1820 the eminent Swedish chemist, Johann Jacob Berzelius, had suggested the mutual benefits of correspondence: ". . . You cultivate a science to which I have devoted the greater part of my time. It would be very pleasant to me if you could maintain a literary correspondence with me. I cannot promise you that my letters will have the same interest as those of an inhabitant of France or England; but, as we are not entirely confined to Sweden, I can perhaps from time to time furnish you with interesting news. . . . If an exchange of the minerals of America for those of Sweden and Norway would be agreeable to you, you have only to let me know, and to tell how you would like this exchange to be effected."

They did exchange specimens, for two years later Berzelius wrote again: ". . . I am very happy to learn that the minerals have arrived in safety, and that you are satisfied with them. I willingly take advantage of your kind offer to ask from you some American minerals, of which almost any would be welcome for a beginning since we have but very few here. . . . I take the liberty of sending you a copy of the French translation of my work upon the Blow-pipe, since you do not read German. . . ." Other papers and volumes went back and forth and Berzelius contributed several communications to the *American Journal of Science*.

Perhaps their most interesting exchange had to do with Beaumont's experiments, alluded to earlier, on human gastric juice. In April 1833 Beaumont, when preparing his celebrated monograph on the subject, "made a special trip to New Haven to consult Benjamin Silliman who told him that Berzelius of Stockholm was 'the man above all others best qualified to investigate the subject of such deep interest to mankind.' He accordingly recommended that Berzelius be sent a liberal supply of gastric juice for analysis—'enough to fill a pint Congress water bottle, carefully marked, sealed and capped with strong leather and twine, and then cased in tin, with the lid soldered on so that no one may open it.' A pint of gastric juice was a large order, for it required half an hour or more to collect a small amount of the fluid from the fasting stomach. This tedious process must have considerably annoyed the bibulous Alexis [the patient] who doubtless thought it a long time between drinks." *

Silliman finally sent Beaumont a full report which contained several good physiological observations, but from Beaumont's standpoint a somewhat unsatisfactory conclusion:

. . . On placing today a piece of veal in a wine glass containing some of the gastric fluid, and standing on a warm stove (stirring occasionally with a glass rod), digestion began very soon and proceeded until the fluid had spent its force, and was renewed on the addition of more fluid.

I regret that I can not contribute something important to our previous knowledge—there is much in physiology that eludes the scrutiny of chemistry. Thought may emanate from the brain, volition may cause the movement of the muscles, sentient and ever rational beings may spring from a seminal drop of very simple composition, and all kinds of aliment may dissolve with the equally mild and simple gastric fluid, but who can explain the proximate, or even the ultimate, cause in any other way than by referring it to a positive law of the Creator—often incomprehensible equally in his nature and in his works.

Berzelius failed to reply until July 1834. Evidently the request had proved embarrassing for he felt that to do anything with the juice chemically he must have fresh samples. His an-

* Cushing, Harvey. "William Beaumont's Rendezvous with Fame," in *Yale Journal of Biology and Medicine*, 1935, *8*, 113-126.

alysis, therefore, proved much less satisfactory than had Silliman's.

In the meantime, from Dr. William Henry, whose textbook of chemistry Silliman had first introduced in this country, came congratulations on Silliman's own *Elements of Chemistry*, with information on the state of the science in England. Similar intelligence concerning the field of geology came frequently from Robert Bakewell, a forthright individualism enlivening all his comments (it should perhaps be mentioned that his views on religion were not those of Silliman). Thus in 1830:

. . . Have you seen Dr. Ure's book on geology? It was intended as a catch for religious people to satisfy them that the world was made, as he says in *"six working days";* but he violates the Mosaic account as much as any preceding writer, for he makes a seventh working-day after the Deluge to create the present race of animals. Dr. Ure is profoundly ignorant of practical geology and places the lias next to the chalk. Dr. Ure is said not to be a practical religionist any more than he is a practical geologist. In this country a pretence to religion and principle is more often esteemed than the reality. He is no true friend to religion who would force astronomical observations to coincide with the literal Scripture phraseology addressed to mankind in their infant state, and never intended to teach the sciences. . . .

I live rather out of the world, and have little new to communicate. A few weeks since, Mr. Mantell, the discoverer of the Iguanodon [a genus of gigantic herbivorous dinosaur], and Mr. Lyell, foreign secretary to the Geological Society, came to breakfast with me. Mr. Lyell has published a work in two volumes, entitled "Principles of Geology," being an attempt to trace present appearances on the globe to causes at present existing and in activity. There is on this subject much diversity of opinion. Dr. Buckland supports the opinion that the surface of our planet has been cut out and made by causes not at present going on—the action of deluges. I have not yet seen Mr. Lyell's book, but I am convinced that we must resort to both ordinary and extraordinary causes to explain geological phenomena. . . .

He mentions Mr. Lyell's book again, after he had read it: "If you have seen it, you will think there is much Scotch amplification. A Scotchman can never write briefly and directly to the point." Of his own *Principles of Geology* (it was Silliman's appendix to the American edition that had aroused Thomas Cooper's wrath) he wrote: "My fourth edition has had a more courteous reception at its birth than the third. Professors Buckland and Sedgwick both sent me their congratulations and approbation, and Professor Jameson, who was formerly much offended by my attacks on the Wernerian system, wrote to my publishers saying that he considered it one of the best English books on geology. Professor Buckland also told a gentleman whom I knew that it was decidedly the book he should choose to place in the hands of his pupils. My third edition received its first approval from you five months after its appearance."

In 1839 Bakewell commented upon a letter of Silliman's about the richness of the coal and iron deposits in Maryland: "The United States present such extensive fields for the exertion of civilized man that imagination toils in vain to delineate the vast accession of moral power and happiness that a few centuries hence may present in your hemisphere. You say that there are no faults in the Maryland coal-fields, but as faults do not make themselves known at the surface, they can only be ascertained by many operations which, I presume, are yet on too limited a scale to have discovered them if they exist beneath the surface."

Later in the year he announced the publication of *The Silurian System* (the name of which he did not approve): ". . . A magnificent geological work, full of plates, sections, maps, and outlines has recently been published—price eight guineas and five crowns to subscribers—by Mr. Murchison, a gentleman of fortune whom, next to Professor Sedgwick, I consider one of our best practical geologists. It is a labor of seven years. . . . Mr. Murchison has kindly presented me with a copy of his work and, if my health and strength permit,

I will send a review of it for your Journal (which will probably be the last labor of mine in geology). . . ."

As Bakewell hinted, his health was beginning to fail, but he continued to write fulsomely about geology, varying it now and then with a plea for a simple universal language between all nations and with amusing discourses on the state of his health in answer to Silliman's regular enquiries: ". . . I have been very unwell for the last month, having had returns of incipient dizziness with severe attacks of flatulence and indigestion, though I am very careful respecting my diet. Mrs. Hannah More allows of two evils in the world—sin and bile. I think she might have admitted wind into partnership. Cowper, in his interesting letters, mentions a religious friend at Huntingdon, who kept a diary, and the most frequent items in it were thanksgivings for delivery from wind. Cowper observes that this diary was more rational than that of the great Dr. Johnson, who makes frequent entries of the lumps of sugar which he left out of his tea and coffee on saint-days and fasts. I am quite satisfied that many cases of demoniacal possessions, mentioned by heathens and Jews, were cases of obstinate flatulence; everything which could be heard and felt, but not seen, was with them spirits."

Bakewell died shortly after Silliman finished his last Lowell Lecture in Boston in 1843, and although his long letters full of facts and pungent humor were greatly missed, Silliman continued to hear geological gossip from other correspondents. Charles Lyell, now Sir Charles, wrote him about his public lectures, a venture Lyell was soon to try in England with considerable success: "I congratulate you on the unexampled success of your lectures to which nothing in this country or in Europe can possibly come up in point of numbers. No one can lecture well to small audiences, or be eloquent to empty benches, as would be the lot of most lecturers on geology here."

Of the new edition of his book he wrote: "I wish, indeed,

there was a bridge of steam across the Atlantic, that I might transport, if not myself, at least the first printed copy of my fifth edition to New Haven. As to American geology, I always feel that I have so much to do at my own door that I have no business to go there for these ten years—for it would be like wishing to geologize the moon in our present infancy of the knowledge of the earth. . . ."

Sir Charles did come to America, however, in 1842 (and again later) and gave lectures at the Lowell Institute even as Silliman had been doing. Silliman was well pleased with a letter he had from Sir Charles written in New York on April 4, 1842: ". . . Now that I have travelled from Niagara to Georgia, and have met a great number of your countrymen on the Continent of Europe and heard the manner in which they ascribe the taste they have for science to your tuition, I may congratulate you, for I never heard as many of the rising generation in England refer as often to any one individual teacher as having given a direction to their taste. *Non omnia possumus omnes,* and if you cannot yourself explore the rocks from Maine to Florida, you may say that you have sent forth pupils who will do it for you."

Two years later he thanked Silliman for a copy of Dana's *Mineralogy* and congratulated him on his daughter's marriage to Mr. Dana. He continued: "I am much obliged to your son [Benjamin, Jr. was then editor of the Journal] for so promptly publishing the abstracts I sent of my papers on American geology. They come out so tardily now in our proceedings that I am glad to have a voice in your Journal."

Sir Roderick Murchison wrote in 1841 as he was about to embark on a study of Russian geology in the Ural mountains: "To your magnificent region I look with intense interest, and I live in the hope of being able to explore its palaeozoic rocks. Already, however, your able countrymen are preparing all the elements for the complete classification of these olden deposits

of America. . . . From what I see, I should be disposed to
think that North America may offer the fullest and most perfect sequence of palaeozoic strata in the world. It is right, therefore, that I should see your grand development last. 'Vedi
Napoli e poi muori [See Naples and then die].' "

Interchange of this nature between the scientists of the two
countries fostered cordial relations, and the only Victoria gold
medal awarded in 1850 by the Royal Geological Society was
given to the American explorer, Colonel John Frémont.
Murchison wrote: "I have quite an admiration of this true
geographer who, under so many privations, has opened up to
us such an enormous mass of land, and has laid down its latitude so correctly. . . ."

Knowledge of the latest discoveries and new thinking on old
problems came from Professor Charles Daubeny of Oxford,
who visited the United States and Silliman in 1837, Sir J. F. W.
Herschel, son of Sir William, the astronomer whose sister had
demonstrated his telescope to Silliman in 1805, Professor Richard Owen of the Royal College of Surgeons, and many others.
Professor William Conybeare, another prominent geologist,
wrote in August 1836 to thank Silliman for gifts of books, etc.,
and added: "An intercourse of the scientific and literary minds
of the two countries, will, I am persuaded, be among the most
efficient means of cementing those feelings of friendship which
it is so very desirable to encourage. I have, therefore, great
satisfaction in forwarding to you the first numbers of a new
scientific journal, which my friends at Bristol have just established."

Professor J. F. W. Johnston, the well-known professor of
chemistry who directed the laboratory of the Agricultural
Chemical Association at Edinburgh, wrote him from Moscow
as he travelled through Russia in August 1842: "What a contrast between the internal progress of your really young country and of this gigantic and almost unwieldy empire, every

wheel of which is moved by one main spring, the tension of which regulates the progress on every hand. Here are vast plains, extensive forests, great rivers, all rich capabilities undeveloped by the great mass of the nobles—even as yet unperceived. . . ."

From Professor Louis Agassiz, the great naturalist, who had not yet come to make his home in America, there came news of the progress of geology in his native Switzerland, and especially of his now classic work on fossil fishes, the first two volumes of which Silliman had already received: "Today I send you the third volume of my work. You know so well how few resources the literature of this department of natural history affords us, that I can but hope for a favorable reception of my essay in your country. You would oblige me greatly by giving a little analysis of it in your Journal. . . .

"A journey in England this year has added largely to the number of species which I knew and which now reaches eight hundred. I should be greatly interested also to learn more of the fossil fishes of America, which I find noticed in the 'Manuals of Geology,' and respecting some of which your Journal has given us valuable information. For a long time I have thus found myself connected with you, but this is the only connection I have with America, and I should think myself very fortunate if this intellectual exchange should become more intimate and direct. I should like especially to ask you for some details as to the discoveries on the subject of fossil fishes brought to light by the active geological researches of the past year. If on my part I can be of any service to you in the little corner where I dwell, I pray you to make use of me."

When Agassiz came to America in 1846, Silliman was of assistance to him in making arrangements and contacts. His contribution to American geology is well known and his Museum of Comparative Zoology (popularly known as the Agassiz Museum), begun during the years of his professorship in natural history at the Lawrence Scientific School at Harvard, is now one of the most distinguished departments of Harvard University. The warm friendship which had developed out of their letters was a source of satisfaction to both men and Agassiz often took advantage of the hearty welcome always awaiting him in New Haven.

One of the most faithful of Silliman's correspondents was Dr. Gideon A. Mantell, a physician who had combined an active practice with outstanding discoveries and contributions to geology. In the autumn of 1830 Silliman had ventured to write for Mantell's publications, offering him in turn the *American Journal of Science* and any of his own works that might be of use. This was the beginning of a friendship which existed entirely on paper for twenty years, but the two friends finally met face to face in 1851, the year before Mantell died. His letters were similar to those Silliman had received from their mutual friend, Robert Bakewell—full of technical information but also including human touches. In June 1834 Dr. Mantell wrote:

. . . Your admirable letter on the harmony between geology and the Mosaic records has been read with great delight and satisfaction by many of our intelligent clergymen, who felt unsettled in their opinions upon these subjects. Can it be obtained apart from the volume? If it can, I shall order some. . . . The volume and atlas on the Geology of Massachusetts [the survey by Edward Hitchcock] reflect great credit on the author, and on the enlightened government who patronized the undertaking. . . .

Lyell is off to Norway and Sweden to examine into the proofs afforded of the gradual elevation of these countries, which is supposed to be still going on. Murchison is off to Wales, to complete his grand geological survey of a part of that principality, which he intends to publish in a separate work, and I have no doubt it will be one of great value and interest, for he has time, talents, and fortune at his command.

Buckland is employed on his Bridgewater Essay (or at least will be, so soon as the Oxford fooleries are over—think of the Duke of Wellington being the Chancellor of our first University—there is no hope for man-

kind while the brute qualities of a mere soldier claim the highest rewards
of *learning!*)—which is to be out in August, the plates will be numerous
and beautiful.

The box I am sending you will contain the copy of Mr. Hawkins' work
—the portrait of the *"inventor"* of the Iguanodon—as my friend Horace
Smith facetiously terms me—and a few scraps of miscellaneous scribblings
of mine, and some fossils.

In 1841, just before Charles Lyell came to America for the
first time, Dr. Mantell wrote Silliman a detailed letter about
his background, concluding:

In person, Mr. Lyell presents nothing remarkable, except a broad ex-
panse of forehead. He is of the middle size, a decided Scottish physi-
ognomy, small eyes, fine chin, and a rather proud or reserved expression
of countenance. He is very absent, and a slow but profound thinker. He
was Professor in King's College, London, and gave lectures there and at
the Royal Institution. . . . He always takes part in the discussion at the
meetings of the Geological Society, but he has not facility in speaking.
. . . As a popular lecturer, he would stand no chance with Buckland or
Sedgwick. He is providing himself with very beautiful illustrations for
his lectures to astonish the Bostonians, and I should suppose the prestige
of his name and his European reputation will insure him a flattering
reception. . . . I understand Mr. Lowell was very anxious to induce
Faraday to come over and lecture on Chemistry. But poor Faraday, like
several of our best men, has overworked himself, and is obliged to lay
by altogether. . . .

Because he knew Mantell would be interested, Silliman
sent him a detailed account of the Lyells' visit to New Haven:
"Mr. Lyell was animated and interesting, often eloquent, and
full of geological zeal, which was fully indulged in excursions
around our noble trap region. . . . We had several good geologists with us, at least five besides Mr. Lyell. Mrs. Lyell made
herself most agreeable in our family. We were charmed with
her winning, affable manners; we endeavored to see that they
were furnished with the comforts of an English home in
America, and they appeared to enjoy being identified so early
with an American family. . . . We wanted nothing, my good

friend, but your presence to have made our interviews as happy as possible and you and your reputation and interests were often on our tongues. . . ."

Silliman was naturally interested in Lyell's preparations for his course of Lowell Lectures and he wrote Mantell: "He is to begin there on the 19th of October and lecture six weeks. He has told me of his huge drawings, and Mr. Bakewell has prepared eight more for him on a huge scale, drawn principally from his own works. He thinks the drawings I have lectured from quite too small and counts much upon the aid from his large drawings. He is anxious that I should be present at his beginning to aid him by my advice. It will be extremely difficult; but I shall try to break away for a few days and hear a couple of his lectures. He has been through the State of New York with Mr. Hall, a clever young geologist of that state, and has written me that he has been much gratified. . . ."

In another letter Silliman wrote Mantell: ". . . I thank you for your remarks upon the Iguanodon, and I should like to know, when you write again, what dimensions you now give to the tail—how much, for example, you have shortened an iguanodon of seventy-five feet in length, as formerly estimated by comparison with the leviathan! I am much amused by the comparison with the leviathan. Owen's splendid work came in the same parcel with your elegant little book on a pebble."

In 1846 Dr. Mantell sent Silliman the news that "Mr. Murchison is Sir Roderick—the Queen having knighted him that he may wear the red sash, cross, and star of the orders the Emperor of Russia bestowed on him." He also mentioned that Dr. Buckland was now Dean of Westminster. Later in the year he wrote: "In the geological world, Murchison and Lyell monopolize everything. Russia and America, roast, boiled, cold, hashed, and fricasseed, are the dishes set before us at Somerset House till, like the poor Frenchman, we exclaim— 'Helas! toujours perdrix! [Alas! Always partridge!]' And, I doubt not, the same viands will be the principal subjects at the meetings of the British Association of Science in the geological section. . . ."

One of the last letters Mantell wrote Silliman before they finally met in London was a description of an anniversary dinner of the Geological Society:

. . . The Archbishop of Canterbury, Sir Robert Peel, the Russian Ambassador were there; and my friend, Sir C. Lyell, the new President, took the chair. Murchison, De la Beche, Buckland, Sedgwick, and almost all our great men were present. The Archbishop made an admirable speech in defence of scientific pursuits, and geological in particular; and Sir Robert a senatorial declamation in the like spirit. Lyell spoke good sense, but was so long in his pauses, and so hesitating, that I was frightened out of my wits lest he should break down. Dr. Buckland made an academical oration, like one got by heart by a young collegiate; and Sedgwick poured forth a flood of eloquence, which, in spite of the discordant tones in which it was uttered (for his voice is most harsh), carried everything before it. The Belgian Ambassador, in capital English with just sufficient foreign accent to add to its interest, gave a luminous address in praise of science, and in just encomiums on his own country for having remained unmoved in the midst of the revolutionary tempest which had swept over the Continent. Murchison made a courtly speech, highly complimentary to the nobles present; and your humble servant, who had to respond as one of the Vice-Presidents, gave a flourish of trumpets, which concluded the entertainment. Sir H. De la Beche has been a capital president. . . .

These few quotations make it abundantly clear that Silliman was in constant touch with the important happenings in the scientific world. This knowledge he disseminated in America through his teaching, his lectures, and his Journal. The Journal, too, carried American advances abroad, and Silliman thus became something of a clearing house for scientific thought between the old world and the new.

CHAPTER XII

The Mining Consultant

EARLY in the nineteenth century the natural resources of the American continent were unexplored—their extent undreamed of—but forward-looking men were beginning to buy up tracts of land suspected of containing rich veins of ore. Having bought the land, generally on speculation, they then sought advice on which to base their mining operations, and since the mining engineer of that period was often the academic geologist, Silliman was frequently called upon during the 1830's and 1840's to make field surveys. In 1830 he examined a stretch of mountains, forests, swamps, and excavations, 120 to 130 miles in extent, in the coal-rich Wyoming Valley in Pennsylvania, in 1836 he surveyed the gold mines of Virginia, in 1838 the iron and coal region of Alleghany County, Maryland. He was also in demand for surveys of a widely different sort, such as a study of the production and manufacture of sugar and an investigation of steam apparatus, both undertaken for the government.

In his mining surveys he usually took along an assistant whose skills he knew—one of his students or his son Benjamin, Jr., who had graduated from Yale in 1837 sharing his father's scientific interests. On these journeys Silliman often spent eight or nine hours a day in the saddle, but more often traversed long distances on foot into territory too wild to be penetrated in any other way. During the Pennsylvania trip Silliman wrote his wife: "I have never in my life gone through a week of such arduous exertion, not even in the mountains and mines of Derbyshire, in the center of England, nor in those of Cornwall, at the Land's End in the same country." But although he was in his late fifties and early sixties during these strenuous years, he seemed able to endure hardships that would have daunted many a younger man.

He was offered generous fees for his surveys, sometimes receiving as much as $1400, plus travelling expenses and the sal-
ary of his assistant. They varied in length, but usually occupied
him for a month or two, and they always entailed a full report.
When the client who engaged him for the Maryland survey
sent the results to England in the hope of inducing English
capitalists to invest in the mines, the reply inferred that the
report must be exaggerated—such wealth was unheard of. Silliman was most gratified when the mining expert they sent over
to repeat the survey corroborated his findings in every detail.

Not only was the actual surveying arduous, but travelling
such distances from New Haven was fraught with hazard. Indeed, he observed that crossing the Atlantic was less dangerous
than travelling within the limits of the United States. He and
Benjamin had a miraculous escape on one journey when a strip
of track pierced one of the cars of their train. It went up
through the seat where they had been seated a few minutes
earlier, pierced the brim of a lady's bonnet, and went on up
through the roof of the car! But he was to live much more dan-
gerously when in 1844, at the age of sixty-five, he undertook an
extensive study of a section of Missouri and Illinois. Following him closely on this momentous journey will provide a clear
picture of what such a survey involved, and what conditions
in "the West" were at that time.

He started out on the 10th of April (1844) by steamer to New
York and thence by rail to Cumberland, Maryland, where he
had to take a stage over the Alleghany Mountains. From
Wheeling, Ohio, he went by steamer down the Ohio to Marietta, where he found that that bright and beautiful town was
peopled from Connecticut. He wrote Mrs. Silliman: "Four
mornings ago I was with you and now I am 600 miles from you.
It is delightful to me to spend a New England Sabbath in a
New England town." He of course attended church services—
which were conducted by a Yale graduate in the morning and a

converted Cherokee in the evening! From Marietta he travelled by steamer to Cincinnati. All along the way he met Yale
men who offered him hospitality and good cheer, showing him
the town and gathering in the townspeople to meet him.

From Cincinnati he took another steamer to Louisville, and
thence down the Ohio to the Mississippi, then up the Mississippi until he reached St. Mary's Landing, Missouri, where he
was meeting his assistant for the survey, Mr. Forest Shepard of
New Haven. In a letter to Mrs. Silliman he described their
passage down the river:

> Our boat was full to overflowing, the saloons crowded with cabin pas-
> sengers, and the lower deck with emigrants and their families, horses and
> lower animals were mingled with children and their parents, in com-
> fortless circumstances. The furnaces beneath the floor of the saloon and
> above the main deck poured out torrents of sparks frightful to behold, as
> driven by the wind they rushed along in showers of fire, in contact with
> the dry warm and unprotected pine boards of the floor above. The hur-
> ricane deck, the upper floor of all, was loaded with furniture, machines,
> and bedding and here too showers of cinders and sparks were falling
> from the chimneys both upon the bedding and upon cotton, paper, and
> other combustibles. Mr. Atwater and I removed the most inflammable
> materials to safer situations, while our reasonable and careful Captain
> Stone, at our suggestion, provided additional buckets of water and he
> himself, with three of his men, kept watch during the three nights we
> were on board. A hose was provided to throw water to every part of the
> ship, but there was only one yawl or boat to convey 200 to 250 people
> to the shore in case of alarm, and should the tiller ropes be burned (the
> tiller chains ordered by law of Congress are not always provided), it
> might be impossible to run the steamer ashore, which in cases of con-
> flagration is the usual course.

St. Mary's Landing was only a river stop with a few houses,
and Mr. Shepard had horses there so that they could start immediately for Brownsville, via Chester, Illinois. They crossed
the river on a ferry and began their journey into wild country.
Late in the afternoon a severe thunder and lightning storm
made their passage through a forest somewhat dangerous be-

cause several trees were struck by lightning. When they came to cross a "considerable river" they discovered that the bridge had settled on one side until it resembled a sloping roof. Even though they dismounted and led their horses, every step was filled with anxiety, for the animals could scarcely keep their footing on the slippery bridge even without mounts, and Silliman expected any minute to be pulled into the dark torrent.

Night had fallen long before they reached Brownsville, drenched and very cold, but the prospect of drying out in the warmth of one of the two taverns kept up their spirits. However, when they arrived, they could not gain admittance to either tavern because both were full of patients sick with a prevailing fever. They tried several houses only to find sickness there also, but they finally were given shelter by an Englishman who lived in a great, barnlike house which had evidently been intended for some other purpose. Most of the window panes were broken and the night wind blew through the one big room in generous blasts. They were able to dry themselves around the fireplace and were provided with food and a bed, but no sooner had they retired than there was an agitated flurry over their heads and they soon discovered that chickens were apparently roosting on the rafters directly above them.

The next morning when they began their work it was still pouring, and their exploration of the coal beds was made difficult by the fact that spring thaws had swollen the streams and rivers they had to cross. Several times they discovered that the water was too deep for the horses at the usual fording places and they were forced to wander off their trail for miles through the woods before they could get to the other side. Eventually they reached their destination and Silliman found the coal highly bituminous and very pure, though not in such large masses as in Maryland.

After a quiet Sunday in Brownsville they set off for the iron mountains. Here again they discovered ample evidence of quantities of ore. Since they were far from towns, they were offered hospitality at the few houses they found on their travels. Although unknown and unexpected, they were nevertheless made welcome everywhere. The accommodations varied considerably—from a comfortable log cabin owned by a wealthy woman to a "comfortless" home where they slept four in a bed. Silliman was surprised that they encountered no snakes in their travels, and only once did a deer or wild turkey cross their path. They were, however, most annoyingly pestered with woodticks.

After a ten-day survey of the iron mountains they journeyed to St. Louis where Silliman spent much of his five-day stay writing his report in order that Mr. Shepard might check his findings before they took leave of one another. However, many Yale College graduates and others to whom he was well known through his account of his trip abroad called upon him and he was happy to be received thus cordially so far from home. St. Louis was then a city of 35,000 and Silliman wrote that "eastern men and eastern institutions decidedly predominate and religion and morals have a strong hold here. . . . I found a very respectable mercantile house from Hartford, that of Collins & Co., and there is much active intercourse between St. Louis and New York and New England."

During the visit a former New Haven man, Mr. Jeremiah Townsend, very kindly offered to take Silliman to some geologically interesting coal beds nearby in Illinois. They started out in his carriage, but at noon instead of early morning which Silliman would have preferred. After crossing the Mississippi he discovered that their driver was uncertain of the way and they were shortly off their route in wild country that became rougher as they progressed. The road was so bad that the twisting and turning of the horses had cracked the carriage tongue. Finally they came upon the main road again just as the sun was sinking. As they were going down a steep hill, Mr. Townsend gave the team the rein, with the inevitable result that the pole broke, terrifying the horses. They proceeded to kick the carriage and the harness to pieces until one of the party had the courage to approach near enough to cut them loose. One galloped wildly off into the forest and was never seen again. Leading the other, they walked some distance to a farmhouse where they engaged a rough lumber wagon from the farmer to take them the rest of the way.

Shortly a fierce thunder and lightning storm overtook them and they soon became drenched to the skin. When they were yet a mile from the ferry, one horse refused to budge another step, and they were forced to abandon the wagon and make their way through deep mud on foot, their path illumined at intervals by sharp flashes of lightning. Arriving at a small cluster of houses on the river bank, they found, as he recorded, that "a party of gamblers in a drinking shop shewed the only light in the place and we were compelled to enquire of them for a tavern which we found by the aid of a candle they furnished us. Thus their good deed shone in the midnight darkness and in their naughty conclave."

Silliman survived this unfortunate incident without unhappy after-effects, and three days later, on May 14th, he left St. Louis by steamer, bound eventually for Chicago. Flooded conditions, with trees and debris whirling in the eddies, made river travel very dangerous and he was outraged to discover, furthermore, that the boat he was on was transporting a large amount of gunpowder. In view of the ever-present possibility of fire which he had described so vividly to Mrs. Silliman on his journey down, he expressed himself very forcibly on the matter—to the effect that if gunpowder was to be transported, it should be done only in boats expressly for that purpose.

However, the trip up the Illinois river was without incident and he reached Peru, Illinois, where on May 16th he was to take a stage to Chicago. This part of his journey proved to be one of the most severe trials he had yet encountered. "We were fellow sufferers on the worst roads I ever saw. They were deep with mud and full of dangerous holes through which the horses could hardly drag the carriage, sometimes when empty of passengers." He found the "boundless" prairies magnificent but had little time to enjoy the scenery. Streams were so swollen that the water often rose over the floor of the carriage at the fords and during the second night, having given his blanket to a fellow passenger who had no coat, he suffered severely with the cold. At about two a.m. the coach broke down. Fortunately it carried the part necessary for its repair, but all of the passengers had to fall to and help. Silliman's assignment was to hold the horses, which were wild and restless, and this added exposure made him shake "as if with the ague."

They had no more than returned to the comparative warmth of the coach when he was called out again to hold the horses while the driver went ahead to explore the road. "Although by far the oldest man of the party, I felt that I was the most vigilant, and not inferior to the younger men in activity. As the coach stopped, my companions being all fast asleep, I was instantly on foot with the coachman at the head of the horses, while he was examining a morass through which we must pass. The gentlemen in the coach being roused by the ceasing of motion, they began to enquire what had happened, and I overheard Mr. Lee as he asked: 'What has become of the old gentleman?' "

After two nights and a day of this sort of travel they welcomed the sight of Chicago, then (1844) a thriving town boasting 9,000 inhabitants. He did not linger long, however, but as soon as possible embarked on a lake steamer bound for Buffalo. Cold winds whipped up high waves and made progress difficult but they passed through Lake Michigan into Lake Huron without accident. He found Lake Huron uninteresting, its shores covered with virgin forest, but Lake St. Clair delighted him, and Detroit was "well built and rising gracefully from the water." At Cleveland he called on Sherlock Andrews, his former assistant, but had only a brief time before the boat left for Buffalo. When they arrived safely on the 26th of May he observed: "I could write many things of lake navigation, grand but terrible—magnificent in the vast extent of these mediterranean seas—in their almost desolate and harborless shores—in their stormy waves and terrific gales and numerous and fearful casualties by burning, by explosion of boilers, by collision, by swamping in the surge and wrecking on the shores." Instead he gave thanks for the continued vigilance of a kind Providence.

The rest of the journey was uneventful. He went by stage and private conveyance to a joyful meeting in Geneseo, New York, with his oldest daughter, Maria, now Mrs. John B. Church. Maria and her two children returned to New Haven with him for the marriage of Henrietta on June 5th to James Dwight Dana. On this occasion, with two hundred and fifty guests joining in the festivities with the happily reunited family, the rigours and dangers of his recent journey seemed far away.

Silliman continued to make field surveys for mining companies for another ten years, the last in April 1855 when he was seventy-five years of age. On this occasion he spent two weeks with Benjamin, Jr. investigating a vein of copper in the Blue Ridge Mountains of Virginia. This again was an exhausting trip, made partly on horseback, partly on foot, and while Silliman did not complain, he let this trip mark the end of his career as a mining consultant.

CHAPTER XIII

The Sheffield Scientific School

1846-1853

THE year 1846 was a significant one for Silliman—he was denied the opportunity to be president of Yale, but his small group of advanced students became the nucleus from which grew a scientific school, a venture that marked the beginning in this country of the university concept of higher education.

In the summer of that year the venerable President Day, after thirty years in office, was forced because of ill health to resign. On August 8th Silliman recorded in his day book: "There has been much agitation of mind here & elsewhere this summer on account of the announced resignation of President Day. No one candidate has such commanding claims as was the case when Dr. Stiles died in May 1795—G.S.S. [his brother] and I being then juniors in Yale College. Dr. Dwight was named almost by acclamation. When Dr. Dwight died January 11, 1817—then there was Professor Day. Professor Woolsey will, I think, be chosen if he will accept (which he does not favor)."

In May 1846 a group of alumni and some of Silliman's friends had begun to suggest him for the presidency, among them his old friend of law school and Philadelphia days, Charles E. Chauncey; also Timothy Pitkin, A. N. Skinner, Thomas Day, Roger Baldwin, Chancellor Kent, and "other men of the same stamp." Silliman assured them that the proposal of his name would be of no use since the President of Yale had always been a clergyman. He might have added that the Corporation, and possibly others, although they recognized that he was Yale's leading figure, would doubtless be horrified at the thought of making a scientist president of Yale. However, the arguments brought forth by his friends in his behalf and their expressions of regard (such as the letter from

Chancellor Kent to Judge Roger Baldwin of New Haven on August 3, 1846) were, he recorded with becoming modesty, a source of gratification to his family:

I understand that at the annual Commencement a President is to be chosen in the room of the venerable President Day, and permit me to say that I ardently hope that our friend, Professor Silliman, may be his successor. I do not know the man within the College catalogue that has a better title to the honor, and who is more fitted to fill the station with reputation to the College and the general and warm approbation of the community. His character is pure and estimable. He has sustained his professional duties for a long series of years with distinguished ability and success. His talents, his learning, his science, his taste, his purity and elevation of character, and his varied and almost universal accomplishments, point him out as the very person that ought to be chosen. . . . I feel an unshaken love and an attachment to Yale College, and I should deeply regret, as one of its ancient alumni, if Professor Silliman (provided he is willing to accept, of which I know nothing) should be passed by. I express these wishes of mine on my own spontaneous suggestion, and hope and trust you will be willing to give to the choice of Professor Silliman your effective countenance. In my humble opinion, the elevation of Professor Silliman to the presidential chair will add diffusive renown to the College, both in this country and in Europe.

Whether the failure to appoint him may be laid to his age, to his long absences from New Haven and the affairs of the College, or (as is more likely) to the fact that he was a scientist is not known, but "the determination and action of the Corporation," he wrote in his daybook, "have been decisive. They elected Professor Woolsey, but in addition to his decided aversion to the office he is apparently determined not to be ordained, a point on which I suppose the Corporation will insist and I understand they passed a vote to that effect." The Corporation triumphed—Woolsey finally submitted to ordination and was inaugurated as President of Yale College on Wednesday, October 21, 1846.

That Silliman was not appointed was the cause of widespread comment, even in the public press:

To the Editors of the Journal of Commerce

Since the late commencement at Yale College, I have heard expressions of surprise that Professor Silliman was not elected to the Presidency of that Institution, and this from gentlemen and scholars who highly estimate the moral excellence and very distinguished scholarship of Professor Woolsey. The long connection of Dr. Silliman with that college, his admirable personal character and manners, and his preëminent services to the cause, not only of chemical but of general science, gave his friends some reason to expect for him, from the Institution to which his life has been devoted, the highest honors it could bestow. Our reply to all inquiries addressed to us has been that we are unacquainted with the peculiar circumstances of the case; that very possibly Dr. Silliman may have indicated a wish that the attention of the Trustees should be directed to some other than himself; that conflicting interests and views may possibly have been harmonized in the present choice, which, if good in itself, may be the better for securing such harmony; but that, at all events, Professor Silliman enjoys a reputation throughout this country and all Europe, not to be elevated or depressed by any station which any one or all of the colleges of this Union could give. His fame is not the property of Yale, or his native State, or of the United States alone; and full well I know that among American names eminent for science and the highest virtues, none is more respected and admired in Great Britain and on the continent than that of Professor Silliman.

But perhaps in his heart Silliman was glad to have been spared the tribulations of a difficult administrative office. In any event, he made no show of disappointment and continued to throw his energies behind every forward-looking movement on foot in the College.

During the spring of 1846 Silliman and Benjamin, Jr., who was then his assistant, had been preparing the way for the creation of two new chairs of science at Yale to fill a need which had become increasingly evident to them through their association with students who had applied for special work. In Silliman's undergraduate courses in geology, chemistry, and mineralogy there had been no opportunity for laboratory exercises, this method of teaching being the customary lectures to which he added demonstrations. Students desiring to delve more deeply into the study of science and to do laboratory research on an advanced level were forced to seek such opportunity in European laboratories, where graduate instruction was available in a few university centers.

Silliman had for some time been accepting a limited number of special students, such as Amos Eaton and John Pitkin Norton, in addition to his assistants, but although they were somewhat casually listed in the College catalogues as Resident Graduates, they received no credit for their experimental investigations. The demand for the opportunity to do advanced work had now increased to such an extent that Silliman and Benjamin, Jr., to whom he turned over his special students when he was away lecturing, realized that the time had come to expand their small, unofficial group into a laboratory, recognized by the College, where students interested in graduate study in the sciences, particularly agricultural chemistry and vegetable physiology, could receive adequate instruction. They accordingly drafted a proposal for the establishment of such a laboratory.

This memorandum, not before made public, stands as a highly significant milestone in the history of higher education in the United States. It recognized that since a large proportion of the country's population earned their livelihood by farming, science should be applied to agriculture as well as to industry. Interest in scientific agriculture had been growing since the days of Thomas Jefferson, and it was further stimulated by the publication of an inexpensive American edition of Davy's *Elements of Agricultural Chemistry,* first published in England in 1813. When Justus von Liebig's *Animal Chemistry* had appeared in 1840, an American edition was issued almost immediately, and Professor Daubeny of Oxford wrote Silliman in 1843: "The subject of agriculture is now exciting much attention in England and the new views of Liebig are opening a new field of research both in vegetable and in ani-

mal physiology." Silliman knew also that Liebig's introduction
of the laboratory method of teaching chemistry had been eminently successful, and he must have watched with interest the
same principle applied by Amos Eaton in his school at Rensselaer where the students "learned by doing." The result of all
this, added to his own experience, was embodied in the proposal. Penned by Silliman, Jr., with his father's interlinea-
tions, it was presented to the officers of the College in the
summer of 1846 [Silliman's additions in square brackets]:

PROPOSALS FOR ESTABLISHING A CHAIR
OF AGRICULTURAL CHEMISTRY AND
VEGETABLE AND ANIMAL PHYSIOLOGY
IN YALE COLLEGE

It is believed that the time has already arrived, when it is not only
desirable for, but incumbent on, every Institution for liberal Education
to make specific provision to meet the wants of a large and constantly
growing class in this community who represent the great agricultural and
landed interests.

Courses of instruction, full and able, have been provided for every
other class of professional students among us, which all combined render
this institution a favorite resort for many who have already passed the
threshold of their academical studies either among ourselves or at other
similar places. Shall we fail to meet the call now daily made by those
whose tastes or circumstances lead them to seek that knowledge which
shall best fit them for the quiet but engrossing pursuits of agricultural
life?

The progress of scientific discovery abroad has of late years led particularly to the practical application of Science to the useful arts, and
unexpected light has been shed by these researches on the important relations existing between the sciences of Chemistry & Physiology & the
processes of Agriculture & of Vegetable and Animal Life.

These departments have grown so rapidly & advanced so far beyond
their former position as to have assumed the rank & importance of
distinct sciences. Their successful cultivation requires the undivided attention of any teacher who would endeavor to give instruction to those
whose taste or position in society leads them to seek for such information.

This instruction can now be obtained only with great difficulty & expense, under the embarrassments of a European residence & the inconvenience often of a foreign tongue. Moreover, the knowledge, even when thus acquired, has to be modified & adapted to ~~an entirely different~~ [our] climate & soil & ~~an unlike~~ [to the peculiar] organization of [our state of] Society.

These & other similar considerations have presented themselves with such force that it has been determined by a few friends of this Institution to make an effort to raise a foundation of Twenty Thousand Dollars to found a Professorship of Agricultural Chemistry & Vegetable & Animal Physiology in Yale College. This effort has been determined on at the present time, on account of the liberal offer of a prominent friend of the Institution, & of the objects here set forth, to devote the sum of Five Thousand Dollars to this purpose, provided the sum of Twenty Thousand in all can be raised within a reasonable time & the department brought into efficient organization.

It is desired that the objects of this foundation may be understood to be entirely separate & distinct from the existing provisions for instruction in Elementary Chemistry so long established in the College. The duties of the proposed office will begin where those of the former end. The students having access to its advantages will be strictly professional & not academical students. At the same time such provisions may be made, as in the wisdom of the government may seem best for the institution, by which [certain] members of the Senior Class [whose taste or views lead them in that direction] may as such enjoy the advantages of the proposed Chair.

Moreover, the emoluments & income of this chair will be derived solely from its own foundation & from such fees & charges as may properly be made for lectures & the private instructions of the Laboratory.

The duties of this Chair will consist primarily of a course or courses of lectures, to be delivered annually at such times as may be hereafter agreed on, upon the subjects peculiar to the foundation. It will also afford, at all times, opportunities to those so disposed to acquire accurate experimental & practical knowledge in the processes of chemical analysis & the application of scientific principles to the nutrition of animals & vegetables. For this purpose, an active & well furnished Laboratory will be provided, with suitable assistants, and a Museum of Agricultural Geology & soil, & all things properly belonging to this department of Science.

The Corporation deferred action on the proposal until their August meeting at which time their favorable vote was expressed in the following resolution:

Whereas, it has been represented to this Corporation that a benefactor of the College proposes to give five thousand dollars for the endowment of a Professorship of Agricultural Chemistry and of Vegetable and Animal Physiology, provided twenty thousand dollars be raised for that purpose.

Resolved that there be established in this College a professorship of agricultural chemistry and of vegetable and animal physiology for the purpose of giving instruction to graduates and others not members of the undergraduate classes; and that the Corporation will now proceed to elect a professor of those branches of science, that while efforts to complete the endowment are in progress he may devote himself to study preparatory to his entering on the duties of that office, it being understood and provided that the support of this professor is in no case to be chargeable to the existing funds or revenues of the College.

Resolved, that there be also established a professorship of practical chemistry for the purpose of giving instruction to others than members of the undergraduate classes, in respect to the application of chemistry and the kindred sciences to the manufacturing arts, to the exploration of the resources of the country and to other practical uses. And that a professor be now appointed to that office whose compensation, till other provision can be made, shall be derived exclusively from fees for instruction and for other services.

This resolution was followed by two specific votes, also passed at the August meeting of the Corporation, one that John Pitkin Norton be appointed Professor of Agricultural Chemistry and Animal and Vegetable Physiology, and that Benjamin Silliman, Jr. be appointed Professor of Practical Chemistry. The early history of the Scientific School turns largely upon John Pitkin Norton, since Benjamin Silliman, Jr. withdrew after two years to accept a chair of chemistry and toxicology at the Medical School in Louisville.

The appointment of these two new professors of science whose duties were in no way to be concerned with teaching the undergraduates of the College, at once raised the question of

JAMES DWIGHT DANA

By Daniel Huntington 1857

BENJAMIN SILLIMAN, JR.

Painted by John F. Weir in 1910 from a photograph
Original in the foyer of Strathcona Hall

the propriety of their assignment to the faculty of the academic college and led directly to a consideration of the desirability of establishing a new department to which they and other professors who might be appointed in the future in similar capacities could be appropriately assigned.

Accordingly, and at the same Corporation meeting at which Norton and Silliman, Jr. were appointed, a committee was formed, consisting of President Day, Professors Silliman, Sr., Kingsley, Olmsted, Woolsey, and Salisbury, to consider the desirability of establishing a new department under which instruction could be given in subjects not otherwise provided for. This committee, of which Silliman was the leading spirit, made a favorable report on August 19, 1847, whereupon the Corporation adopted the committee's recommendations which were as follows:

I. There shall be a fourth department of instruction for other than undergraduate students, who are not in the departments of theology, medicine and law, to be called the Department of Philosophy and the Arts. The department is intended to embrace philosophy, literature, history, the moral sciences other than law and theology, the natural sciences excepting medicine, and their application to the arts.

II. Instruction in this department may be given by professors not belonging to the others, by professors in the academic departments, and by such others as the president and fellows may approve. But no second course of lectures on the same branch may be given, without the consent of the previous lecturer.

III. All graduates of this or other colleges, and all other young men of fair moral character, may be allowed to pursue such studies included in this department as they may desire. But dismissed students of this or other colleges and undergraduate students, without express leave of the academical faculty, shall not enjoy the privileges of this department.

IV. The instructors in this department may make such arrangements as respects remuneration for their instruction, as they may think proper.

It was the creation of this department, which subsequently became the Graduate School of Yale University, that for the first time in an American college established postgraduate work, soon to lead to the conferring of the higher academic degrees. It also led, within the next few years, to the development of that type of undergraduate education typified by the courses offered by the Sheffield Scientific School. Both results were truly epoch-making events and constitute Yale's greatest single contribution to higher education.

But of all this, John Pitkin Norton had no inkling in the beginning. In his early teens, spent at Farmington, Connecticut, he is said to have exhibited an unusual inquisitiveness for all kinds of natural phenomena. He had no aptitude for the classics and spent the greater part of his time attending to the chores on his father's farm. During the winter of 1840-41 he entered Silliman's laboratory as a private pupil and attended lectures on chemistry, mineralogy, and natural science. He then spent a winter at Harvard College studying chemistry and anatomy, but he was drawn back to Silliman during the two following winters.

Since there were no opportunities in the United States for studying the application of chemistry to agriculture, Silliman secured an opening for him in Scotland with Professor J. F. W. Johnston at the laboratory of the Agricultural Chemical Association in Edinburgh. The superior quality of his work during the two years he spent there prompted Johnston to send an enthusiastic report to Silliman, which the latter immediately passed on to President Day (during the August Corporation meeting) to gain support for his proposal of Norton for one of the new professorships. After his appointment, Norton returned to Europe, this time to the laboratory of Professor G. J. Mulder of Utrecht where he devoted nine months to intensive study to fit him specifically for his teaching responsibilities at Yale.

The new School of Applied Chemistry, as it was called, made its first public announcement in 1847: "Professors Silliman and Norton have opened a Laboratory on the college grounds, in connection with their departments, for the purpose of practical instruction in the applications of science to the arts and agriculture." The laboratory was set up in the house formerly occupied by the presidents of Yale and the two professors paid the College a rental fee of $150 a year and provided their own apparatus. Their only source of revenue was the interest on the $5,000 donated for the establishment of the professorship of agricultural chemistry and the laboratory fees and tuition paid by students—which amounted to a small proportion of their expenses.

Eight students came the first year—students serious in purpose and enthusiastically eager to make the most of this unusual opportunity for laboratory instruction. Operating on principles very radical for those times the new school allowed the student investigators complete freedom to find their own way into the world of science. With help and guidance from the professors they performed their own experiments, gaining self-reliance and confidence as they progressed and the ability to draw their own conclusions from facts which they themselves had disclosed. The lights in the building now called "the Lab" often burned far into the night.

There was inevitable criticism of this new method of teaching and some doubted the educational value of puttering around in what appeared to be little more than a trade school or workshop. But students came in numbers which surprised not only the critics but the College authorities. Although they granted the request of the hard-pressed professors that the rental fee for the laboratory be temporarily revoked, they gave it no other support, either financial or moral. But Norton's belief in the school was unshakable—it was through science that the United States would reach the level of the European countries and men would learn it in such laboratories as the one at Yale. In 1849 the withdrawal of Benjamin Silliman, Jr. was a severe test of his courage, but he went on

alone, with the help of young voluntary assistants, endeavoring
to strengthen and formalize the curriculum and to inaugurate
examinations to test the students' accomplishments.

In 1850, Norton presented to the Corporation a letter, endorsed by Professors Olmsted, Salisbury, Silliman, Sr., and
Dana, suggesting that it might be found advantageous to adopt
a practice somewhat analogous to that of the German universities and award a degree, such as Doctor of Philosophy, to
students who had completed a thorough course of study and
passed examinations in three separate branches of scientific
study. He further suggested that it might be proper and best
to give a first degree or diploma to those students who had
advanced to a certain extent in chemistry alone and were able
to pass examinations in its several branches.

As a result of Norton's suggestion the Corporation in July
1852 established the degree of Bachelor of Philosophy and
specified in some detail the requirements for this degree within
the Department of Philosophy and the Arts. The length of
the course was then two years, later extended to three years,
a practice that was continued by the Scientific School until
1918-19 when it was changed to four years. The new degree
was to be granted to students who had resided at the College for
the full two years, who had passed a successful examination in
three branches of study, and who showed proficiency in either
German or French.

In addition to his unceasing labors in the laboratory, Norton was devoting all the energy he could spare to furthering
the use of scientific methods in agriculture in the country at
large. He contributed freely to agricultural journals, spoke
before agricultural societies, and used every means at his disposal to stimulate interest in applying science to the cultivation of the soil. But he gave too freely of his own strength in
his devotion to these varied activities, and he died of pneumonia on September 5, 1852, just before commencement, at

the age of thirty. His last efforts were expended in the examination of the candidates for the new degree to be granted for the first time that year. Several months after his death President Woolsey received a poignant letter from Norton's father:

Farmington — Jan^v 12th 1853.

Revd T. D. Woolsey
    Pres Yale College

Dear Sir—My deceased son, the late Professor John P. Norton, in a brief will executed a few hours before his death, left all his property to his wife, Elisabeth P. Norton. He remembered his laboratory however in his dying moments, expressing the earnest wish that it might be continued, and requesting that if it were continued, all his property therein, excepting two balances which he wished given to his assistants, William J. Craw and Mason C. Weld, should be given to Yale College. In fulfilment of this request, and with the consent and approbation of his widow, to whom the property belongs, I herewith transmit a copy of an inventory of the same, made by Messrs Craw and Weld, and valued by their estimate, after deducting the two balances above referred to, to twenty-two hundred dollars and twenty-one cents. And I hereby make over and deliver to you as President of Yale College, the whole of said property in said laboratory (except the two balances) the same to be hereafter the sole property of the College.

Very respectfully   Your ob^t serv^t

John T. Norton, Executor of J.P. Norton, dec.
also in behalf of Elisabeth P. Norton

Behind the scenes Silliman, Sr. had offered what help and encouragement he could to his former student. The young professor and his old preceptor saw the same vision for the future, and in 1852 Silliman, Sr. sponsored the proposal that a School of Engineering be created to function along the same lines as the School of Applied Chemistry. The Corporation, impressed by the interest shown in the latter school, looked upon the proposal favorably and on July 27, 1852 established a new professorship of civil engineering, William Augustus Norton to be the first incumbent. Professor Norton (who was unrelated to John Pitkin Norton) came from Brown University where he had been giving instruction in civil engineering. He was trained at the United States Military Academy and he had taught natural and experimental philosophy there after his graduation in 1831. He remained at Yale for thirty-one years.

In the meantime, John Pitkin Norton's place had been filled by a man who had the same remarkable qualities of leadership. A Yale graduate of the Class of 1842, John Addison Porter had also studied science abroad, having spent two years with Justus von Liebig. Porter possessed not only a high degree of scholarship but a thorough understanding of the unlimited possibilities for the practical application of science. He was thus ideally suited for the task of carrying forward the hopes and plans of the founder of the laboratory.

At the end of the first twenty-five years, the school which had developed out of Silliman's small group of advanced students was well established and John Pitkin Norton's vision had been realized. The curriculum had been enlarged and broadened to provide for undergraduates who wished to prepare for a scientific career without first completing the academical course. There was now a substantial endowment, a faculty of 28 members and a student body of 201, of which 28 were graduate students. The Schools of Applied Chemistry and Engineering, which had been grouped together under the title of the Yale Scientific School in 1854, became the Sheffield Scientific School in 1861, in honor of its most generous benefactor, Joseph E. Sheffield (father-in-law of John A. Porter). His gifts of considerable sums of money and a completely equipped building, together with the contributions of other citizens of New Haven, placed the School (which still received no support from Yale College) on a firm financial foundation.

Before he died, Silliman had the satisfaction of witnessing the degree of Doctor of Philosophy granted for the first time in America by Yale College to three graduates of the Scientific School—one of them to J. Willard Gibbs (in 1863), probably the greatest scientist this country has yet produced. The Ph.D degree proved a powerful incentive to scholarship at Yale, and it soon was adopted by other universities in this country and in England. Not only had Silliman succeeded in making the sciences an essential part of general education, but he had also planted the seed of graduate education that was shortly to extend from the sciences into other fields of learning. He watched with particular interest the development of education at the graduate level in the Lawrence Scientific School at Harvard, which was founded a year after the scientific school at Yale.

Something of the vigorous spirit that prevailed in the Scientific School and attracted outstanding men to its faculty also spread to other departments in the College. In this stimulating intellectual atmosphere appeared able figures such as George J. Brush and William H. Brewer, two of the first to receive degrees from the School; James Dwight Dana, for many years the leading American geologist; Daniel Coit Gilman, Dana's biographer and president of Johns Hopkins University for twenty-five years; General Francis Amasa Walker, who became president of the Massachusetts Institute of Technology; Samuel J. Johnson, founder of agricultural experiment stations in this country, Addison E. Verrill, the zoologist, and Othniel C. Marsh, first curator of Yale's Peabody Museum of Natural History—these and many others whose reputation and contributions to science were such as to make the School known throughout this country and abroad.

In 1945 Yale College at long last absorbed the undergraduate science program, and Sheffield became again, as it was in the beginning, a school primarily for graduate instruction. In 1947 the Sheffield Scientific School can look back over a hundred years of solid achievement. Conceived on a plan far in advance of the time, it has continued to maintain its leadership in scientific education.

CHAPTER XIV

Europe Revisited

1851

ON AUGUST 8, 1849 Silliman in a communication to the Yale Corporation signified his desire to retire at Commencement the following year. "An earlier retirement would, as I conceive, be inconsistent with the interests of the Institution, and with existing duties, both to the College proper, and to the Medical School; and I am therefore willing to serve for another year." If the reasons behind his desire to retire were asked, he said he would reply: "I am daily admonished by the rapid flight of time, and often by the departure of my contemporaries, that my work is nearly done. Having now attained to the age of seventy, and fifty years of my life having been passed in the service of the College, I feel that I am entitled to a discharge, and that a younger man ought, ere long, to fill my place. In the retrospect I have the satisfaction to add, that from my colleagues and from my fellow-men, I have received sympathy and encouragement, and from the Corporation, both confidence and efficient aid; but of those venerated men who under President Dwight, invited me, in my youth, into the service of the College, not one remains. The time of my own departure from the College is at hand, and when it shall arrive, I shall leave this long-cherished institution with deep affection and earnest solicitude for its prosperity, and shall never cease to pray that God may continue to regard it with favor, and to bestow upon it His blessing." President Woolsey, in communicating the Corporation's reaction to this letter and their request that he continue for a time longer, closed with: "It will give me a feeling of loneliness and desolation when you leave us."

On January 18th (1850) Mrs. Silliman died after a lingering illness, and with the future thus abruptly altered, Silliman decided to continue with his college duties, hoping that work might help him to bear the sorrow and loneliness which her passing caused him. He wrote in his daybook on their wedding anniversary: "This is the anniversary of my happy marriage 41 years ago—a day ever to be remembered with gratitude. Now all is in retrospect. My dear wife has been removed from me—it will be seven months tomorrow and I am a bereaved man—submissive, since God has done it, but desolate and a mourner whenever I withdraw from society, whether by night or by day."

In June he reluctantly parted with his youngest daughter Julia, who had taken her mother's place as head of the house. When she married the Reverend Edward W. Gilman, an elder brother of Daniel C. Gilman, on June 5th seventy of their combined families and friends attended the wedding. "The young people came from the library," Silliman wrote, "as did formerly Oliver Hubbard and Faith and James Dwight Dana and Henrietta, and the company comfortably filled both parlors. . . . The occasion passed off with reasonable cheerfulness and sobriety; my emotions were solemn and pensive—almost sorrowful, but I shewed a cheerful although grave demeanor. Many thoughts pressed upon my mind. My dear wife so recently removed . . . the assembling of all my children, perhaps never to meet here with me again, the parting with the last of them from my house now left entirely desolate . . . and my own advancing years—all these things made this to me more a scene of sorrow than of joy although I could and did participate in the happiness of the married pair."

When the Gilmans departed for his parish in Lockport, New York, Silliman presented his son-in-law with a letter mentioning "some points which may be very important to your mutual happiness." It was a letter from his heart, and the fifth of the eight points he covered revealed something of his own marriage: "A husband whose duties require frequent composition, will often find advantage by reading his writings to his wife. Sensible women have great tact in discovering anything wrong; by a kind of instinctive perception, they discover and point out what man's more obtuse intelligence may have overlooked. On this point I write feelingly, from experience, having profited much on this subject, and on all subjects, by the advice of my late dear wife, who was almost invariably my confidant and counsellor."

A visit to Julia in her new home in September assured him of her complete contentment and put his mind at ease. In the meantime, Commencement had turned his thoughts in a happier direction. Yale this year celebrated the one hundred and fiftieth anniversary of its founding (the founding date having been considered 1700 instead of 1701 in those days), and nearly 1,000 alumni thronged New Haven—twice as many, it is said, as were ever gathered on any previous occasion, and the proceedings were marked by great enthusiasm and hilarity. Distinguished graduates of the College and scholars from other colleges were present for the occasion and Oliver Wendell Holmes, although a graduate of Harvard, wrote a humorous poem, *Astræa,* "abounding in capital hits at all sorts of humbugs," which he read before the Phi Beta Kappa Society.

At the special exercises on Wednesday morning, August 14th, it was announced that Professor Silliman, who had proposed to resign from his chair, had consented to continue in office. The tremendous applause which greeted this announcement filled his heart with profound gratitude. In his daybook he appended a paragraph from the *New York Observer* with the thought that it might be interesting to his children when he was gone.

On Wednesday morning at half past nine the alumni assembled in the College Chapel. Professor Silliman was called to the chair. It was gratifying to the many graduates of the College present to see this distinguished man, who has done so much for their Alma Mater, still erect and firm as a pillar of granite. He has passed the age of 70 years, but 'his eye is not dim nor his natural force abated': May he long be spared to give to the Institution the benefit of his great talents and fame.

"This," he wrote, "is an instance of the very kind treatment which I have often received from my countrymen; commendation beyond my desert and which I do not feel to produce any emotion of vanity but rather the opposite."

The Commencement exercises, which occupied almost the entire day, were held on Thursday in the Center Church which was "crowded by beauty above and learning below, to the almost entire exclusion of fresh air." That evening President Woolsey opened his house to all the alumni and "other gentlemen of education attendant upon the exercises." The next day the many sons of Yale who had gathered to renew their memories of its pleasant and fruitful shades, returned to the widely scattered fields of their various labors.

The hospitality of the Silliman house was extended as usual to friends of the College attending the celebrations and to those who sought out Silliman personally. Through the years many scholars and scientists, some young, others who had already achieved fame, had been welcomed and entertained in this house, near the heart of the College but far enough removed to offer a quiet retreat. Mrs. Silliman had been an hospitable hostess, reserved but gracious, and always thoughtful of the comfort of her guests. The daughters, attractive and with keen minds and eager interest in anything which concerned their beloved father, added their own contribution to the friendly atmosphere of the Silliman household. The warm affection of the whole family for one another, the mutual interests of father and son, the unostentatious comfort of their manner of living, and above all the stimulation of conversation with Professor Silliman himself in his book-lined study made any visit a memorable occasion. Silliman's dignity and kindliness and his unquenchable enthusiasm for science were not easily forgotten, especially by those from other countries who perhaps did not expect such simplicity in a man whose name was venerated on both sides of the Atlantic. On this occasion Silliman recorded: "Professor Agassiz and lady were our guests for ten days and most agreeable people they are. Mr. Reginald N. Mantell [son of Dr. Gideon A. Mantell] arrived from England early in commencement week and remained with us. Count de Pourtalès and lady and Mr. Geavel, friends of Agassiz were also among our guests; also Professor Brown of Dartmouth College, and my old friend, Robert Hare. Our house has been full and indeed we have hardly been without company during the summer. The celebrated poet Dr. Oliver Wendell Holmes was also with us for a night and a most pleasant man he is."

In 1851 Silliman obtained a six-month leave of absence from his college duties and on March 5th departed for Europe accompanied by Benjamin, Jr. and his daughter-in-law (Benjamin had married Susan Forbes in May 1840), her sister, his eldest grandson, Walter S. Church, and George J. Brush, who was one of Norton's pupils in the School of Applied Chemistry. The return, after forty-five years, to the scene of the treasured experiences of his youth brought back pleasant memories. Again he kept a journal, this time for his children, especially his son. "For his sake chiefly, I consented to cross the ocean again, and to put forth all requisite energy in travelling, at a period of life when most men desist from wandering, and seek the quiet of home." The journal was published in 1853 in two volumes (totalling 986 pages), which for practical information and minute detail would rival a modern Baedeker. Indeed, it would almost appear that Silliman had missed his calling in life when he pursued science instead of preparing guidebooks for travellers! This travel diary also was very well received and there were many enthusiastic reviews.

The party crossed on the *S.S. Baltic,* a U.S. mail side-wheeler;

after a comfortable passage they dropped anchor in the
Mersey at 8:30 a.m. on Monday, March 17, the passage having
been accomplished in eleven days and twenty-one hours. Silliman adds that a Cunard steamer which had left at the same
time, not being forced to deviate from its course because of
ice, had arrived a day earlier. On boarding the *Baltic* Silliman
made a careful examination of the ship and he records in detail its physical characteristics which contrasted so sharply
with the 400-ton sailing vessel, *Ontario,* on which he had
crossed in 1805: the *Baltic* displaced 3,200 tons, was 287 feet
in length with a beam of 46 feet and a hold 32 feet deep. The
side paddles were 36 feet in diameter with 26 floats, i.e.,
buckets, on each wheel. Each paddle was rimmed with 300
pounds of iron and it took six men to lift one in place.

We see in all this the minute interest of a man who had spent
his life putting scientific principle to useful application. He
even records the steam pressure, the position of the machinery
in relation to the rest of the ship, the performance of the en-
gines, stoking, fire hazards, and the admirable system of temperature control through the use of steam tubes to the state-
rooms. And he was likewise interested in some of the more
mundane things about a ship that would claim the attention of
any traveller. There were 50 persons looking after the machinery, 48 of whom were stokers. There were 30 to 40
stewards, 20 to 25 sailors, and 3 officers, making a total of 140
in the crew as contrasted with only 70 passengers. The furnishings were "very elegant, rich enough for a nobleman's villa.
Of mirrors large and small there were about fifty, indeed they
are in such excess that a passenger cannot look in any direction
without meeting his own image." The table was amply supplied "and had the best attendance; articles of animal food
were packed in ice; of luxuries there was a great abundance."

This journey was something of a triumphal tour for Silliman. He would not only return to the happy days of young

manhood as he revisited familiar landmarks in England, but he would visit many places and institutions in Europe rich with historical association, and above all, he would have the pleasure of meeting face to face many with whom he had become acquainted through correspondence or the *American Journal of Science*. Wherever he sought out these scholars or scientists, he received a warm welcome. Dr. Gideon A. Mantell of London wrote in his diary after Silliman's arrival: "At half past seven this evening my beloved friend and correspondent and I met for the first time, after an interchange of thought and feeling more than 30 years, in my little study: he was accompanied by his son. We met as old familiar friends: he was what I had anticipated; a fine, hearty, good humoured, intellectual countenance, and a frame upright and vigorous as a man of 50."

At Liverpool where they had disembarked on March 17th, they had been cordially welcomed by another friend with whom Silliman had kept in touch by letter—John Taylor, a chance stagecoach acquaintance of 1805 and now a prosperous merchant who had made every arrangement for their comfort and entertainment. Liverpool and Birmingham had grown and changed almost beyond recognition as had London, where they arrived on March 26th after nine days of sightseeing in Chester, the celebrated Vale of Llangollen, and Oxford to which they later returned.

Their purpose in hurrying to London was to attend a meeting of the Geological Society at Somerset House with Dr. Mantell. Here among scientific men Silliman received an enthusiastic reception. His friend, Sir Charles Lyell, announced to the audience that "the meeting might hope for some additional illustrations on this subject [the paper of the evening was on glaciers] from Professor Silliman and his son, who do us the honor to attend on this occasion." Although unprepared, Silliman responded appropriately, commencing his remarks by saying that they were happy to see "the eminent men whose writings we have so long perused with instruction and pleasure, and to listen to their living voices." Having made these introductory remarks, Silliman showed his independence of mind by politely taking issue with Lyell's theory of glaciers— which Lyell accepted in good part.

Silliman had a similarly cordial reception at Oxford when he returned the next day to spend more time with his old friend, Dr. Charles Daubeny, later Aldrichian Professor of Chemistry, who had visited in New Haven in 1837. They had much in common, for Daubeny was struggling to secure recognition for the sciences at Oxford. Gibbon, who in the eighteenth century had found Oxford plunged in 'port and prejudice,' would have found things little improved had he visited the University in the first part of the nineteenth century. Silliman was especially disappointed to discover that science had little place or encouragement at this venerable institution.

It is obvious that Oxford has imbibed very little of the spirit of modern improvement. We are assured that physical science is not favored by the great body of the University, and indeed it appears to be decidedly discountenanced. The classics—very valuable, as indeed they are, and always deserving a high place in a course of general education—are here, along with some portion of mathematics, and with the moral and intellectual sciences, especially logic, the great absorbing topics, and there has been little change from the courses of former centuries. Neither Dr. Buckland (now Dean of Westminster), nor Dr. Daubeny, both of them men eminent in their professions, the former in mineralogy and geology, the latter in chemistry and botany, could obtain more than a meagre class, not on an average twenty pupils, in a University which has 6000 members on its books, and 1500 in actual attendance.

A Parliamentary inquiry into the condition of the universities has elicited, among other documents, a report by a distinguished professor of Oxford, of which I have a copy. It presents a table of the attendance for a series of years, on the lectures of the different professors of science, and one is astonished to find that it is rare that any professor has more than ten or twelve, some only five or six, pupils, and some of the chairs are even at zero. Some of my American friends who have visited Oxford with an introduction from myself to Dr. Buckland, and have been by him invited to his lectures, have been astonished to find perhaps only a dozen pupils.

No wonder that the spirit of Dr. Buckland, a noble man of high talents and attainments, seconded by great zeal and industry, and eloquence, should have been discouraged by classes which would be meagre indeed even in any of our infant colleges in the youngest States of the Union. He is said to have ended his last course in Oxford, with only three pupils! Dr. Buckland's lecture-room could hardly have accommodated with seats more than twenty or twenty-five.

Dr. Daubeny's lecture-room is new, and was well fitted up with all necessary conveniences and appendages, but it was small; perhaps the seats would receive thirty or forty. The impressions of a transient stranger may be erroneous; but I will quote the remarks of an Oxonian, one of the sons of the University, a man of science, a scholar, and a man of world-wide fame. It was in London he remarked to this effect: that so strong is the University in wealth and patronage that they are able to go on in their own way, despite the influence of the age, and of public opinion. The great object, he remarked, among the fellows, was to obtain livings in the church, and to this end their studies were mainly directed. He did not doubt that should some college decide that they would study Chinese alone, they would be able to carry it out.

In consequence of the movement now making by government, it is expected that more attention will be paid to science; that the attendance will, hereafter, be rendered obligatory, and that, therefore, larger classes may be expected. Even the eminent gentleman, himself a distinguished professor, who expressed this hope and expectation, did not venture to propose, in the pamphlet alluded to, more than partial courses of science, containing great leading principles, and selections of facts, without going fully into any of the sciences.

It was a great disappointment to Silliman not to meet at Oxford William Buckland, whom he knew through his geological classics, *Reliquiae Diluvianae* and the *Bridgewater Treatise*, and through correspondence of many years. Shortly after he had become Dean of Westminster, Buckland had completely lost his mind through overwork.

As in every university he visited while abroad, Silliman explored the libraries and the museums. He was delighted to find a head of the extinct Dodo in the Ashmolean Museum and to discover that the collection at the Radcliffe Library was especially rich in natural science. (He recorded that there were 400,000 books in the Bodleian Library and 200,000 in the Radcliffe, as well as innumerable manuscripts, for he never failed to ascertain the number of volumes in each library he visited).

Back in London, Silliman observed several changes—the junction of the Strand and Charing Cross at the head of Parliament Street had been "invaded by the splendid Trafalgar Square," which brought to mind the day he had seen Nelson in the Strand with an admiring crowd at his heels, and later when he embarked from Plymouth to his death at Trafalgar. One change he found decidedly for the better was that the British Museum was now open to the public and one could stay as long as desired instead of being hurried out as in 1805 after two hours. Indeed, the changes made him feel like a Rip Van Winkle who had awakened from a sleep of more than twice twenty years. "In my own comparatively young country, rapid and great changes are, of course, to be expected; but in this old country, which has been civilized for a thousand years, we might with more probability expect to find all things to continue as they were. It is however not so; science and art have, in this age, and in this country, given a wonderful impulse to the human mind; and their results, joined with those of a higher moral, intellectual and philanthropic character, are already such as no human sagacity could have foreseen, nor can we even now discern the extent of the career of progress which may be coming."

France, to which he repaired next, offered no comparisons because he had been denied entrance when formerly in Europe. One of the first places he visited in Paris was the Cabinet of

Comparative Anatomy of Cuvier—"probably the most extensive and complete in existence." And he of course went to the famous School of Mines where he was particularly interested in their museums. He comments on the beauties of the Louvre, the Gobelin tapestries, and Sèvres porcelain (for he invariably visited all the great shrines, repositories of art, industries, and public buildings of interest), but his first and chief concern was always science—the men, the equipment and arrangement of their classrooms and museums, and then the geology of the region. He was especially gratified in Paris to have an opportunity to attend a session of the then all-powerful French Academy:

The French Academy is the great center about which the whole world of science, in a certain sense, revolves. I had the honor of being escorted to one of its weekly sittings on Monday afternoon at three by the venerable Cordier, now I believe the only surviving member of that large corps of savants who accompanied Napoleon to Egypt. His little work on the internal heat of the earth, presenting decisive proof that the temperature increases as we descend, made a great sensation in the scientific world, and however it may at first have appeared to savor of extravagance, his startling conclusions have been fully established. Although M. Cordier has passed fourscore, he is still erect, active, animated, affable, and warm in his address. By him I was introduced to the distinguished geologist, M. Constant Provost, professor of geology in the Sorbonne. M. Provost has been the steady and able opponent of the elevation theory of MM. Elie de Beaumont and von Buch. Sitting by his side in the center of the long hall where the Academy holds its sessions, I had, for a brief space, opportunity to scrutinize the array of leading minds by which I was surrounded. Before me, elevated upon the tribune, and with the baton of his office, sat M. Rayer, the distinguished physician—and president for the year. On his left, was the striking form of the perpetual secretary, the illustrious Arago, his face strongly marked by dark and shaggy eyebrows, and deep lines of thought. There was the amiable and dignified Biot, with his little velvet cap. Bousangault, Payen, and Dumas, the chemists—Brongniart, Milne Edwards, Elie de Beaumont, Leverrier, and many others equally well known. Some of these I now saw for the first time, as they were kindly pointed out to me by M. Provost. . . .

On April 14th, after a two-week stay they left Paris and proceeded across France, visiting Lyons, Avignon, Nismes, Arles, and Marseilles. In the latter city he was interested in the public health measures that had been strictly enforced since the town had been stricken by the plague in 1721. In 1839 it had again been desolated by cholera which carried off victims at the height of the epidemic at the rate of 1,000 or 1,500 a day. The great hospital of Marseilles "covers 50 acres and contained the whole French Army on its return from Egypt, in which country, however, and the vicinal regions, most of the soldiers who left France in that expedition found their last home, being thinned out frightfully by the casualties of war, and by disease, and by many modes of privation and suffering. It is said, that if, at the present day, a case of plague appears in any vessel at Marseilles, the vessel is sunk, and the goods are burned."

From France the party travelled by land to Genoa via Nice and the Cornice Highway. Italy, particularly Rome, stirred Silliman's imagination—seeing the Pantheon, the Coliseum, the Appian Way, St. Peter's was like stepping backward into history, and he was filled with a deep emotion which inspired some of his best descriptive writing—and some of his most extravagant superlatives. Thus in his diary entry for May 5th we find him quite overwhelmed by the Eternal City:

In the morning I awoke, and behold I was in Rome! My first returning consciousness brought a more realizing conviction than I felt last evening, that I was indeed in Rome. Rome, famous long before the Saviour appeared on earth—Rome, conqueror of the then known world—Rome, the seat of learning, arts and eloquence—Rome, heathen in the midst of all its splendors, and persecuting and destroying the Christians—Rome, prostrated by barbarians, still not destroyed—Rome, nominally Christian in after ages, then, and for centuries, a persecuting power, in cruelty rivalling her own heathen era—Rome, often torn by factions or possessed by foreign armies, and still great in her desolation;—in this very Rome, where Paul preached and died, I had now indeed arrived, and thus was about to connect the present with the past by surveying its ruins, physical, mental, and moral.

But he could also exercise a more poetic restraint:

The glory of the bay of Baiae [Naples] is departed for ever. The bright Italian sky indeed sheds its lustre over the placid waters, and the rising sun gilds ruined villas and temples; but the fisherman draws his seine where once anchored the Roman fleet, and dries his net upon the strand where Cicero recreated his leisure hours by gathering with his friend the smooth pebbles and polished shells whose lustrous porcelain still adorns these shores.

The ruins of departed empires claimed much of Silliman's attention and he also visited many churches. The incomparable beauty of the European cathedrals filled him with aesthetic appreciation, but he approached evidences of living Catholicism gingerly, feeling uncomfortable when a witness to the richness and color of their ritual and a manner of worship he did not know or understand. St. Peter's and the Vatican inspired him with silent reverence, the Vatican containing as it does "the richest collections of antiquities and things illustrative of man's history and his powers, and what he has done and suffered, that the world affords." In addition to his long description of St. Peter's in the journal, he added six additional pages of comment in an appendix.

But the most thrilling experience of all was beholding with his own eyes Vesuvius, Mount Etna, Stromboli, and the Mont Blanc. "To ascend Mount Vesuvius was a pleasure I had never expected to enjoy. I had most carefully studied its history and watched its movements for fifty years, and was therefore fully prepared not only to understand its teachings, but to enjoy the gratification of seeing this classical volcano." To see Stromboli "whose volcano has been in a state of restless activity for more than 2000 years" he was on the deck of their Sicily-bound steamer at four a.m., and he awakened the other passengers so they too could enjoy the sight. They had no more than passed

Stromboli before "over the comparatively low curve of the
Sicilian coast, we descried the 'Snowy Etna, the pillar of
Heaven,' towering far above all other objects." Of Etna he
wrote: "Who has not wished to see this grand storehouse of
volcanic fire, whose action preceded the records of history and
the legends of tradition, and whose energy is still displayed in
undiminished vigor!" They climbed Etna as far as the Val del
Bove, but only Benjamin, Jr., and George Brush attempted the
strenuous ascent to the cone. Silliman described the Val del
Bove, 3500 feet above the Mediterranean, with such vividness
that one could almost imagine oneself there beside him:

The grandeur of this scene far surpasses all powers of description. . . .
It is a vast volcanic amphitheatre with almost vertical walls of ragged
rock, black and forbidding. The area has been a scene of the most tremendous action of fire. Compared with this natural amphitheatre of
Etna, the Coliseum of Rome is a toy. The area of the Val del Bove would
contain 10,000 such Coliseums, and London itself could be included in its
vast capacity. It has been well remarked that, compared with Etna, Vesuvius is a cabinet volcano. There lies the Val del Bove, amidst the awful
solitudes of Etna; itself desolated by internal fire, its enormous piles of
lava, and its now quiet volcanic cones, attesting that below is the focus
of latent energy. Still this area is depressed far below the giant power, the
great cone of Etna, that, in close proximity, impends over it, and holds
it, as a vassal, in subjection. In some future eruption, Etna's cone may
pour into this profound gulf such floods of molten rock as may fill it again
up to the general slope of the great dome, or convert it into an overflowing fountain of fire, which shall pour its floods of lava down the
declivities and into the valleys below, as has more than once happened
already.

After leaving Sicily, the party spent over a month exploring
the beautiful and historic landmarks of Naples, Leghorn, Pisa,
Florence, Bologna, Venice, and Milan, before they proceeded
to Switzerland. In Geneva, where they first stopped, Silliman
of course visited the University. He also called on the distinguished Professor Auguste de la Rive who opened his town
residence especially to receive Silliman and who accompanied

him to the house where Horace Benedict de Saussure, credited
with naming the science of geology, had lived. Silliman paused
at the grave of Sir Humphry Davy who, only a year his senior,
was already well started on his distinguished career when Silliman had called on him at the Royal Institution in 1806—
paused long enough to copy the inscription on his tomb:

Hic Jacet
Humphry Davy
Eques, Magnæ Britanniæ Baronelus,
Olim Regiæ Soc. Londin. Præses.
Summus Arcanorum Naturæ Indagator
Natus Penzantiæ Cornubiensium
XVII. Decemb. MDCCLXXVIII
Obiit Genevæ Helvetiorium
XXIX. Mai MDCCCXXIX

From Geneva they went to Lausanne to deliver a letter to
the mother of his friend, Louis Agassiz, then living in Cambridge, Massachusetts. "Although nearly fourscore, her health-
ful person was erect, tall, and dignified, while her animated
and warm address placed us instantly at ease. . . . As soon as
we explained to her our intimacy with [Louis]—that he had
been often a guest in our families—that we had the pleasure
of knowing his interesting American wife—and when we added
a friendly notice of her son's domestic happiness, and of his
high standing and success in his adopted country, her strong
frame was agitated, her voice trembled with emotion, and the
flowing tears told the story of a mother's heart. . . ."

At the library at Berne, where they went from Lausanne,
Silliman was interested in a manuscript volume on heraldry
of Swiss families in which his own family name and coat of
arms was pointed out to him by the librarian. It is interesting
that a portrait of the illustrious physiologist, Albrecht von
Haller, also claimed his attention, for Haller and Silliman
were in many ways alike. Their knowledge was encyclopedic,
they both wrote incessantly and neither one gave himself suffi-

cient leisure for original thought. At the Stadt Bibliothek in Berne is preserved Haller's correspondence with distinguished contemporaries in the 18th century bound in sixty-seven volumes. Silliman's correspondence, if it were ever fully collected, would match Haller's both in extent and in the number of correspondents. Between Silliman and Haller, however, there was one great difference, for Silliman, like John Hunter, the great Scottish surgeon, his near contemporary, founded a school; he had a large following of pupils who carried on with his traditions when he withdrew from active work. Haller had pupils in his early days but when he died there was no disciple on whom his mantle could fall.

From Berne the party proceeded to Heidelberg via Basel and Strasburg. Here Silliman sought out Professors Leonhard and Bronn with whom he had long corresponded. Unfortunately Professor Bronn was ill, but Leonhard received him cordially and showed him his excellent geological collections and lecture rooms. At the University of Bonn, Silliman was welcomed by Professor Frederick Reaumer of the department of geology and paleontology, who had spent three years in the United States and was now glad of an opportunity to return Silliman's kindness.

In Berlin the Sillimans attended a meeting of the Geographical Society on the invitation of the well-known physical geographer, Karl Ritter. Silliman writes: "We received a warm welcome to Berlin, and throughout the interview of the evening the most kind and cordial treatment." He was also extremely gratified to have an interview with the renowned Alexander von Humboldt. After a week of exploring the city, they journeyed to Freiburg to visit the School of Mines of Professor Werner, because, Silliman recorded: "My early professional studies created in me a high admiration of this school of mines, founded in 1765; and of Werner, its illustrious ornament, whose name was, for half a century, of decisive authority upon all questions relating to the sciences connected with the mineral kingdom." Although great advances had been made since the time of Werner in the knowledge of minerals, and although his views of geology later proved limited and in some cases erroneous, nevertheless "he, more than any other man in his time, imparted interest and gave impulse to these studies, so fruitful in important results both to science and the arts." Freiburg then, was "a capital point in our rapid glance at Germany." The young men in the party wanted to descend into the mines, but Silliman, who had done enough of this in his earlier years, preferred to write or to wander about the town where the man who had strongly influenced his early thinking in geology had once walked these same streets.

Dresden, Cologne, Leipzig, Antwerp, and Brussels were covered in a week (August 6-13); they then stopped in Paris and London once more before they sailed from Liverpool on September 2d. Dr. Mantell entertained them again before they departed and took them on a tour (with geological intent) to the Isle of Wight and the chalk pits of Lewes. Wherever they went there were comparisons to be made—in London, comparisons between the present and the past. The Museum of the College of Surgeons, for example, founded by John Hunter, which Silliman had visited many years ago, was now set up in a large building in Lincoln's Inn Fields. On the continent he was constrained to make comparisons with America. The trees of Bonn reminded him strongly of the New Haven elms. In fact, some of his New Haven friends and others from America, had found Bonn both an agreeable residence and by its great literary advantages, conducive to learning. In Pisa he found some of the girls "blooming with New England complexions, but not veiled by New England gravity and reserve." In Neuchâtel, which had a population not exceeding 7000, less than one-third that of New Haven, he was forced to make the observation that it was "greatly beyond us in the munificent endowment of an institution for popular education, which is, in fact, a great University in almost every thing except the name." (He appends a footnote to "popular education" in his journal to the effect that "Yale College has a different, and, in some respects a higher destination!") In physical improvements, such as roads and bridges, and in agriculture, he also found that Europe led America, and he hoped that his countrymen might follow their "noble example" more than they had done hitherto. However, he concluded his observations with the consoling thought that "considering the comparative youth of our country, much has been done; and we may hope that long before we have enjoyed, like Europe, a thousand years of civilization, we shall not be behind the nations of the old world in noble institutions. We have even now not a few, and they are, year by year, coming into existence."

Although he had covered a large territory with astonishing thoroughness, Silliman had nevertheless missed a few things he had wanted to see—he regretted that he had been unable to explore the tertiary basin of Paris and the volcanic district of Auvergne, and most of all he regretted not being able to revisit Scotland "and especially Edinburgh, which is, in my memory," he wrote, "associated with very interesting recollections of my youth. . . . Imperative duties and engagements at home alone prevented my waiting for the next steamer, that good old Scotland might have been seen again, but it is still loved as of yore."

After an uneventful voyage of twelve days' duration, they were back in America on September 14th. Silliman went immediately to Brooklyn "to the house of that brother to whom the narrative of my early travels was addressed, and who was permitted now to witness the happy conclusion of another foreign tour, performed in the evening, as the early one was in the morning, of life. . . . The next day restored me to my own house in New Haven, to the warm welcome of many friends, and the affectionate embraces of my children."

However, the house proved unbearably lonely after the first excitement of his return was over. On September 17, 1851 he married Mrs. Sarah Isabella Webb of Woodstock, Connecticut, long a friend of the family and a relative of the first Mrs. Silliman. Her concern for his comfort and her companionship were a source of happiness to him in the remaining years of his life.

CHAPTER XV

His Successors
1853

IN SEPTEMBER 1852 Silliman made a second attempt to retire, setting the date as July, 1853. He wanted to go "before compelled to by infirmity and to march out of the camp with colors flying." The Corporation realized that the time had come when they would have to release him and accordingly they sent him the following resolutions, passed at their annual meeting on July 26, 1853:

Resolved, that this board entertains a high and grateful sense of the eminent services which Prof. Silliman has rendered to the College during his long term of office, and regrets that the approach of old age makes him feel it to be expedient to resign his professorship.

Resolved, that he be requested to continue in the Academical and Medical Faculties, as professor emeritus, with the right of a vote in these faculties, if he shall see fit to attend their meetings.

Resolved, that until Prof. Dana shall be able to commence his instructions, Prof. Silliman be requested to continue his lectures in Mineralogy and Geology, and that the Prudential Committee be authorized to decide what compensation shall be rendered for this service to the College.

Resolved, that the President of this Board be requested to communicate these resolutions to Prof. Silliman.

At a meeting of the Alumni Association on July 22, 1853 Denison Olmsted offered a resolution "that the Alumni have heard with deep concern of the resignation of Professor Silliman; that they cherish the warmest attachment to his person, and entertain a high appreciation of his labors for Yale College, and for the promotion of knowledge and virtue throughout the world." Olmsted then followed with a particularly happy, informal appreciation of Silliman's services to Yale which ended:

. . . The almond tree indeed is white with blossoms; but no wonder, since that tree has struck its roots so deep in the soil, and spread its branches so far that not only we, but our fathers and to some of us, our fathers' fathers have taken shelter beneath its shade.

His mantle descends upon his son and his son-in-law, each of whom will wear it gracefully and will, we trust, make its folds still more resplendent. He carries with him the sincere respect, nay the warm affection of every son of Yale, and the highest estimation of all the world. To all of us who represent here today the thousands whom he has instructed in science and whom he has attracted to virtue by the lustre of his example, it will ever be among our most cherished recollections that we were pupils of Professor Silliman.

Leaving the scene of his long labors was made easier by this spontaneous expression of regard and affection and by the fact that James Dwight Dana and Benjamin, Jr. had been chosen as his successors.

THE CHAIR OF CHEMISTRY

Benjamin, Jr. took over his duties immediately as Professor of General and Applied Chemistry with joint assignment to the Yale Scientific School and the Medical Institution of Yale College. In his Reminiscences Silliman recalled his son's proclivities:

In early life, in his schoolboy days, he was not fond of the study of language, particularly of Greek and Latin and therefore, after entering College, he did not take that stand to which his talents entitled him. From his earliest days, however, he manifested mechanical talents of a high order. He was not inclined to folly and he took great delight in visiting shops and manufactories, not only to see but to understand their curious processes. In two instances when he was missing from his school for several days together, it was found that in one instance it was to learn the art and mystery of forming the moulds for the casting of iron and in another that of making hats. He had no propensity to engage in the follies of boys or to resort to improper places of amusement.

His love of mechanics was so strong and his talents in that line were so decided, that almost as soon as he had reached his teens I indulged him in the possession of tools of which he made so good use that a shop was fitted up for him in a wing of the house with ample conveniences, including a lathe of iron constructed by himself and a furnace with bellows, anvil, etc. was added.

In College he early discovered a love of natural science and the mathematics and his mechanical training harmonized well with these more mature developments. During his College life he was of course familiar with the doings in the Laboratory and he therefore very naturally passed into the situation of assistant as soon as he had finished his undergraduate course in 1837. He had become in the meantime, a good writer, and was in all respects qualified for the place which he filled with ability and to my entire satisfaction during twelve years from 1837 to 1849 having served in the department more than twice as long as any one of his predecessors. Of course he became familiar with the sciences which we cultivated and he was able to lecture occasionally in my place in the College and in popular courses to the citizens of New Haven and other places. Thus easily did Benjamin, Jr. slip into his father's place. His textbook, *The First Principles of Chemistry for the Use of Colleges and Schools,* which first appeared in 1847, had gone into its forty-fifth printing by 1858. His *First Principles of Physics* which came out in 1859 enjoyed similar popularity.

The younger Silliman is best known for his important discovery of the nature of petroleum; indeed he is generally regarded as having inaugurated the petroleum industry in the United States for it was he who recognized that rock oil is in reality a mixture of different hydro-carbons which can be separated one from the other by fractional distillation. His celebrated report, begun in April 1853, was privately published in New Haven in 1855 under the title "A Report on the Rock Oil, or Petroleum from Venango County, Pennsylvania, with Special Reference to Its Use for Illumination and Other Purposes." On the basis of this report, prepared at the request of a group of promoters, a company was launched which drilled the Drake well at Oil Creek, Pennsylvania, and it was this well that marked the beginning of the oil industry in the country at large. Silliman's report was reprinted in 1871 in the *American Chemist* (vol. 2, pp. 18-23) with the following editorial comment:

. . . At the time Prof. Silliman made this research, all that was known of the "rock oil" of Pennsylvania was that on the waters of Oil Creek, in Venango County, the oil oozed out in pits dug in the soil and floated on the surface of the water as a dark green dichroous oil of high density (882° B.). No artesian well then existed, or had been ever thought of as a possibility. Drake's well was sunk more than two years after the report of Prof. Silliman was written. In reading this report now, after sixteen years of experience in the development of this important industry, we are struck with the fact that its author very nearly exhausted the subject, and anticipated and described most of the methods which have since been adopted by manufacturers. He even suggests the distillation by high steam, which has since been adopted with so much success by Merrill, in the preparation of his neutral heavy oil. He also noticed the peculiar breaking up of the heavier oils into lighter products, under the continued action of heats far below their boiling points, now called "cracking." He remarks that when "exposed for many days in an open vessel at a regulated heat below 112°, the oil gradually rises in vapor, etc., gradually and slowly disappearing, and finally leaving a small dark and pitchy residue."

Benjamin, Jr., like his father, was frequently called upon by mine owners, business executives, and promoters as a field consultant and in the course of dividing his time between his academic and promotional activities he seems to have developed something of a double personality. His scientific writings were couched in sober and restrained language but when he wrote a field report on oil his enthusiasm was unbridled, and according to Mr. E. DeGolyer, the eminent oil geologist, "he saw millions in everything."

Silliman went several times to California, once during the Gold Rush and again in 1864 just before his father's death. He had become much interested in the geology of oil, and so great was his enthusiasm about the potentialities of California as an oil-producing region that he came back from his 1864 survey and lectured in various cities on the state's resources. He even induced some of his colleagues in the Scientific School to invest money, among them William Dwight Whitney and

William H. Brewer. But Silliman did not inherit his father's business caution; his advice was not always sound, and both Whitney and Brewer lost rather heavily. In addition, Whitney's brother, Josiah Dwight Whitney, director of the California Geological Survey (later Professor of Geology at Harvard), was in violent disagreement with Silliman as to where the oil was in California—Whitney contending that it was in the northern part, Silliman in the south. All this combined to make Silliman unpopular in New Haven, and for a time feeling against him rose to such a pitch that it was not politic to mention his name. Brewer and Whitney even tried to have him ousted from the National Academy of Sciences.

Time has proved Silliman right, for California has been one of the most important oil-producing states in the nation and all of the production has come from the southern part of the state. As an able man of science, Silliman's name has been cleared—but perhaps he should have been wiser than to persuade his friends to invest in his ventures.

On the occasion of the celebration of the centennial of the discovery of oxygen, held at Northumberland, Pennsylvania, August 1, 1874, Silliman, Jr. issued in the columns of the *American Chemist* a useful historical monograph entitled "American Contributions to Chemistry." Well-written and accurate bibliographically, this monograph stands as an indispensable source for those interested in the history of science in the United States.

THE CHAIR OF GEOLOGY

If one judges a teacher by his pupils, then it must be said of Benjamin Silliman that he was a great teacher; for although he did almost no research himself, he inspired others and provided opportunity for investigative work of the highest order. His most outstanding pupil was James Dwight Dana, later his son-in-law, who probably contributed more to American geology and mineralogy than anyone after Silliman's time. Bailey Willis, Professor Emeritus of Geology at Stanford University, has said of Dana that he was a great thinker possessing constructive imagination and extraordinary mental grasp, and that he collected and collated the observations of his contemporaries with indefatigable industry until he became a clearing house for the exposition of geology. He commented: "As a college student in the late eighteen-seventies had I been asked why the earth was cooling, contracting, I might have answered: 'Because Dana says so.'"

Although Dana was not an outstanding student in college, Silliman in recommending him for an appointment in the Navy after graduation had written that "the candidate evinced uncommon interest in physical science and his attainments in chemistry, geology, and mineralogy were of the most respectable character and such as indicate ingenuity, industry, and perseverance." Dana had come to Yale College in 1830 from Utica, New York, because he wanted to study under Silliman. He had unusual opportunities to pursue the interests which Silliman had awakened when his Navy appointment as mathematics instructor took him on an eighteen-month cruise in the Mediterranean. The account of Vesuvius that he sent his preceptor in a letter so impressed Silliman that he published it in the *American Journal of Science,* and when Dana returned in the autumn of 1835, he invited him to become his personal assistant.

Daniel Coit Gilman, Dana's biographer, believes that this was probably the turning point of his career, for he was now established among men of kindred tastes in a stimulating intellectual atmosphere which offered the best opportuniity then available in this country for the study of science. Silliman proved a sympathetic mentor who gave his assistant much free time for the development of his fields of special interest, for

THE SILLIMAN FAMILY

Back Row: Benjamin, Jr., Faith (Mrs. Hubbard)
Front Row: Julia (Mrs. Gilman), Benjamin, Sr., Maria (Mrs. Church),
Henrietta (Mrs. Dana)
Background: Portrait of Harriet Trumbull (Mrs. Silliman, Sr.)

Courtesy of Miss Dana

HARRIET SILLIMAN LATE IN LIFE

Courtesy of Miss Dana

MARIA TRUMBULL SILLIMAN
(Mrs. John B. Church)

Miniature by A. Robertson

Courtesy of Miss Dana

HENRIETTA FRANCES SILLIMAN
(Mrs. James Dwight Dana)

Miniature by N. Jocelyn in 1843

Silliman had an extraordinarily modern view of education—he envisaged the ideal milieu for intellectual growth as a university where promising young men of the staff would be given a minimum of teaching responsibility and the opportunity to devote the remainder of their time to research and study. Granted this degree of freedom, those with real ability come to their full stature, while the incompetent and those who lack seriousness of purpose soon fall by the wayside.

Such a doctrine was heresy in almost every academic institution of that time—a young tutor or instructor labored under a heavy teaching burden and was expected to attend daily prayers and other religious observances, which left him little or no opportunity for study or research on his own initiative. When Silliman provided for students in his laboratory the opportunity to develop their latent talents in independent effort, he not only paved the way for the graduate school but he created an environment which produced men like Dana and others who became great American educators.

At the end of his first year in Silliman's laboratory Dana committed to press a brief study (December 1836), written primarily for his own use, entitled *A System of Mineralogy: Including an Extended Treatise of Crystallography*. When it appeared in the spring of 1837 the book was enthusiastically received both here and abroad and quickly placed its twenty-four-year-old author in a position of authority among the mineralogists of the time. Revised and enlarged, it went into six editions and became a scientific classic that for sixty years was the standard textbook in the field.[*] Although his *Manual of Geology* (1862) showed a "breadth, philosophy, and originality of treatment that have seldom been attempted," the earlier work was considered by many to be his most original contribution.

[*] The first volume of the 7th edition was published in 1945 and the other three volumes are in a forward state.

Following the appearance of his *Mineralogy* Dana would probably have continued his studies in New Haven had his friend Asa Gray, Professor of Botany at Harvard, not induced him to join the United States Exploring Expedition under Captain Charles Wilkes, as geologist and mineralogist. The Wilkes expedition (which in the end did not include Dr. Gray) sailed from Norfolk, Virginia, in six vessels in August 1838 to spend the next four years studying the major islands in the Pacific from the Aleutians to the Antarctic wastes. Dana and his colleagues brought back an enormous volume of scientific data, and he spent the next thirteen years preparing for publication the three official reports of the expedition assigned to him. The first two years were spent in Washington, but in 1844 he returned to New Haven to marry Henrietta, Silliman's third daughter, and settled down to spend the rest of his life at Yale.

By 1856 he had finished his reports and felt that he was ready to take over his share of Silliman's duties. On February 18th he gave his introductory lecture in the Geological Hall in the form of an historical résumé of geology at Yale, closing with the following references to America's first professor of geology:

And while the Science and truth have thus made progress here, through these labors of fifty years, the means of study in the Institution have no less increased. Instead of that half bushel of stones, which once went to Philadelphia for names, in a candle box, you see above the largest Mineral Cabinet in the country, which but for Professor Silliman, his attractions and his personal exertions together,—would never have been one of the glories of Old Yale. And there are also in the same Hall, large collections of Fossils of the Chalk, Wealden and Tertiary of England, which following the course of affection and admiration, came from Doctor Mantell to Professor Silliman, and now have their place with the other "Medals of Creation" there treasured, along with similar collections from M. Alexandre Brongniart of Paris. Thus the stream has been ever flowing, and this Institution has had the benefit—a stream not solely of minerals and fossils, but also of pupils and friends. . . .

We rejoice that in laying aside his studies, after so many years of labor, there is still no abated vigor. Youth with him has been perpetual. Years *will* make some encroachments as they pass: yet Time, with some, seems to stand aloof when the inner Temple is guarded by a soul of genial sympathies and cheerful goodness. He retires as one whose right it is to throw the burden on others. Long may he be with us, to enjoy the good he has done, and cheer us by his noble and benign presence.

Frequently the students, breaking over the academic rule, manifested their approval of his remarks by loud applause. Silliman, well pleased, wrote in his autobiography: "I feel that I have a right to rejoice that the great subject of geology and its connected sciences has passed into his hands; that he once my pupil is now my successor, and that on the foundations which it was my province to lay down, a superstructure is being reared by his hands whose strength will ensure for it perpetuity, and whose richness and beauty will, like the Parthenon, continue to be admired by those who shall follow in long succession where we have guessed the way."

During the first years of his professorship Dana gave considerable time and thought to the reorganization of the Scientific School (he had become formally attached to its faculty in 1855) and to ways and means of increasing the endowment. The preliminary step was a forceful address before the alumni in August, 1856. This was followed in the same year by a pamphlet of thirty-two pages entitled: *Proposed Plan for a Complete Organization of the School of Science connected with Yale College* which embodied some of the more liberal methods of kindred institutions in Europe that he sought to introduce at Yale.

Although he rarely attended the meetings of the Governing Board of the Scientific School he always took the deepest interest in its growth and advancement and could always be relied upon for "sympathy, counsel, and influence." His biographer adds that "there is no doubt that the early distinction of this School is due to Dana and [William Dwight] Whitney [one of the foremost linguistic scholars of his generation] whose names were a guarantee the world over that the methods here adopted were wise and commendable. . . ."

Franklin B. Dexter, later Secretary of Yale College, in recalling his undergraduate days, wrote of Dana as he remembered him: "Professor James D. Dana was perhaps forty-five years of age when I first saw him, but was already eminent, even to my untaught apprehension. He was in appearance as remarkable as he was in reality. Though not of commanding stature, in every other respect he was a most striking figure. His compact, wiry frame was instinct with life and vigor, and a glorious, buoyant energy seemed to radiate from every feature and every limb. As is well known, his intense, incessant mental activity wore out his physical strength and restricted his enjoyments in social and domestic life; but the elasticity of his tread and alertness of his look bore witness until late in life to the unconquerable strength of his will. . . . As a member of the faculty he was conscientious in attendance on his duty, but not greatly interested in the petty details of business and rather impatient of the needless waste of time. In the grasp of principles he was a recognized leader; the expansion of the elective system in the College in 1876 was due to his inspiration."

Dana occupied the Silliman Professorship of Geology and Mineralogy for forty years. His effectiveness as a teacher has been evaluated by his biographer in the following terms:

There is a certain standard of professional life which measures the value of a teacher by the number of recitations that he hears, or by the skill with which he exacts attention to the lessons of a class-book. Not so should the greatest teachers be estimated. They are the greatest who can awaken in their followers a love of knowledge and show them how this knowledge may be obtained or verified. To this class Dana belongs. His power was that of inspiration and of guidance. He could arrest the attention of his hearers, fill their minds with an enthusiastic love of science, and inspire them with certain principles which they would not forget as long as life continued.

Silliman had given the first chair of geology a tradition of inspired teaching; Dana carried this tradition forward, and he added much to its prestige and to Yale's eminence in science.

CHAPTER XVI

Professor Emeritus
1853-1864

THE Yale from which Silliman retired in the eighteen fifties was quite a different college from that to which he had been called as Professor of Chemistry and Natural History half a century before. When President Dwight was inducted into office in 1795, the College occupied a small parallelogram of 334 feet on College Street and 246 feet on Chapel, and the faculty consisted of Dwight, Professor Meigs, and three tutors. The Broadside of 1796, the first regular annual "catalogue" of Yale, and probably the first published by any college in the United States, was printed on a single sheet and contained 117 names. In 1802, when Silliman was appointed to his chair, President Dwight added two other professorships—Mathematics and Natural Philosophy to which Jeremiah Day was appointed, and Hebrew, Greek and Latin Languages to which James L. Kingsley was called. And at the turn of the century Dwight succeeded in acquiring for "the College grounds" all the land bounded by College, Chapel, High, and Elm Streets, now referred to as the "Old Campus."

By 1850 the College had grown to 386 undergraduate and 145 professional students, and buildings had been added including a Library, a chemistry "laboratory" (formerly the Commons), a building devoted to the display of minerals and to instruction in geology and mineralogy, another "laboratory" (formerly President Day's house) where the scientific school was developing under the name of the School for Applied Chemistry, a medical institution, and a gallery of art. By 1861 the faculty consisted of six active professors in the humanities, six in medicine, five in theology, two in law, and eight in science. The College also had a graduate school (in addition to the schools of law, theology, and medicine), and in this year

248

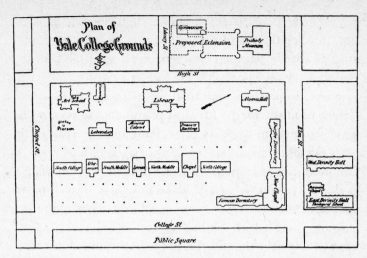

PLAN OF THE YALE COLLEGE GROUNDS SOME YEARS AFTER
SILLIMAN'S DEATH

offered for the first time the degree of Doctor of Philosophy.

In physical plant, in students, in faculty, Yale College had
advanced steadily, but the most encouraging growth lay in the
curriculum which had been expanded from its narrow offer-
ings in the classics and a smattering of the "pure" sciences
(mathematics and astronomy) to include not only physics,
chemistry, geology, mineralogy, etc., but the applied sciences
as well. Silliman, who had had a leading hand in all this, had
good cause to rest on the fruits of his labors, but the habits of
a lifetime were too strong, and retirement was to him only a
change of occupation with less pressure.

A PLEASURE TRIP

In June of 1854 he and Mrs. Silliman received an invitation
to a unique celebration that offered not only pleasure and re-
laxation, but an opportunity to participate in an historic event.
Two prominent citizens of New Haven, Henry Farnam and

Joseph E. Sheffield, in their capacities as engineer and financier, had just fulfilled their contract (six months ahead of schedule) to build a railroad between Chicago and Rock Island. It was decided to mark the opening of the line by inviting more than 700 persons "to pass over the road in the cars of the train to its western terminus on the Mississippi and then to proceed by a fleet of steamers to the City of St. Paul and the Falls of St. Anthony, an additional distance of nearly 500 miles."

With no duties or responsibilities, Silliman particularly enjoyed this excursion, especially since the party, travelling in comfort in twenty "private" cars, passed over a portion of the same route along which he had struggled ten years before. Their swift trip over the prairies in modern railroad carriages was in sharp contrast to the old stagecoach lumbering through almost impassable mud in 1844 when he had made his study of the iron mines of Illinois. On this occasion there was no sleeping three or four in a bed in windowless houses with chickens roosting overhead. Silliman observed that "only twenty years had passed since this region was transferred to our dominion [*i.e.,* entered the union] and now it is full of the stir of a high civilization." In every town and village along the route the townspeople were assembled in holiday mood to greet them and something of the lively spirit of the hour is conveyed in a letter Silliman wrote to his daughters:

. . . We left Chicago at 8 o'clock in two trains of more than twenty cars and passed rapidly and safely over the grand railroad of 180 miles in 8 hours, stops included. It conducted us through the most magnificent prairies both level and rolling—almost boundless and dotted with here and there a village or town. Our flight was in strong contrast to my toilsome passage over the same prairies in 1844 when two days and the intermediate night were consumed in struggling in a stagecoach through half the distance from Peru to Chicago.

The people were out all along the road in their gala dresses—flags were waved and shouts of gladness were blended with the roar of cannon. It was the jubilee of this great country and it was finished at Rock Island on the Mississippi, the western terminus, by a vast gathering of people with all the demonstrations which I have mentioned and the addition in the evening of splendid fire works and instrumental music from a brass band on board of one of the five steamers which lay in the stream waiting for us. . . .

The morning disclosed to us the most splendid scenery, which during Tuesday and Wednesday grew more and more grand and beautiful. Tuesday at 9 o'clock we turned into a small lateral river which conducted us at the distance of six miles from the Mississippi to the flourishing town of Galena of 10,000 people. High hills sloping on both sides to the river are bright with new houses and were swarming with a delighted population assembled to greet our squadron of steamers, now six in number, stretching along in line and gay with flags and their overflowing members shouting from the decks a warm response to the volleys of hurrahs and the booming of cannon from the shores.

Piles of lead in massive ingots lay along the quays and told the great business of the place as it is descried from the rich mines in the vicinity. Soon a veteran pioneer, the first settler at Galena in 1819, a tall bony man named Green, appeared on a gray horse, dismounted and came on board our steamer, the *War Eagle,* and made an enthusiastic speech full of western fire, and Rev. Dr. Spring replied in a few brief but pertinent remarks.

The shore was lined with wagons and all sorts of strange machines to give the excursionists a ride to the mines 5 or 6 miles in the country. Oliver [Hubbard] and I mounted the first wagon with Dr. Spring and others, and had we been made of rubber, I believe we should have gone bouncing over the sides, but we endured the solid pounding (no springs nor cushions, only a buffalo robe). At the mines a long board table was covered with bottles of champagne and kettles of water with cracked ice. After ascending from the mine (here not very deep and entered by ladies as well as men) the corks flew out of the bottles and inspiration followed. Again old Mr. Green took the stump and poured out anew his fluent periods, to which I, a cold water man, was summoned to respond—like an ice cream after hot toddy. Returned to our boats, the fleet was soon under way again and followed by shouts with waving flags until the cannon were heard no longer. . . .

When rain kept the passengers in the saloon the next day Silliman was called upon to entertain them by giving a geological description of the region through which they were passing. On June 8th they arrived at St. Paul, the capital of Minnesota—"2000 miles above the Gulf of Mexico. . . . As the town stands on a high bluff, it is conspicuous at a distance and makes a very handsome appearance. It was said at the time of our visit to contain 5 to 6 thousand inhabitants. Large warehouses, several churches, and a spacious and elegant Capitol, half a mile from the town, would hardly permit one to believe that a man to whom we were introduced built the first house in 1849." Their trip to the Falls of St. Anthony so exhausted him that he felt he must forego the Governor's reception and ball in the evening given for the entire party.

From St. Paul they began their return trip the next day. As they passed through the Great Lakes to Buffalo, Silliman studied the geology of the region at every opportunity and recorded in his daybook many facts of historical interest about the various cities at which they stopped. On the 24th of June he rejoiced that they were again at home, after a safe and interesting tour of four thousand miles.

His trip to the Blue Ridge Mountains of Virginia in April of the following year in a professional capacity and his lecture tour to St. Louis in December were the last of his extended journeys. From that time on he left New Haven only to attend scientific meetings or to make visits to his brother in Brooklyn or to his children.

A VARIETY OF INTERESTS

His grandchildren, of which he had twenty-six at this time (later thirty), were a source of particular pleasure to him. He welcomed their visits to New Haven, and when they were ill he invariably went to them immediately as he had to his own children. His daughters, accustomed to leaning on him in their own younger years, still called him whenever they were in need of reassurance or moral support—this although he was now approaching his eightieth birthday. His letters to them were filled with warm affection, and here more than anywhere else one finds evidence of wit and humor. He often took one or another of the children on his lecture tours, and in writing to those who were left at home he was in the habit of leaving space at the bottom of his letters so that whichever child was with him could add his or her bit. Thus, Benjamin, Jr. writes to Faith and Oliver Hubbard at the end of one of their father's letters written during a lecture course in New York: "Nearly all the news Pa has told you, for as Hetty says, he is a great monopolizer of both news and paper, indeed for the sake of their successors, those who monopolize news, had best also use up the paper." Scrawled all around Benjamin, Jr.'s contribution to this joint letter Silliman had added: "Prof. Parks [who had been assisting him in the demonstrations] sends his best respects . . . especially to Prof. Hubbard. Prof. Parks' brown wig underwent spontaneous combustion a few evenings since —as he came home from the lecture to our parlor and lifted his hat, the tangled brown forest and the covering burst into a blaze with a bit of phosphorus, but it was soon subdued."

In another letter Silliman had a little fun at Benjamin's expense: "The heat—therm. 83° and 84°—is enervating, especially to us who came from freezing cold down to Alabama and are now in summer weather. And the mosquitos who like New England blood and especially that of a young and fat subject like B.—— are very busy and we have to be fortified by our mosquito nets . . . every night."

On yet another occasion, when Mrs. Silliman was away from home, he sent off to her a letter in which the whole family had participated. The letter commenced: "My dearest, I begin a letter tonight that it may be ready on Monday and take a large sheet that there may be room enough, although it is very probable that it may not all be filled. Your letter dated this a.m. would have decided me as to the Buffalo overture even if I had been more inclined to it than I was; I shall therefore write them a negative and hope, with you, that nothing will occur this winter, should our lives be spared, to prevent my remaining quietly at home. . . ."

Silliman proceeded to fill a considerable portion of the large sheet and his thoroughness in covering the news prompted nineteen-year-old Julia to say when it came her turn: "As usual, Father has left very little to be told but love. . . ." She then added some domestic details her father had not included. "Hettie and I get on nicely, we find no difficulty with Bridget, though she is not so pleasant to deal with as Mary. Mr. Fisk's dining here was unexpected and we found our dinner rather short, so Hettie went begging and was so lucky as to find a nice piece of sparerib at Susan's [Mrs. Benjamin Silliman, Jr.] so that we made out very well."

Henrietta began her contribution with: "Dear Mamma, Pa has here a sheet of paper about as big as the mainsail of a vessel—and the quill pen I have picked up would answer well for a mast. . . . I have made my purchases with reference to Phil. and am to have a dressmaker this week. . . . I do not like the idea of leaving you, dear Mamma, but I tell them here it is good policy for you will all learn how to appreciate me. . . ." In the other parts of the joint letter there was at least one more complaint that "Father had told all the news."

A letter written to Faith in 1851 described the first gas lighting in their house. "I am now writing by the splendid light of a gas Argand lamp, pendant from one of the gas chandeliers at the height of about 20 inches above the table in the middle parlor. It is a positive luxury; it is almost as bright as the sun and being screened by one of those fancy covers, it is as mild as the moon. . . . Mr. Bakewell was in this evening and I was alone. . . . I went round and lighted for his gratification the whole house—13 rooms and 23 jets. It is beautiful and I only regret that dear mother could not have enjoyed it, for no one would have liked it better." The lighter side of his life was re-vealed in many other letters in like vein—heartwarming, human documents that balanced the somewhat ponderous quality of his scientific writings.

Although he lived much in the past as he worked at putting his correspondence and records in order, he lost none of his keen interest in people, scientific matters, and college and current affairs. In July of 1857 Mr. George Peabody, one of the greatest financial figures of the time, came to New Haven to visit his nephew, Othniel C. Marsh, then a sophomore at Yale. Silliman called on him, and while Marsh's biographers, Charles Schuchert and Clara Mae LeVene, suggest that this was purely a matter of courtesy on his part, the idea evidently occurred to him at this time that Peabody might be interested in the Scientific School, then in the midst of its campaign to secure endowment. Accordingly he later addressed a letter to him, and although his immediate object was not attained, when Peabody in 1863 decided to leave Yale a hundred thousand dollars for the promotion of natural science, he named Silliman one of the trustees to administer the fund. This was announced to Silliman in a letter from O. C. Marsh, who had become deeply interested in the future of the Scientific School during his postgraduate study there in 1861 and 1862. Marsh, who was then studying abroad, wrote:

Hamburg, May 25, 1863.

My dear sir: I take great pleasure in announcing to you that Mr. George Peabody has decided to extend his generosity to Yale College and will leave a legacy of one hundred thousand dollars to promote the interests of *Natural Science* in that Institution.

He has expressed a wish that the five following persons should act as his Trustees in employing this legacy for the attainment of the above object:—

Prof. B. Silliman	Prof. B. Silliman, Jr.
Hon. James Dixon	O. C. Marsh
Prof. J. D. Dana	

In order that the matter may be definitely arranged, Mr. Peabody suggests that the Trustees, as soon as convenient, decide upon a plan which
seems to them best adapted to promote the object proposed, and to em-
body the main features of this plan in a clause to be inserted in his
will. . . .

The gift eventually amounted to $150,000, of which $100,-
000 was to be used for a museum of natural history. Although
the site for the building was not selected until 1874, ten years
after Silliman's death, nevertheless he must have been deeply
gratified to know that an adequate science museum—for which
he had struggled for sixty years—was at last being provided
at Yale through this generous gift; gratified, too, that he could
participate in the early plans. It is to be regretted that he did
not live to see his dream realized in the work of Marsh, who
became Professor of Paleontology (the first in America) in the
Scientific School and curator of the Peabody Museum of
Natural History.

Having been throughout his life a proponent of scientific
gatherings, Silliman continued to make an effort to be present
at all meetings which were held within a reasonable distance
from New Haven. In August of 1856 he went to Albany, New
York, to attend the meetings of the American Association for
the Advancement of Science, the organization that in 1848 had
evolved from the American Association of Geologists of which
he had been a charter member and the first president. A new
Geological Hall had been built on State Street modeled after
the Museum of Practical Geology on Jermyn Street, London, and a ceremonial was held for its dedication in a tent with
a capacity "variously estimated from 3 to 5 thousand." Professor Dewey, President Hitchcock, Professor Henry, Professor Davies, and others were the speakers. Although Silliman
always enjoyed recognition, he never courted praise, and expressions of injured feelings such as the following are almost
never found in his daybook: "I was not invited to speak but

many afterwards expressed regret that I had not been heard. This course appeared singular when they were giving the history of geology in this country and when an individual was present whose life for a half century had been coeval with its origin—whose personal exertions in the cause had been unceasing and whose 'Journal of Science' had been the great power wheel which had kept all in motion. It appeared singular indeed that he should have been neglected. It could hardly have been supposed, when some gentlemen spoke who had been instructed by me and most of whom were my personal friends, that my name should have been forgotten. Since my seat was in front upon the stage, I could not have been overlooked. But I do not complain, altho' while I was receiving privately many marks of respect I am unable to explain this public omission."

Three years later at the Springfield meeting of the Association he proved to be the oldest living member present, and appreciation of his attendance prompted Dr. Alexander G. Bache to propose a resolution that somewhat compensated for his disappointment over the fancied slight at the Albany meeting: "Resolved that this Association express its gratification at the presence of our octogenarian friend at our meetings and we hope that we may often meet him, as he now is, with his eye undimmed and his natural force unabated."

During the year 1858 a variety of events claimed his attention—first, he was deeply interested in the great religious revival which was sweeping across the country. "New York," he wrote, "presents a very interesting spectacle—even Wall Street has its prayer meetings." Under the heading "Fruits of the Revival in New Haven," he listed the number in each congregation in the town that had seen the light.

In August he recorded "the greatest discovery of the age"— the laying of the first successful transatlantic cable, and he expressed his satisfaction in Dr. Bacon's sermon on the contributions to science in the past two centuries. During that month there occurred another event, of more local significance, but also an experiment—Yale College sponsored an art exhibit at the Trumbull Gallery. Daniel Coit Gilman, then Librarian of the College, made the arrangements, and the railroads co-operated by offering special rates. Three hundred guests were invited to the opening and people attended the exhibition in droves to see pictures on loan from New York and private Connecticut collections, as well as the local art treasures. New Haven was said to have become temporarily the "Yankee Athens." The visitors, according to Silliman, seemed much gratified.

During these years Silliman had more time to read and he enjoyed many books for which he had not hitherto had the leisure. He was glad to have, on two occasions, an opportunity to discuss with Washington Irving his *Life of Washington,* a biography that had particularly impressed him. One is disappointed not to find in the list of books read in 1860 Darwin's *Origin of Species* which was then rocking the scientific world. However, since Dana, a much younger geologist, at first took a conservative view of Darwin's theory of natural selection, it is improbable that Silliman would have immediately espoused the new and radical concept even though Asa Gray gave it a long and favorable review in the *American Journal of Science* for March 1860. Meanwhile Silliman had become involved with another issue close to his heart.

THE CIVIL WAR

Although reared in a family which had kept slaves—and perhaps because of this circumstance—Benjamin Silliman had always been stoutly opposed to slavery; during his first trip abroad in 1805 he had inveighed while at Liverpool against the iniquities of the traffic in African natives. On several occasions, such as his lecture at New Haven on July 4, 1832 on the re-colonization of the slaves, he had endorsed plans for their voluntary return to Africa. Indeed, his outspoken views had often led to conflict with colleagues in the South. In 1854 Missouri, a slave state, had been received into the Union in open defiance of the Missouri Compromise of 1820 which had prohibited slavery in states north of latitude 36° 30′ and in states formed north of that line. When Kansas came up for statehood the issues soon to be fought out in the Civil War were the cause of bloody conflict between "border ruffians" from the proslavery state of Missouri and the crusading Northern settlers who sought to establish Kansas as a free state.

Feeling in the North ran high; in Boston there were public demonstrations and at a meeting in New Haven on February 15, 1856 funds were subscribed in support of a group of colonists who had elected to go out from Connecticut to Kansas to join the freedom-loving settlers who were then trying to defend their rights. They were fairly well equipped but lacked rifles for self-protection. On March 21st at a crowded meeting in North Church the Reverend Henry Ward Beecher from Brooklyn followed Mr. Lines (who was leading the party to Kansas), Dr. Bacon, and the Reverend Mr. Dutton "in an eloquent and powerful appeal of more than one hour and he urged the immediate supply of rifles." Silliman was then called upon to press the appeal. He finally consented to make a few remarks, suggesting that whatever was done be done at once and pledging himself to supply the first rifle. The result was that "in the course of half an hour 27 rifles were entered with the names of the donors and Rev. Mr. Beecher pledged himself to supply enough more to make up 50. . . . The rifles cost $25 each, those pledged in New Haven cost $675 . . . the proceeds of the evening in admission money and contributions were $1,000."

A few days later (April 3, 1856) he records:

A great clamor has been raised against Mr. Dutton and myself on account of the rifles. It has been used for electioneering purposes by the administration papers to influence the approaching election. I care not what they say about me, I feel that I did right. There was danger that the party—more than half of them—would be obliged to go out unarmed not merely among bears and wolves and panthers but among murderers and robbers. The invaders of Kansas from Missouri have proved their title to both these appellations by murdering three peaceable settlers, robbing many more and maltreating clergymen and all whom they could bring under their power. A general massacre at Lawrence was undoubtedly prevented by the armed preparation of the people.

It matters little that these rifles were obtained in a church; it was a holy cause and time and place were comparatively unimportant.

Some members of Silliman's immediate family and even his brother questioned his participation in the issue but he went steadfastly ahead. He soon found himself both reviled and praised in the public press throughout the country and he received more letters (some scurrilous and many anonymous) than he was able to read, let alone acknowledge. Finally at the earnest solicitation of his friends he published a letter in the Washington *National Intelligencer* of April 21st stating that he was not disposed to apologize for suggesting that arms be given to the emigrant colony, adding that the "real issue in the present case is whether the arming which is conceded to persons emigrating from all other parts of the country, whether going to Kansas to settle or to vote, should be denied to the emigrants from New England." This quieted most of his critics, including Senator Benjamin of Louisiana, "many years ago an unworthy member of Yale College," who had slandered Silliman in the Senate for his part in the affair. The letter, addressed to the Honorable John P. Hale, who had defended him in the Congress, brought him into correspondence with many who shared his views and particularly with the venerable patriot Josiah Quincy, Sr. with whom he had a lively correspondence.

When President Buchanan authorized the use of Federal troops to support the proslavery Kansas invaders, forty-three citizens of Connecticut in July 1857 addressed a memorial to the President protesting under the Constitution of the United States against this illegal usurpation of the rights of citizens. "We call your attention," the memorial reads, "to the fact of . . . 'levying war against a portion of the United States' by employing arms in Kansas to uphold a body of men and a code of enactments, purporting to be legislative but which never had election or sanction or consent of the people of the territory." The document was drafted by Alexander Twining and among the signers were President Woolsey of Yale, the Sillimans, Eli Ives, Josiah W. Gibbs, and Eli W. Blake.

The New Haven broadside brought forth an extended reply from Buchanan in which he effectively sidestepped the issue and "avowed most ultra pro-slavery doctrines." The memorial, addressed to the President personally, was not made known until Buchanan's reply was given wide publicity. After the reply had been discussed by the original signers at a series of meetings, a somewhat devastating rejoinder was sent to the President. Thereafter the three documents—the memorial, Buchanan's reply, and the memorialists' rejoinder—were issued as a twelve-page pamphlet (by John Wilson, a Boston printer) and widely circulated. The rejoinder, which meanwhile had appeared on September 22d in the public press in Washington, New York, New Haven, and Boston, had been drafted by the Reverend Nathaniel W. Taylor, but probably because Silliman was better known than the other signers he was singled out for abuse by the press favorable to the administration, and the document became widely referred to as "the Silliman letter."

On February 9, 1858 Senator James Dixon of Connecticut also elected to take issue with President Buchanan on the subject of using Federal troops to support the proslavery elements in Kansas. In the body of this speech he came to Silliman's defense and two days later the *New York Tribune* published an account of his remarks:

Senator Dixon of Connecticut delivered in the Senate the other day one of the best speeches upon the Kansas question which has been made since Congress came together. He examined the famous Silliman letter to the President, and in the course of his remarks eulogized Prof. Silliman in the following happy manner:

"And now, Sir, who is Benjamin Silliman, that he should be assailed by name in the Government organs, as if he were not entitled to address a respectful message of expostulation, or, if there were need, of reproof, to the President of the United States? One of the great lights of modern science—known, celebrated, distinguished among the few who have adorned the arts and shed new light on the studies most cultivated by civilized man; the peer, the friend of Humboldt, of Davy (while he yet lived), of Arago, of Agassiz, of Chevreul, of Cotta, of De la Beche, of Jean Baptist Dumas, of Faraday, of Leverrier, of Brongniart, of every great contemporary name made illustrious by devotion to science—known all over the world, when many of our distinguished countrymen are still unknown; the honored instructor of three generations of young men, in that far-famed university beneath whose classic shades he is passing his last days, the guide, the philosopher, the friend, whose teachings and whose counsels have been enjoyed by more of our public men than those of any man now living; the honored professor, at whose feet your own Calhoun sat for many years, when he, a young man, went to New England, as the young men of Rome went to Greece, to learn philosophy. There, Sir, under the instructions of Silliman, and Dwight, and Kingsley, his great intellect was cultivated, adorned, and strengthened. There he learned to wield that invincible logic which enabled him successfully to encounter the giants of other days—the Websters, the Clays, the Bentons —in the Senate, with constant victory; or, if not with victory, without ever having been compelled to acknowledge defeat. I know not, Sir, how many members of this body were trained by the same men or their successors; one, at least, I see near me (Mr. Benjamin), who has left in those halls a traditionary record of eminent scholarship, of high talent scarcely surpassed by his distinguished position on this floor. But this with deference I say, that whatever honors may be in store for any member of this body; whatever just claims to undying fame the talents, the acquirements, the eloquence, the public services of the most distinguished here may give him; there is not one among these honored Senators who may not deem himself satisfied, all the hopes of his youth more than fulfilled, all the labors of his manhood more than rewarded, if he may finally reach the measure of fame enjoyed in his ripened years by Benjamin Silliman. No office could elevate him; no honors could extend his reputation; no added celebrity could make his name familiar where it is now known among civilized men. It is inscribed in the immortal records of learning, and can never be forgotten, till the knowledge of humanizing arts and sciences shall fade from the memory of mankind.

On this panegyric Silliman commented: "I wrote a letter of thanks to Mr. Dixon for his true and honorable vindication of the New Haven correspondence and for his too generous commendation of me which some, and perhaps many, would regard as extravagant. . . . I do not feel that I can honestly appropriate all Mr. Dixon's glowing commendations but my friends approve of them and I have not yet heard of any rejoinder, which I expected—it may yet come—and if it comes I shall care nothing for it."

The handwritten reply which Silliman received from Mr. Dixon gave him particular pleasure:

Washington, Feb. 20, 1858.

Dear Sir: I thank you for your kind approval of my humble effort on Kansas etc., a corrected copy of which I send you herewith.

Allow me to say that the allusion to yourself has called forth from Senators and Representatives of all parties, as well as from various private citizens, by letter and otherwise, warm approbation, as being more than deserved by the distinguished subject of my remarks. I felt that I was taking a great liberty in using your name in so public a manner, but I felt also that your own position and the public interest justified and required it. . . .

I am, Sir, With great respect and esteem, Your obedient servant, James Dixon.

The financial panic of 1857-58 contributed to the growing tension in the South and finally John Brown's heroic march on Harper's Ferry in October 1859 set the stage for the great conflict between the North and the South. While Silliman sympathized wholeheartedly with John Brown's motives, he was alarmed that anyone unsupported by the authority of government should thus take the law into his own hands: "This invasion was rash and could never have been successful among a people of any energy. Whenever slavery comes to an end in this country, I trust it will be by peaceful means and not by bloodshed. It would be happy if this explosion should diminish the value of slave property and thus discourage the slave trade."

The early days of the war can be followed in Silliman's diary. He was, like the rest of the country, anxious concerning the result of the election of a Republican, 'Abraham Lincoln, Esq. of Illinois,' to the presidency. During the following year (1861) he made these entries:

April 23. Near the close of Mr. Buchanan's administration it was discovered that the corruption developed by the Goode report in the session of 1859-60 had extended to every department of the government and that treason had for many years been plotting the destruction of the Constitution and the establishment of a southern slave sovereignty. The story is long and is fully published in the papers of the day. Nearly all the slave states have now declared for disunion and have proceeded to form a constitution based upon slavery and they have established a Southern confederacy with a constitution ostensibly excluding the slave trade, but it is believed that as soon as they are established, they will again open that trade. They have seized nearly all the forts and arsenals situated in the rebellious states—the mint of New Orleans, the post offices in several cities, and a considerable number of the small vessels appointed to aid the government as cutters, &c.

May 13. It is stated that 30,000 troops are now in Washington and it is believed that the Capitol is now safe from any attack that may be made upon it. There is, however, still great cause for vigilance and effort as the rebels, rendered desperate, are collecting their armies and are hovering in Virginia in uncertain numbers—they boast of 50,000 but no doubt this number is greatly exaggerated.

By order of government, and to prevent their falling into the hands of the enemy, the Navy near Norfolk was burned and with the naval buildings, eleven ships and vast warlike stores and buildings were destroyed and vast treasures were thrown into the water.

At Harper's Ferry also a great manufactory of arms and an immense collection of arms were destroyed or greatly damaged. These steps were disgraceful to us although necessary—but the Virginians have come in and possessed themselves of both places, although now in ruins, but it is said that much of the property will be saved by the rebels.

June 5. An immense rising of patriotic men in the North and North West has placed hundreds of thousands of men at the command of the government and millions on millions of money are tendered by the States, by cities, and by individuals and associations for the defence of the government. It is stated on apparently good authority that there are now 45,000 men—efficient troops—assembled in Washington and its vicinity and other thousands are ready or preparing to march to the Capitol.

General Scott proceeds with extreme caution. The federal troops occupy Alexandria, behind which are intrenchments to prevent surprise. Arlington Heights are also occupied with formidable breastworks a mile in length and seven feet high. The heights of Georgetown are also occupied and those north of Washington. The Chesapeake is commanded as well as its rivers by our troops and the great fortress, Fort Monroe. Several attacks have been made by our troops and hitherto with success.

Our armies and those of the N. and N.W. perplex the rebels as they know not where they will strike next and their armies are suffering from starvation and disease.

Nov. 2. We have suffered two defeats—one at Bull Run July 31—a panic seized our troops after they had won the day and they rushed pell mell into Washington. October 21—another defeat was sustained at Leesburgh —with great slaughter. There have been numerous battles in Western Virginia and Missouri, generally they were won by the loyal troops.

In February 1863, when Mr. Lincoln came to appreciate that the government needed technical advice in connection with the conduct of the war, a National Academy of Sciences was created through an Act of Congress. Silliman was one of the fifty scientists who were named charter members. The bill responsible for the new organization passed the Senate March 3, 1863 and an organization meeting was held on April 22d of the same year at New York University at which Alexander D. Bache was elected president. Silliman was unable to attend but he was made chairman of the Class of Natural History. He was not present either at the first scientific meeting of the Academy held in Washington in January, 1864, but since the second formal meeting of the Academy was held at New Haven (on August 3, 4, and 5, 1864), he took part in the sessions although then within a few days of his eighty-fifth birthday. He has left the following account of the meeting:

Prof. Alexander D. Bache, president of the Academy being prevented from attending, Prof. James D. Dana, being vice president, opened the meeting in the Linonian Hall in the Hall of the Alumni. Only 20 or 21 members were present among whom the gentlemen of Cambridge were prominent. . . . An evening meeting was held in the room of the Brothers on the opposite side of the hall and there some nominations were made which were reported on Friday to the meeting. . . . On Saturday morning several communications were made. The most remarkable was by Prof. Newton on the shooting stars. He had been at great pains to collect many historical facts—for this purpose he diligently examined the scientific journals in our library and I presume many more.

He made many important deductions and the piece was highly approved and ordered to be printed. It was regarded I believe as the crowning piece of the occasion and gained much credit for our young professor. At the private meeting of the Sections I nominated Prof. George J. Brush but there was no room to elect him which will I trust be done in the future.

CLOSING YEARS

Concurrently with all these activities Silliman had been engaged since the beginning of his retirement on a project which he describes on March 4, 1862:

A memorable day—being the anniversary of President Lincoln's inauguration and what a year of agitation and anxiety—and the war not yet over! It is a memorable day with me in another respect—I have this afternoon finished my historical account of my labors in science out of Yale College. Before beginning on them I wrote first an account of Col. Trumbull and the Trumbull Gallery of pictures and then some notices of the Trumbull family and of old Lebanon. Col. Trumbull and the gallery was begun June 18 and finished July 24, 1857, pp. 129.

My own reminiscences were begun December 11, 1857 and finished this day—in hand 4 years 2 months but with very many interruptions, sometimes of months at a time. The MS is in 9 bound quartos, size large letter paper, from 50 to 100 and 200 and 250 pp. in all rising of 1700 pp. and two small quartos will I suppose add nearly 200 more. I have written this work for my children, not for the public, although with my private journal it will form a storehouse of materials should they ever be needed. I thank God that I have been carried through this labor, which has been also a pleasure, without faltering.

While preparing his memoirs he also reread and arranged his voluminous correspondence, separating his letters concerning the *American Journal of Science* (the editorship and financial responsibility for which he had turned over to Benjamin, Jr. and Dana in 1851) from his personal correspondence with friends and scientific colleagues. For example, during 1857 he had arranged and bound up the 130 letters he had received from his friend Dr. Mantell, who had died in 1852.

Although busy with his various activities and in excellent health for a man of his years, Silliman became increasingly aware that his contemporaries were slipping away. His day-book was largely taken up with obituary notices and at each Commencement he made note of the fact that fewer and fewer of his classmates remained. The loneliness that sometimes took possession of him as his friends and associates one by one fell away made him turn more and more to the solace of his religion. In 1857, the year before Robert Hare died, he wrote him a warmly tolerant letter despite his concern over the fact that Hare had turned to spiritualism:

. . . You and I are now old men, and the time is not remote—it may be very near—when we shall pass into the real world of spirits, into the presence of God. . . . You may remember that, at an early period, we conversed much and freely on the Christian faith; but, as we did not agree, and as I saw no hope of convincing you, while you, with a spirit of candor and kindness, appeared not to wish to invalidate my belief, we tacitly dropped the subject. But, during more than half a century, we have maintained a friendly communion on matters of science, a warm personal friendship, with a frequent interchange of offices of kindness. . . . Your course as a man of science has been honorable, and duly and justly honored by your country and in other lands. . . . It would have been happy if your public career had ended with science. . . . You will be hurt—I fear you will be offended—by my plainness; but when you realize that this is the strongest proof I have ever given you of that friendship which you yourself have valued, and which has been coextensive with our acquaintance, and almost with our lives, you will then perceive that these are indeed the faithful wounds of a friend. . . . Pardon me if, in my honest zeal for your welfare in both worlds, I have transcended the limits of that kindness and courtesy which we have always maintained towards each other, and I beg you to accept this letter as a proof that I am still, as ever, Your faithful friend, B. Silliman.

Silliman's appreciation of Hare published anonymously after his death in the *American Journal of Science* contained a lucid evaluation of his scientific contributions but did not express so clearly as did the above letter the depth of his affection. Hare's death affected him profoundly.

Within a short time, Parker Cleaveland, another friend of long standing, succumbed and of him Silliman wrote: "Professor Cleaveland was one of my earliest scientific associates. We interchanged many letters, especially in earlier years, but we met only twice. He came to New Haven in the spring of 1814 soon after the Gibbs cabinet was arranged here and this contributed to attract him to this place. In 1818 I attended the commencement at Bowdoin College and lodged at Prof. Cleaveland's house. . . . Mr. Cleaveland's Mineralogy was a very valuable work. It was constructed upon the plan of Brongniart's Mineralogy, an excellent treatise which I adopted early as the basis of my lectures on mineralogy in Yale College. . . ."

In 1859 he was even more affected by the death of his devoted pupil, Denison Olmsted, whom he referred to as "among the most distinguished of my professional assistants." With the loss of each of his friends, Silliman felt more and more lonely and when Jonathan Knight, ten years his junior, died during the summer of 1864 he wrote beside the printed obituary pasted in his daybook: "Dr. Knight and the late Dr. Eli Ives were both named by me to President Dwight for professorships in the Medical College. I am now the only survivor of the Medical Faculty of that Institution."

Silliman sustained a fall in August of 1864 from which he apparently recovered, but his health began to fail toward the middle of November. He himself recorded the cause: "I attended the College Chapel last Sabbath, November 3, in my usual health and might have so remained had I not gone out again in the evening. There was a very large audience assembled to hear the statements of four gentlemen, Dr. Parish and others, respecting the Sanitary Commission in relation to the Army and the country. The discussions were very interesting and showed the immense importance of this institution [which became the Red Cross] and the sister institution of the Christian Communion to the suffering soldiers and to the Army. So great is the insufficiency of the public provision for sick and wounded men that the Army could evidently not have kept the field but for these institutions and especially the Sanitary." He continued:

The air was so heated by a large audience in addition to the fires and lights that when we withdrew (Mr. Skinner being with me) a wintry wind struck me and the next evening I became a sufferer. Pain seized my chest externally and became at the time of retiring so severe that we used friction and in the night the pain was transferred to the arms, from the shoulders to the elbows and became worse than ever. In the morning, after a sleepless night, the pain became seated between the shoulders and in the back of the head.

In the course of the day the pain subsided but left me unwell; the stomach refused to retain food, some fever supervened and I became decidedly an invalid, so I remained through the week and was confined to the house. I am gaining a little from day to day with a little appetite and some power of retaining food. I am not able to attend public worship at present but am thankful that I am able to employ my time usefully at home.

On Monday, the 21st, he was considerably improved: "I have been able to resume my pen," he records, "and am gradually recovering my usual state of feeling. But the shock has been rather severe and to an old man serious. As the cause is apparent I must avoid in the future the exposure to a cold night air which brought on the attack." On Tuesday he pasted an anecdote in his journal quoting Lincoln as having said, when asked if he loved Jesus: "When I left home to take this chair of State I requested my countrymen to pray for me, I was not then a Christian. When my son died, the severest trial of my life, I was not a Christian. But when I went to Gettysburg, and looked upon the graves of our dead heroes who had fallen in defence of their country, I then and there consecrated myself to Christ; *I do love Jesus.*" Silliman wrote in a firm hand beside the clipping—"More to his honor is this brief paragraph than all that his country can bestow."

There is then a final entry beside an obituary of the Reverend Dan Huntington, who had been two years ahead of Silliman at Yale and who had died on Monday, the 21st, at the age of ninety: "In his last years he returned [after espousing Unitarianism] with great satisfaction and was welcomed to the worship and communion of the orthodox Congregational church." Thus did Benjamin Silliman lay down his pen on the day before his death on Thursday, Thanksgiving morning, November 24, 1864. He slipped away peacefully and without immediate warning after his morning prayers in bed. He had just repeated the Lord's Prayer and the hymn, "Trembling before Thine awful throne." Daniel Coit Gilman, in a long appreciation published in the New Haven *Daily Palladium* on November 26th, spoke for many when he wrote:

Prof. Benjamin Silliman, for more than sixty-five years the much beloved and honored officer of Yale College, died at his residence in this city early Thursday morning (Nov. 24) at the age of 85. As the intelligence of his decease was spread from neighbor to neighbor and from

BENJAMIN SILLIMAN IN 1857

By Daniel Huntington
Original in Library of Silliman College

SILLIMAN COLLEGE, YALE UNIVERSITY, IN 1947

friend to friend through the community, universal grief mingled with the joys of the bright Thanksgiving morning; but as one and another heard the circumstances of his declining days and hours, it seemed to all as if there could have been no end more beautiful and fitting to a life so pure, so happy and so good. . . .

Both in college and in his intercourse with men elsewhere, Professor Silliman has had the rare magnetic power of kindling the enthusiasm and awakening the co-operation of all whom he wished to reach. He was so kind of heart as well as clear of head, so sympathetic and courteous, as well as so sagacious and enterprising that he carried with him the affectionate admiration, the unqualified respect, and, in later years, the veneration and gratitude of pupils and friends through the length and breadth of the land. . . .

The grace which crowned all other graces was the purity and simplicity of his Christian character. His was the Charity which thinketh no evil, which suffereth long and is kind. His was the Faith which in the hour of sorrow and disappointment knows where to repose with cheerful submission. His was the Hope that never despairs. Few men have lived a more happy life than Professor Silliman. Few live to be surrounded by so many children and grand-children, bestowing day by day the warmest tributes of love and honor. Few die so much lamented.

The benign spirit of Professor Silliman hovers over the college at Yale University which was named in his honor. There, several of his portraits have come to rest in Library and Common Room, and the students repeat the grace that he so often said under his own hospitable roof:

"May God bless all those who are bound to us by ties
of friendship, consanguinity, or grace."

CHAPTER XVII

Silliman's Legacy to Science and Education

NEARLY a hundred years have passed since Benjamin Silliman closed the door of his laboratory for the last time and turned over his duties to his successors. He died a distinguished man, well known in university circles in America and in Europe, much loved by the thousands of men who had passed through Yale College during the years of his professorship, respected and revered by those who came long after his familiar figure was gone from hall and campus. Evidence of their affection was poignantly expressed in the indignation aroused by his overturned statue with which this story of his life began.

Silliman had the rare good fortune to be born at the precise moment when his particular talents could be put to their most effective use. It is not often that the man and his time are so perfectly matched—he did not have to "ripen" it. At the turn of the century the American people, their freedom now won, were beginning to feel the need of extending their boundaries—physical, economic, and moral. This necessity for growth in good time brought pressure to bear on the institutions of learning where men were being prepared to take the lead in their country's expansion. The teaching of the classics (with their emphasis on an ordered and disciplined society, freedom of the spirit, and the cultivation of the beautiful and the good) combined with the teaching of religion (which emphasized the dignity of the human soul) had produced the strong and self-reliant characters so needed in the formative years of a young nation.

Before 1800, however, economic necessity had begun to dictate a new order. The classical education, effective as it had been for developing the kind of citizen needed for the stern task of settling an unexplored country, did not serve the purpose of a people who, having established themselves, were now turning to industry and commerce and to the development of the country's natural resources. Silliman, with his feet planted firmly on orthodox Puritan ground and his face turned toward a future in which science would stand side by side with the classics and theology, was the connecting link between the old and the new. No one was better suited than he by birth, training, and natural endowments to introduce these changing concepts of education, to awaken in the public mind an interest in science which would serve to open the way to its useful application, and to win over those who instinctively greet change with suspicious opposition. He was in truth the ambassador of science in the new world—his portfolio, an unimpeachable character and a contagious enthusiasm.

Silliman's original contributions to science were few—in chemistry he improved the oxyhydrogen blowpipe of Robert Hare and with it successfully fused the heavy metals, including platinum; in geology his extensive field observations produced few original deductions, save for those concerning the development of valley soil from weather erosion of certain rock formations. These scientific advances were not of the character that would bring him special distinction as a scientist. But distinction he did undeniably achieve, and this through his outstanding success as a teacher. He not only carried his teaching outside the college walls, but he extended the instruction within the college to a graduate level. He thus influenced the intellectual life of the country as did few others in the nineteenth century for he in truth paved the way for Charles Eliot and Daniel Coit Gilman who were so effectively to implement his doctrines.

Van Wyck Brooks in *The Flowering of New England* accords Silliman a place of considerable distinction in broadening the intellectual horizons not only of New England, but of the nation as a whole:

At Yale, for instance, the great centre of learning, the second capital of the New England mind, a notable school of science had arisen, with Benjamin Silliman as its presiding spirit. Harvard, with all its literary prospects, had nothing to show as yet, or for years to come, beside this genius of the laboratory, who formed for Yale its collection of minerals and its physical and chemical apparatus, along with the *American Journal of Science*. Silliman's pioneer work in science might have been expected to offset the obscurantist theology of the college, for Yale, like the other and lesser centres of learning, Williams, Amherst, Bowdoin, Brown and Dartmouth, those minor Paley's watches, continued to be stoutly Orthodox. Through Silliman's *Journal,* the science of the world passed into the mind of the nation; and Yale was in other respects nationally-minded, with broader political sympathies than Harvard and a much more all-American student-body. But it was isolated from the great-world interests, outside the field of science, that were so soon to stir Boston and Cambridge; and this, in addition to its religious thinking and the relative poverty of the institution, portended little good for literature.

Henry A. Beers, for over forty years Professor of English Literature at Yale College, wrote in *Scribner's Monthly* in 1876 that "there has always been in the training given at Yale a certain severity. Discipline, rather than culture; power, rather than grace; 'light,' rather than 'sweetness,' have been, if not the aim, at least the result of her teaching. Her scholars have been noted for solid and exact learning." Silliman was reared in this environment and it proved completely appropriate for the growth and fruition of his sober scholarship and intense religious convictions. Possessing an uncomplicated nature, he moved forward steadily on his appointed course without being slowed down or diverted by the opposition often aroused by the eccentricities of genius. He had no need to waste time or energy struggling against an "inner demon."

The original contributions Silliman made to science were the result of practical thinking rather than intuitive reasoning. Alexis Caswell in his memoir of Silliman for the National

Academy of Sciences says: "It seems to me that the *utility* of *science*, in its broadest sense, was always uppermost in his mind. He is always tracing abstract principles to their practical applications. In his several books and papers, he aims at the accomplishment of useful ends. His style of writing looks to this. It is direct, simple, perspicuous. Its only object seems to be to expound clearly the subject under consideration. It is business-like. It reads as if the author had too many important matters on his hands to occupy himself in the mere refinements of style."

Silliman's modification of Hare's blowpipe (which he named the 'compound blowpipe') was prompted by a desire to make its use more practicable by eliminating the danger of explosion. His adaptations of Henry's *Chemistry* and Bakewell's *Geology* were designed to make these excellent texts more useful in America. His travel diaries were 'practical' guides to other travellers. The idea behind the *American Journal of Science* was also utilitarian, for he knew that progress in science was impossible unless scientists could have some channel of ready intercommunication.

Along with this pragmatic cast of mind, he had a purposefulness that never let him rest until he had pursued every problem and every opportunity to the very end. He never laid down the challenge implicit in the first professorship of chemistry at Yale and the first professorship of geology in America. In his public lectures he often put forth far more energy than the occasion demanded, simply because he could not do less. The task of extending knowledge of science was his, and he never slackened his efforts even though he be drawn into byways far afield from his college professorship and into a multitude of activities that taxed even one of his tremendous energies. In the founding of a medical school and later of a scientific school he saw the multiple opportunity to extend science at Yale and to make it work for the good of society. Indeed he threw his

weight behind every movement at Yale which held promise
of a broadening influence on the students or on the community.

But it required more than a practical purpose and perseverance to push his diverse projects to a successful conclusion,
and it was in this sphere that his consummate diplomacy served
him so well. Whether because he was above petty bickering or
uncharitable thought, or because he hated bitterness and controversy, whether because his training for the bar enabled him
to resolve opposition tactfully, or because of his natural kindliness of manner—whatever the reason, he had extraordinary
success from the very first years of his professorship in bringing people to think as he did, in enlisting not only their interest but their enthusiastic cooperation in whatever project
he chose to sponsor. His ability consistently to win for science
the support of the Yale Corporation, composed almost entirely
of theologians, was phenomenal. Here he was notably aided by
his strong religious faith and his personal warmth.

Although his early training at home did much to make him
thus at ease in society, there can be no doubt that his experience
abroad enhanced his ability to foster friendly exchange. Silliman could easily have become a narrow-minded provincial
had it not been for this early contact with a world far outside
his own. Here he acquired an international viewpoint which
he never lost. To his visits to the museums of art, natural history, and science of the old world he undoubtedly owed his
lifelong enthusiasm for procuring similiar collections for Yale.
His interest in the Perkins and the Gibbs Collections of
minerals and in the Trumbull art collection, which he eventually obtained for the College, brought to Yale cultural influences that were all a part of his broad vision of science as
the handmaiden of the arts.

Although Benjamin Silliman was not a creative scientist,
he was nevertheless a great figure in science. He achieved

more in his capacity of ambassador and teacher than he could ever have done had he confined his activities to the laboratory. Again to quote from Alexis Caswell:

We have already referred to the distinction between the discoverer of new truths and him who diffuses them abroad and gives to them their practical applications. The former is testing the powers of nature by the crucible and the balance and all those reagents which bring into play the affinities of matter; the latter is acting upon the intellectual powers of the community, and putting in motion far and wide over the land those mental agencies which result in wider general knowledge, higher culture, sounder practical judgments, and more productive industry. It is sometimes difficult to say which of these two classes of laborers confers the largest benefits upon the world. Nor, indeed, need we attempt to decide upon their respective merits. It is sufficient that they are both necessary to the highest ends of science. It was the fortune of our friend to act, for the most part, as the diffuser of knowledge. . . .

It might be said of Professor Silliman that 'his influence on science was chiefly exerted through the medium of his pupils and his intercourse with general society.' . . . Among the pupils of half a century how many have caught the enthusiasm of the master and given their energies to science, and placed their names high on the list of its honored cultivators! How many hundreds and thousands of those who, in different cities, have listened to his eloquent lectures, have learned to appreciate science, and gather refined pleasure from its culture, and give to it their hearty patronage! How regularly and widely has his Journal carried to the reading public intelligence of the latest discoveries, and the best practical applications of science!

Silliman's course lay for the most part in unchartered fields, but his character was such that as each new demand was made upon him he was able to meet it, not brilliantly or spectacularly, but with conservative wisdom. The public praise and honors which deservedly came to him he accepted as his just due with grace and modesty. Religious humility kept him from taking more credit than was becoming.

As a teacher of science and its chief advocate in the early nineteenth century, he will never be forgotten. To Yale men he will always return in the words of 'Ik Marvel' (Donald G.

Mitchell) whose gentle and fanciful writings touched on rural pleasures and who is remembered chiefly for his *Reveries of a Bachelor*. In this he wrote with nostalgia for the Yale of the '40's and '50's:

I happened only a little while ago to drop into the college chapel of a Sunday. There were the same hard oak benches below, and the lucky fellows who enjoyed a corner seat were leaning back against the rail, after the old fashion. The tutors were perched up in their side-boxes, looking as prim and serious and important as ever. The same stout Doctor read the hymn in the same rhythmical way; and he prayed the same prayer, for (I thought) the same old sort of sinners. As I shut my eyes to listen, it seemed as if the intermediate years had all gone out; and that I was on my own pew-bench, and thinking out those little schemes for excuses or for effort, which were to relieve me or to advance me, in my college world. . . .

In the corner above was the stately, white-haired professor [Benjamin Silliman], wearing the old dignity of carriage, and a smile as bland as if the years had all been playthings; and had I seen him in his lecture-room, I daresay I should have found the same suavity of address, the same marvellous currency of talk, and the same infinite composure over the exploding retorts.

And so we leave this man who has been variously called 'Patriarch and Guardian of American Science' and 'Father of American Scientific Education.' Hundreds of Yale students pass his statue each day as they go to and from their classes unmindful that Silliman was more than a bygone worthy of Yale. But a few of the more thoughtful may pause to recognize this statue as a symbol of the growth of science on which rests much of our present national vigor.

Bibliography and Sources

Although the *Life of Benjamin Silliman, M.D., LL.D.* by George P. Fisher (New York, Scribner & Co., 1866, 2 vols.) has been used for reference, nearly all quotations in the present biography of Silliman have been taken from original source material in the Yale University Library and other historical repositories possessing Silliman papers. A few quotations from letters, especially to and from foreign scientists, are taken from Fisher since the originals were widely scattered in 1897 and have not yet been recollected. Direct quotations, the source of which is not indicated, come either from his nine-volume Reminiscences (mentioned in the Preface) or from the original manuscripts of his seventeen-volume daybook or his student and travel diaries, the specific source being obvious from the context. Quotations from family letters are taken from those in possession of Miss Maria Trumbull Dana or of Silliman College; other letters, such as those in the Historical Society of Pennsylvania, the Ridgway Branch of the Library Company of Philadelphia, and the New York Historical Society, have been indicated in footnotes.

MANUSCRIPTS OF BENJAMIN SILLIMAN

Student Diary, July 27, 1795-May 15, 1796, 4 vols.
Account Books (3):

  (1) *Minutes of matters connected with my voyage to Europe, New Haven, February 24, 1805.*

  (2) *Exhibit no. 1, being an account of personal expenses incurred during a tour to England and other countries by B. Silliman on business for the President and Fellows of Yale College during the years 1805 and 1806.*

  (3) *[Miscellaneous accounts, 1806-1808]*
Origin and progress in chemistry, mineralogy, and geology in Yale College and in other places, with personal reminiscences, 9 vols. [1857-62]
The Trumbull gallery and the artist, its founder. [1857]
Daybook, 1840-1864. 17 vols.

PRINTED SOURCES

BALDWIN, E. *History of Yale College, from its foundation, A.D. 1700, to the year 1838.* New Haven, Benjamin & William Noyes, 1841, 343 pp.

CHAMBERLAIN, J. L., Ed. *Yale University—its history, influence, equipment and characteristics.* Boston, R. Herndon Company, 1900, 259 pp.

CUNINGHAM, C. E. *Timothy Dwight 1752-1817. A biography.* New York, Macmillan Company, 1942, 403 pp.

DANA, J. D. *Manual of geology.* Philadelphia, Theodore Bliss & Company, 1863, 798 pp., 2 plates.

DICTIONARY OF AMERICAN BIOGRAPHY. New York, Charles Scribner's Sons, 1928-1937, 20 vols. and supplements.

DICTIONARY OF NATIONAL BIOGRAPHY. London, Smith, Elder & Co., 1908-1909, 21 vols. and supplements.

FISHER, G. P. *Life of Benjamin Silliman, M.D., LL.D.* New York, Charles Scribner and Company, 1866, 2 vols.

HORNBERGER, T. *Scientific thought in the American colleges 1638-1800.* Austin, University of Texas Press, 1945, 108 pp.

LEWIS, W. S. *The Yale collections.* New Haven, Yale University Press, 1946, 54 pp.

MORISON, S. E. *The Oxford history of the United States 1783-1917.* London, Oxford University Press, 1927, 2 vols.

PARSONS, F. *Six Men of Yale.* New Haven, Yale University Press, 1939. (See especially "Ezra Stiles," pp. 35-63; "The young Silliman in Nelson's England, 1805-1806," pp. 64-84)

SMITH, E. F. *The life of Robert Hare—an American chemist (1781-1858).* Philadelphia, J. P. Lippincott Company, 1917, 508 pp.

YALE UNIVERSITY. *Historical register, 1701-1937.* New Haven, Yale University Press, 1939, 589 pp.

CHAPTER I

[BAGG, L. H.] *Four years at Yale.* By a graduate of '69. New Haven, Charles C. Chatfield and Co., 1871, 713 pp.

DEXTER, F. B. *Biographical sketches and annals of Yale College 1792-1805.* New York, Henry Holt and Company, 1911, v, 176-236. (Includes a bibliography of Professor Silliman's own writing.)

— *Sketch of the history of Yale University.* New York, Henry Holt and Company, 1887, 108 pp.

— *A selection from the miscellaneous historical papers of fifty years*. New Haven, Tuttle, Morehouse & Taylor Company, 1918, 397 pp. (See especially "Student life at Yale College under the first President Dwight 1795-1817," pp. 382-394)

STILES, E. *Literary diary*. Ed. by F. B. Dexter. New York, Charles Scribner's Sons, 1901, 3 vols.

CHAPTER II

In this chapter we relied almost entirely on Silliman's own Reminiscences.

CHAPTER III

SILLIMAN, B. *A journal of travels in England, Holland and Scotland, and of two passages over the Atlantic, in the years 1805 and 1806*. 1st ed., New York, Ezra Sargent, 1810, 2 vols.; 3d ed., New-Haven, S. Converse, 1820, 3 vols.

CHAPTER IV

MORTON, S. G. *A memoir of William Maclure, Esq*. Philadelphia, T. K. and P. G. Collins, 1841, 39 pp.

SILLIMAN, B. Sketch of the mineralogy of the town of New-Haven. *Memoirs of the Connecticut Academy of Arts and Sciences*, 1810-1813, *1*: 83-96.

SILLIMAN, B. and KINGSLEY, J. An account of the meteor, which burst over Weston in Connecticut, in December 1807, and of the falling of stones on that occasion. *Memoirs of the Connecticut Academy of Arts and Sciences*, 1810-1813, *1*: 141-161.

SILLIMAN, B., Jr. *American contributions to chemistry*. Philadelphia, Collins, Printer, 1874, 176 pp. (Reprinted from the *American Chemist* for August-September and December 1874)

TRENT, J. C. Benjamin Waterhouse (1754-1846) and the introduction of vaccination into America. *North Carolina Medical Journal*, 1944, 5: 9-11.

CHAPTER V

DAVIS, N. S. *Medical education and medical institutions in the United States of America, 1776-1876*. Washington, Government Printing Office, 1877, 60 pp.

DAVISON, W. C. John Morgan (1735-1789), founder of the first American medical school, *North Carolina Medical Journal*, 1944, 5:11.

MORGAN, J. *Discourse on the institution of medical schools in America.* Philadelphia, William Bradford, 1765, 63 pp. (Also Baltimore, Johns Hopkins Press, 1937)

NORWOOD, W. F. *Medical education in the United States before the Civil War.* Philadelphia, University of Pennsylvania Press, 1944, 487 pp.

STILES, E. Plan of a university. (Unpublished manuscript) December 3, 1777, 6 pp.

WELCH, W. H. The relation of Yale to medicine. An address delivered October 21, 1901, at the two hundredth anniversary of the founding of Yale College. *Yale Medical Journal,* 1901, 8:127-158.

YALE UNIVERSITY. SCHOOL OF MEDICINE. *The laws of the Medical Institution of Yale College* [including the catalogue]. New-Haven, Oliver Steele, 1813, 16 pp.

—*Memorial of the centennial of the Yale Medical School.* New Haven, Yale University Press, 1915, 60 pp. (See especially Steiner, W. R., "The evolution of medicine in Connecticut with the foundation of the Yale Medical School as its most notable achievement," pp. 11-33)

CHAPTER VI

SILLIMAN, B. *A tour to Quebec in the autumn of 1819.* London, Sir Richard Phillips and Co., 1822, 128 pp.

CHAPTER VII

American Journal of Science. First Series, 1818-1845; Second Series, 1846-1871; Third Series, 1871-1895; Fourth Series, 1896-1920; Fifth Series, 1920- . (Centennial Number 1818-1918, July, 1918, *46*:1-416)

ROBINSON, V. *Victory over pain.* New York, Henry Schuman, Inc., 1946, 338 pp.

CHAPTER VIII

FENTON, C. L. and M. A. *The story of the great geologists.* Garden City, N.Y., Doubleday, Doran and Co., Inc., 1945, 301 pp.

GEIKIE, A. *The founders of geology.* London, Macmillan and Co., 1897, 297 pp.

HUTTON, J. Theory of the earth; or an investigation of the laws observable in the composition, dissolution, and restoration of land upon the globe. *Transactions of the Royal Society of Edinburgh,* 1785, 98 pp., 2 plates.

SILLIMAN, B. *Consistency of the discoveries of modern geology with the sacred history of the creation and the deluge; being a supplement to the second American from the fourth English edition of Bakewell's Geology.* New Haven, Hezekiah Howe & Co., 1833, 80 pp.

CHAPTER IX

McALLISTER, E. M. *Amos Eaton—scientist and educator—1776-1842.* Philadelphia, University of Pennsylvania Press, 1941, 587 pp.
MERRILL, G. P. *The first one hundred years of American geology.* New Haven, Yale University Press, 1924, 773 pp.

CHAPTER X

SIZER, T. *John Trumbull—museum architect.* Windham, Conn., Hathorn House, 1940, 34 pp.

CHAPTER XI

AGASSIZ, Elizabeth C., Ed. *Louis Agassiz. His life and correspondence.* Boston, Houghton, Mifflin and Company, 1887, 2 vols.
CUSHING, H. William Beaumont's rendezvous with fame. *Yale Journal of Biology and Medicine,* 1935, 8:113-126.
MYER, J. S. *Life and letters of Dr. William Beaumont.* St. Louis, C. V. Mosby Company, 1939, 327 pp.

CHAPTER XII

Silliman's Reminiscences were the principal source for this chapter.

CHAPTER XIII

CHITTENDEN, R. H. *History of the Sheffield Scientific School of Yale University 1846-1922.* New Haven, Yale University Press, 1928, 2 vols.
—The story of the founding of the Sheffield Scientific School. In: *Inventors and engineers of old New Haven,* New Haven Colony Historical Society, November 1939, pp. 83-108.
DAVY, H. *Elements of agricultural chemistry.* Hartford, Hudson and Co., 1819, 2d American ed., 304 pp. (1st ed., London, 1813)
FLEXNER, A. *Daniel Coit Gilman—creator of the American type of university.* New York, Harcourt, Brace and Company, 1946, 173 pp.

FULTON, J. F. Science in American universities, 1636-1946, with particular reference to Harvard and Yale. *Bulletin of the History of Medicine*, 1946, 20:97-111.

YALE UNIVERSITY. SHEFFIELD SCIENTIFIC SCHOOL. *Fourth Annual Report, 1868-9.* New Haven, Tuttle, Morehouse & Taylor, 1869, 76 pp.

CHAPTER XIV

LYELL, C. *A second visit to the United States of North America.* London, John Murray, 1849, 2 vols.

MANTELL, G. A. *The Journal of Gideon Mantell—surgeon and geologist.* Edited by E. C. Curwen. London, Oxford University Press, 1940, 315 pp.

SILLIMAN, B. *A visit to Europe in 1851.* New York, George P. Putnam & Co., 1853, 2 vols.

CHAPTER XV

GIDDENS, P. H. *The beginnings of the petroleum industry.* Harrisburg, Pennsylvania Historical Collection, 1941, 195 pp.

GILMAN, D. C. *The life of James Dwight Dana.* New York, Harper and Bros., 1899, 409 pp.

WILLIS, B. American geology, 1850-1900. In: *Proceedings of the American Philosophical Society*, 1942, 86:34-44. (One of the papers in a symposium on "The early history of science and learning in America")

WRIGHT, A. W. Memoir of Benjamin Silliman (1816-1885). *Biographical Memoirs, National Academy of Sciences*, 1913, 7:115-141.

CHAPTER XVI

NATIONAL ACADEMY OF SCIENCES. *A history of the first half-century, 1863-1913.* Washington, 1913, 399 pp.

SCHUCHERT, C. and LeVENE, Clara M. *O. C. Marsh—pioneer in paleontology.* New Haven, Yale University Press, 1940, 541 pp.

CHAPTER XVII

BROOKS, Van W. *The flowering of New England 1815-1865.* New York, E. P. Dutton & Co., 1937, 550 pp.

CASWELL, A. Memoir of Benjamin Silliman, Sr. 1779-1864. *Biographical Memoirs, National Academy of Sciences*, 1877, *1*, 99-112.

MARVEL, I. [Mitchell, D. G.] *Reveries of a bachelor.* 1850, 298 pp.

Acknowledgments

We wish to thank the publishers of the following books for permission to quote from them:

E. P. Dutton & Company, Inc., for Van Wyck Brooks' *The Flowering of New England;*

J. B. Lippincott Company, for Edgar Fahs Smith's *The Life of Robert Hare;*

C. V. Mosby Company, for Jesse S. Myer's *Life and Letters of Dr. William Beaumont;*

University of Pennsylvania Press, for Ethel M. McAllister's *Amos Eaton;*

The Walpole Society, for Theodore Sizer's *John Trumbull —Museum Architect;*

Yale University Press, for Charles Schuchert's and Clara M. LeVene's *O. C. Marsh;* Francis Parsons' *Six Men of Yale;* and George P. Merrill's *The First One Hundred Years of American Geology.*

Index

Fish, Rebecca P., 5
Fisher, A. M., 121
Fisher, G. P., x, 80, 173
Foot, Lyman, 85, 148-9
Forbes, Susan, *See* Silliman, Mrs. Benjamin, Jr.
Fowler, W. C., 148
Fox, C. J., 51-2, 54
Freiburg School of Mines, 130, 233
Frémont, John, 190
Fulton, Robert, 47, 52-3

Gates, Horatio, 165
Geology and mineralogy, study in Britain, 48, 60, 65, 132; around New Haven, 71; introduced in chemistry lectures, 71; collections at Salem and Cambridge, 73, 83; Perkins Cabinet, 75; first course in mineralogy, 75; Weston meteor, 76 *et seq.*; American Geological Association, 79, 140; mining surveys, 79, 139, 174 *et seq.*; Gibbs Cabinet, 70, 82 *et seq.*, 141 *et seq.*; first course in geology, 88; early work in U. S., 79, 118, 150-4; early geologists, 130-4; conflict with Holy Writ, 134-9; American Assn. of Geologists and Naturalists, 181; public lectures, 174 *et seq.*; methods of teaching, 206
Gibbon, Edward, 225
Gibbs, George, 70, 73, 82, 86, 111, 117, 119, 140, 142; Gibbs Cabinet, 70-1, 98, 109, 151, 276; on loan, 82 *et seq.*; purchased, 141 *et seq.*
Gibbs, J. Willard (1839-1903), 216
Gibbs, Josiah W., 125, 261
Gibbs, Ruth, *See* Channing, Mrs. W. E.
Gilman, D. C., 217, 219, 242, 258, 273; evaluation of Dana, 246; obituary of Silliman, 270
Gilman, E. W., 219
Gilman, Mrs. E. W. (Julia Silliman), 115, 219, 254
Goodrich, C. A., 143-4, 167
Graduate education, 207, 210-12, 214, 216-17
Gray, Asa, 244, 258
Greville, Charles, 54
Gridley, T. L., 95-7
Griswold, Charles, 125

Guettard, J. E., 130-1
Guthrie, Samuel, 125

Hadley, A. T., 102
Hale, J. P., 260
Hall, James, 194
Hall, Sir James, 88, 131, 133
Haller, Albrecht von, 232-3
Hamilton College, 148
Hancock, John, 4
Hare, Robert, 25-6, 31, 109, 140, 147-8, 155, 182, 222; blowpipe, 273, 275; death, 267-8
Harvard University, 23, 62, 178, 274; Lawrence Scientific School, 192, 217; Medical School, 83, 90
Henry, Joseph, 123-4, 256
Henry, William, 75, 186, 275
Herschel, Caroline L., 59
Herschel, Sir J. F. W., 190
Herschel, Sir William, 59
Hillhouse, J. A., 107
Hillhouse, James, Sr., 33, 75, 100, 164
Hitchcock, Edward, 125, 140, 147, 154-5, 192, 256
Holmes, O. W., 220, 222
Hope, T. C., 65, 88, 132-3
Hopkins, Mark, 125
Hubbard, O. P., 148, 158, 251, 253
Hubbard, Mrs. O. P. (Faith W. Silliman), 100, 115, 158, 253-4
Humboldt, Alexander von, 233, 262
Humphreys, David, 86
Hunter, John, 58, 233
Huntington, Daniel, 270
Hutton, James, 78, 89, 131-3, 136

Irving, Washington, 182, 258
Ives, Eli, 85, 100, 125, 151, 261, 269

Jackson, Andrew, 170
Jackson, C. T., 178
Jameson, Robert, 88, 132, 187
Jefferson, Thomas, 77, 207
Jenner, Edward, 83
Johns Hopkins University, 217
Johnson, S. J., 217
Johnson, Samuel, 188
Johnston, J. F. W., 190, 212

Kent, James, 80, 204-5
King's College (later Columbia), 90

bull and three other children die, 111-13; period of ill health, 112-15; birth of two more daughters, 115; death of Mrs. Silliman, 218; remarriage, 236

Professor Emeritus: pleasure trip to West, 249-52; trustee of Peabody Museum of Natural History, 256; involved in controversy over slavery, 259 *et seq.;* death, 270

Characteristics: cheerfulness, 156-7, 162; close-knit family, 116, 162, 221, 252-4; composure, 163, 177, 278; *confessio fidei*, 15, 17, 20; conscientiousness, 9, 177; diary habit, 9, 44-5, 80, 112, 222, 266; diplomacy, 93, 102, 160, 271, 276; enthusiasm, 44, 71, 93, 147, 175, 221; excellence as lecturer, 161-3, 173-5, 180, 188, 277; financial problems, 18-19, 108, 121-2, 176, 179; gracious manners, 18, 71, 147, 157, 159, 161, 181; impatience with pettiness, 161; kindliness, 16, 154, 156, 159-60, 162, 221, 233, 271, 276; middle-of-the-road tendencies, 127, 133, 136, 140; physical appearance, 17-18, 146-7, 157, 159-60, 224; perseverance, 121, 123, 144, 275; practicality, 117, 161, 222-3, 274-5; religion, 5, 7, 9, 13, 20-1, 26, 48, 69, 115, 135-9, 160, 181, 219, 267, 269-71, 273-4, 276; sense of humor, 18, 34, 41, 47, 54, 60, 179, 251, 253; success as teacher, 145, 154, 238, 241, 243, 262, 271, 277; thoroughness, 44, 170, 182, 223, 227, 235; untiring worker, 56, 117, 123-4, 143, 168, 173, 179, 182, 196, 267, 275; voluminous correspondent, 123, 184, 224, 232-3, 255, 267

Children: Maria Trumbull, *b.* June 16, 1810 *d.* Jan. 13, 1880; Faith Wadsworth, *b.* Dec. 18, 1812 *d.* Feb. 26, 1887; Jonathan Trumbull, *b.* Aug. 24, 1814 *d.* June 27, 1819; Benjamin, Jr., *b.* Dec. 4, 1816 *d.* Jan. 14, 1885; Harriet Trumbull, *b.* June 18, 1819 *d.* Aug. 25, 1819; Charles, *b.* July 6,

1820 *d.* Sept. 19, 1820; Edward, *b.* Oct. 4, 1821 *d.* July 22, 1822; Henrietta Frances, *b.* Apr. 30, 1823 *d.* Jan. 31, 1907; Julia, *b.* May 26, 1826 *d.* Apr. 17, 1892

Published books: A journal of travels in England, Holland and Scotland, and of two passages over the Atlantic, in the years 1805 and 1806, 1810*; A tour to Quebec in the autumn of 1819,* 1822*; Elements of chemistry, in the order of lectures given in Yale College,* 1830-31*; A visit to Europe in 1851,* 1853.

Pupils and assistants listed, 147-9

Silliman, Mrs. Benjamin (Harriet Trumbull), 78, 85, 100, 108, 111-13, 166, 221; death, 218; letters to, 179, 197-8, 253

Silliman, Mrs. Benjamin (Mrs. Sarah I. Webb), 236

Silliman, Benjamin, Jr., 112, 115, 128, 180, 182, 189, 210, 213, 253, 255, 267; assistant to father, 148, 158, 174, 176, 196, 203, 206; birth, 110; marriage, 222; petroleum industry inaugurated, 239; School of Applied Science, 208 *et seq.,* successor to father, 238 *et seq.*

Silliman, Mrs. Benjamin, Jr. (Susan Forbes), 222, 254

Silliman, Benjamin D., 148, 156

Silliman, Charles, 113

Silliman, Ebenezer, 5

Silliman, Edward, 113

Silliman, Faith W., *See* Hubbard, Mrs. O. P.

Silliman, Gold S., 3-6, 23

Silliman, Mrs. Gold S. (Mary Fish), 4-6, 18, 20, 69, 111

Silliman, G. Selleck (1777-1868), 4, 6-7, 11, 13, 18, 40, 70

Silliman, Mrs. G. Selleck (Hepsa Ely), 70

Silliman, Harriet, 112

Silliman, Henrietta F., *See* Dana, Mrs. James D.

Silliman, J. Trumbull, 108, 111-12

Silliman, Julia, *See* Gilman, Mrs. E. W.

Date Due
